MODERN APPROACH TO
INORGANIC CHEMISTRY

ENGLAND: BUTTERWORTH & CO. (PUBLISHERS) LTD.
                  LONDON: 88 Kingsway, W.C.2

AUSTRALIA: BUTTERWORTH & CO. (AUSTRALIA) LTD.
                  SYDNEY: 6/8 O'Connell Street
                  MELBOURNE: 473 Bourke Street
                  BRISBANE: 240 Queen Street

CANADA: BUTTERWORTH & CO. (CANADA) LTD.
                  TORONTO: 1367 Danforth Avenue, 6

NEW ZEALAND: BUTTERWORTH & CO. (NEW ZEALAND) LTD.
                  WELLINGTON: 49/51 Ballance Street
                  AUCKLAND: 35 High Street

SOUTH AFRICA: BUTTERWORTH & CO. (SOUTH AFRICA) LTD.
                  DURBAN: 33/35 Beach Grove

U.S.A.:   BUTTERWORTH INC.
                  WASHINGTON, D.C.: 7235 Wisconsin Avenue, 14

MODERN APPROACH TO
INORGANIC CHEMISTRY

A TEXTBOOK FOR

HIGHER NATIONAL CERTIFICATE

AND

GENERAL DEGREE STUDENTS

C. F. BELL, M.A., D.PHIL., F.R.I.C.

Senior Lecturer in Inorganic Chemistry,
Brunel College, London

and

K. A. K. LOTT, B.SC., PH.D.

Lecturer in Inorganic Chemistry,
Brunel College, London

LONDON

BUTTERWORTHS

1963

First published 1963
Reprinted 1963
Revised and reprinted 1964

QD33
'B38
1964

Suggested U.D.C. number : 546

Made and printed in Great Britain by
William Clowes and Sons, Limited, London and Beccles

To J. AND S.

PREFACE

In the last two decades there has been a great resurgence of interest in Inorganic Chemistry. This was initiated by the discovery of the fission of the uranium atom in 1939 and the subsequent exploitation of this for military purposes, culminating in the atomic bomb explosions over Japan six years later. A vast programme of research and development, at first in Britain and then in the United States, led to the production of the atomic bomb and to the preparation of the first transuranic elements, neptunium and plutonium. More recently, the artificial radioactive elements beyond plutonium up to and including element 103 have been made. It has also proved possible to isolate radioactive isotopes of technetium, promethium, astatine and francium and so to fill the remaining gaps in the Periodic Table.

Research into fluorine compounds was stimulated by the war-time requirements for fissile uranium: the development of nuclear reactors in peace-time as a source of power led to an intensive search for new materials and resulted in comprehensive studies of the physical and chemical properties of many of the less familiar metals like niobium, zirconium and beryllium: new techniques were devised to separate a mixture of substances rapidly and efficiently into its components: finally, the availability of radioactive isotopes for almost all elements has resulted in their widespread use in industry, medicine, for analytical purposes and in many other fields.

Other major, recent developments in Inorganic Chemistry include the great progress in the synthesis of new complexes between metals and organic compounds, which followed the discovery of ferrocene in 1951, the increasing interest in inorganic polymers and the production of materials of extremely high purity for use as semi-conductors.

This book is primarily intended for Higher National Certificate and General Degree students but we hope that it will also be useful in the first years of more advanced courses such as the Graduateship of the Royal Institute of Chemistry and the Diploma in Technology. We feel it is essential for a student at this level to have some knowledge of modern ideas on atomic structure, the Periodic Table and chemical bonding. Emphasis should also be given to structural and stereochemical aspects, co-ordination and the concepts of oxidation and reduction and of acids and bases. The student can use this basic knowledge to gain a fuller understanding of the comparative chemistry of the elements and should then be equipped for a detailed and systematic study of the elements.

Our aims in writing this book have therefore been two-fold. Firstly, to provide a modern approach to the subject of Inorganic Chemistry, taking into consideration that many students may have only a limited mathematical background, and secondly, to introduce some of the great advances made in recent years. Considerations of size have precluded a more detailed description of the chemistry of individual elements and one of the standard reference books should be consulted for this.

PREFACE

We wish to express our thanks to several of our colleagues for their help: especially to Dr S. C. Bevan for his numerous helpful suggestions and criticisms throughout the writing of this book and to Mr G. M. Saul for his comments on much of the manuscript. We are grateful to Mrs S. Bell for help in the preparation of the final typescript.

C.F.B.
K.A.L.

Brunel College,
London, W.3.
  December, 1962

CONTENTS

                                                                    Page

PREFACE vii

1. ATOMIC STRUCTURE — 1 1
   THE ELECTRICAL NATURE OF MATTER 1
   RADIOACTIVITY 7
   NUCLEAR FISSION 19
   NUCLEAR FUSION 20
   TRANSURANIC ELEMENTS 21

2. ATOMIC STRUCTURE — 2 23
   QUANTUM THEORY AND ATOMIC SPECTRA 23
   WAVE MECHANICS 29
   PERIODIC CLASSIFICATION AND ELECTRONIC CONFIGURATION . . 34

3. VALENCY 39
   THE ELECTROVALENT BOND 41
   THE COVALENT BOND 54
   POLYATOMIC MOLECULES AND HYBRIDIZATION . . . 60
   SHAPES OF INORGANIC MOLECULES AND IONS . . . 65
   ONE- AND THREE-ELECTRON BONDS 67
   ELECTRON DEFICIENT MOLECULES 69
   HYDROGEN BONDING 69

4. THE STRUCTURES OF THE ELEMENTS AND THEIR
   COMPOUNDS 72
   THE CLASSIFICATION OF CRYSTALS 72
   THE STRUCTURE OF THE ELEMENTS 74
   BONDING IN THE CRYSTALLINE STATE 77
   THE CLASSIFICATION OF THE ELEMENTS ACCORDING TO THEIR
   STRUCTURE 81
   THE STRUCTURE OF INORGANIC COMPOUNDS . . . 88
      FACTORS WHICH DETERMINE THE OCCURRENCE OF SIMPLE IONIC
      STRUCTURES 93
      NON-STOICHIOMETRIC COMPOUNDS 101
      INTERSTITIAL COMPOUNDS 102
      THE MINERAL SILICATES 103

5. REACTIONS IN WATER AND IN NON-AQUEOUS
   SOLVENTS 108
   OXIDATION AND REDUCTION 108
      VARIATION OF THE MAGNITUDE OF STANDARD ELECTRODE
      POTENTIALS 111
      THE EFFECT OF NON-STANDARD CONDITIONS . . . 113

1*   ix

Page

CALCULATION OF EQUILIBRIUM CONSTANTS 115
DISPROPORTIONATION AND STABILIZATION OF VALENCY STATES . 116
ACIDS AND BASES 117
THE BRONSTED–LOWREY CONCEPT OF PROTONIC ACIDS . . 118
THE RELATIVE STRENGTH OF ACIDS AND BASES . . . 120
THE ACIDIC AND BASIC PROPERTIES OF HYDRIDES . . . 121
THE PROPERTIES OF HYDROXIDES AND OXY-ACIDS . . . 122
EXTENSION OF THE PROTONIC CONCEPT TO NON-AQUEOUS
SOLVENTS 123
REACTIONS IN NON-AQUEOUS SOLVENTS 126
HIGH TEMPERATURE REACTIONS IN LIQUID MEDIA . . . 131

6. CO-ORDINATION CHEMISTRY. 133
INTRODUCTION 133
STEREOCHEMISTRY 134
THE STABILITY OF COMPLEX COMPOUNDS 138
CHELATION 141
COMPLEXONES 145
FACTORS INFLUENCING THE STABILITY OF COMPLEXES . . 147
THEORETICAL ASPECTS OF CO-ORDINATION CHEMISTRY . . 151
THE ELECTRONEUTRALITY PRINCIPLE 152
VALENCE-BOND APPROACH 152
CRYSTAL FIELD THEORY 157
THE MOLECULAR-ORBITAL AND LIGAND-FIELD THEORIES . . 161
METAL CARBONYLS AND RELATED COMPOUNDS . . . 161
COMPLEXES BETWEEN METALS AND UNSATURATED HYDROCARBONS . 164

7. THE DISTRIBUTION AND EXTRACTION OF THE
CHEMICAL ELEMENTS 170
DISTRIBUTION 170
EXTRACTION 172
THEORETICAL PRINCIPLES OF EXTRACTION BY PYROMETALLURGY 181

8. SOLVENT EXTRACTION AND ION EXCHANGE . . 186
SOLVENT EXTRACTION SYSTEMS 186
APPLICATIONS OF SOLVENT EXTRACTION . . . 188
LIQUID METAL SYSTEMS 190
ION EXCHANGE 190

9. THE COMPARATIVE CHEMISTRY OF THE REPRESENTA-
TIVE ELEMENTS 195
HYDROGEN 195
DEUTERIUM 197
TRITIUM 198
GROUP 0 — THE INERT GASES 198
GROUP I — REPRESENTATIVE ELEMENTS 200
GROUP II — REPRESENTATIVE ELEMENTS 203

CONTENTS

		Page
Group III — representative elements	. . . . .	205
Boron and aluminium	. . . . . .	206
Gallium, indium and thallium	. . . .	209
Group IV — representative elements	. . . . .	210
Group V — representative elements	. . . . .	216
Group VI — representative elements	. . . . .	228
Group VII — representative elements	. . . .	238

10. THE COMPARATIVE CHEMISTRY OF THE TRANSITION ELEMENTS 247
Properties of the transition elements	. . . .	247
Group IV A	. . . .	253
Group V A	. . . .	255
Group VI A	. . . .	257
Group VII A	. . . .	258
Group VIII	. . . .	260
Group I B	. . . .	264
Group II B	. . . .	269
Group III A	. . . .	272

APPENDIX 1— PHYSICAL MEASUREMENTS IN INORGANIC CHEMISTRY 275
Diffraction methods	. . . .	275
Spectroscopy	. . . .	276
Thermochemistry	. . . .	277
Magnetism	. . . .	279
Dipole moments	. . . .	280

APPENDIX 2— COMPOUNDS OF THE NOBLE GASES . 282

INDEX 285

ATOMIC STRUCTURE — 1

THE ELECTRICAL NATURE OF MATTER

DALTON's atomic theory was put forward at a time (1805) when the existence of comparatively few elements had been demonstrated and experimental studies upon their properties had led to the concept of an indivisible atom characteristic for each element. Towards the end of the nineteenth century, however, this concept of indivisibility began to show its failings. In particular, work by FARADAY on reactions in electrolytic cells and studies by CROOKES, PERRIN and THOMSON on the conduction of electricity in gases under reduced pressure indicated that the atom was essentially electrical in character and led STONEY (1891) to propose a unit of electrical charge known as the *electron*.

A great deal of evidence for the existence and nature of electrons comes from the investigations carried out on *cathode rays* formed in electric discharge tubes at pressures of approximately 10^{-2} mm of mercury. At such pressures the gases were found to exhibit considerable electrical conductivity and the tubes became filled with a form of radiation that was observable only when it impinged upon the walls of the tube or a fluorescent screen. This radiation was subjected to a thorough investigation which led to the recognition of certain characteristic properties:

(*a*) The rays travelled from the cathode to the anode in straight lines.

(*b*) Deflection from their path could be effected by the application of either magnetic or electric fields.

(*c*) The rays possessed measurable mass and a negative charge.

It soon became apparent that these rays were actually streams of electrons and that their characteristics were independent of both the electrode material and the residual gas in the discharge tube. These facts were demonstrated by SIR J. J. THOMSON (1897) in experiments involving the deflections experienced by the rays in magnetic and electric fields. The basis of the method was to apply these fields at mutually perpendicular directions to the line of travel of the rays, the individual effects of the two fields being to deflect the rays in opposite directions. When applied simultaneously, therefore, the values of the field strengths could be adjusted so that no deflection from the original path occurred. The apparatus used by THOMSON is represented in *Figure 1.1(a)* and the effect of the two fields is shown in *Figure 1.1(b)*.

The electrons on entering the electric field of intensity X undergo an attraction towards the positive plate. The force of attraction is given by the product of the charge upon the electron e and the field intensity; this produces an acceleration d^2y/dt^2 which is related to the force of attraction by the Newtonian equation

$$m\frac{d^2y}{dt^2} = Xe \qquad \cdot \quad \cdot \quad \cdot \quad \cdot \quad (1)$$

where m is the mass of the electron.

Integrating equation (1) twice with respect to t and evaluating the integration constants leads to the expression

$$y = \frac{1}{2} X \frac{e}{m} t^2 \qquad \cdots \cdots \quad (2)$$

and substituting for the velocity v ($=x/t$) of the electrons gives

$$y = \frac{1}{2} X \frac{e}{m} \frac{x^2}{v^2} \qquad \cdots \cdots \quad (3)$$

In the magnetic field the lines of force are in the opposite direction. An electron of charge e, moving a distance dx in a time dt, is equivalent to an electric

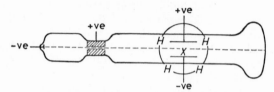

Figure 1.1(a). Thomson's apparatus for determination of e/m for electrons

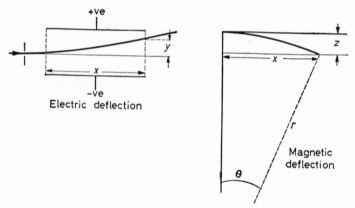

Figure 1.1(b). Electron deflection in applied electric and magnetic fields (from ADAM, N. K. *Physical Chemistry*, Clarendon Press, Oxford, 1956)

current i such that $i\,dt = e$. The electron is thus subject to a force $Hi\,dx$ tending to deflect it from its course (H being the magnetic field strength). This magnetic deflection causes the electron to be directed in a circular path of radius r such that

$$Hi\,dx = m \frac{v^2}{r}$$

which by substituting for i and v becomes

$$He = m \frac{v}{r} \qquad \cdots \cdots \quad (4)$$

An angular deflection (θ) of the electron also occurs in a time t such that

$$\theta = \frac{v}{r} t$$

and this is accompanied by a corresponding linear deflection z, after travelling a distance equivalent to x along the original path. Simple geometrical considerations lead to the relation

$$x^2 = z(2r-z)$$

which for small deflections becomes

$$x^2 = 2rz \qquad \cdots \qquad (5)$$

Substituting from equation (5) for r in equation (4) gives the expression

$$z = \frac{1}{2} H \frac{e}{m} \frac{x^2}{v} \qquad \cdots \qquad (6)$$

By adjusting the values of the two fields it may be arranged that no deflection from the original path occurs. Hence $y=z$ or $v=X/H$. From measurements of the electron deflection made when one or other of the two fields is switched off, the value of e/m can be determined using either equation (3) or (6).

An evaluation of the charge on the electron was achieved by R. MILLIKAN (1909) and the value so obtained allowed an estimate of the mass of the electron to be made as approximately 1/1820 that of the mass of the hydrogen atom.

More recent methods have enabled greater accuracy to be obtained both in the determination of e/m and of m, and these results are summarized in *Table 1.1*. From these figures the ratio of the mass of the electron to that of the hydrogen atom is 1/1837.

Table 1.1. Some values of e/m, e *and* m *for the electron*

	Thomson and Millikan	Recent workers
e/m	$5 \cdot 20 \times 10^{17}$ esu/g	$(5 \cdot 27305 \pm 0 \cdot 00007) \times 10^{17}$ esu/g
e	$4 \cdot 774 \times 10^{-10}$ esu	$(4 \cdot 80286 \pm 0 \cdot 00009) \times 10^{-10}$ esu
m	$9 \cdot 36 \times 10^{-28}$ g	$(9 \cdot 1083 \pm 0 \cdot 0003) \times 10^{-28}$ g

Cathode rays are not the only phenomenon observable in discharge tubes that have been of fundamental importance in elucidating the electrical nature of the atom. GOLDSTEIN found, by using a perforated cathode, that another kind of ray was also produced. Such rays moved in the opposite direction to the cathode rays and it was concluded that they were composed of positively charged particles. Using different gases it was found that, unlike cathode rays, these positive rays had ratios of e/m that were dependent on the nature of the residual gas in the discharge tube. It is now known that *positive rays* are formed by ionization of the gas molecules by the stream of electrons from the cathode. From an intensive study of positive rays has come our present knowledge of the atoms of the common elements.

By using methods similar to those for determining e/m of the electron it was shown that the largest value of this ratio for positive rays was obtained when hydrogen was the residual gas in the discharge tube.   The positively charged particle formed in this instance had a mass 1836 times that of the electron and a charge equal in magnitude, but opposite in sign, to that of the electron.   The *proton*, as this particle became known, is one of the fundamental constituents of matter.

The first systematic investigation of these rays was undertaken by THOMSON (1910–1914) using his 'parabola method'.   This measured the effects, recorded on a photographic plate, of the simultaneous application of electric and magnetic fields to the positive rays.   Development of the plates showed parabolic traces.   Each parabola corresponded to particles of the same ratio of e to m.   These particles fall at different points along the parabola according to their velocities.   The parabolic relationship can be derived from combination of equations (3) and (6) which gives $z^2 = k(e/m)y$.   By comparison with traces from elements of known atomic weight THOMSON was able to estimate the atomic weights of other elements.   Thus, using neon gas in the apparatus, two lines were observed that corresponded to atomic masses of 20 and 22; this suggested the presence of two kinds (or *isotopes*) of neon atoms.

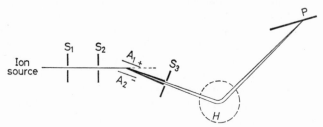

Figure 1.2. Aston's mass spectrograph

The method of measuring masses of elements in this manner was further developed by ASTON who devised the mass spectrograph, an instrument capable of focusing the positive rays as linear rather than parabolic traces. The principle of this method is shown diagrammatically in *Figure 1.2*.   A fine parallel beam of positive rays from a discharge tube is selected by slits S_1 and S_2 and passes through two parallel plates A_1 and A_2 by means of which an electric field may be applied.   The beam, on entering the electric field, diverges upon attraction to the negatively charged plate because of the differences in charge, mass and velocity of the individual particles.   A band from this wide beam is selected by S_3 and passes into the field (H) of a powerful electromagnet whose polarity and direction are such that the particles are bent back in the manner shown.   Adjustment of the field strengths enables particles of the same e/m to be focused on a single line on the photographic plate P. The standard used in the measurement of the atomic masses was that of the oxygen atom.   Lines from oxygen are obtained at positions corresponding to O_2^+, O^+ and O^{2+} respectively.   Using this instrument ASTON not only confirmed the existence of the two isotopes of neon but also found isotopes for chlorine and argon.   Further development was made when the method was applied to solids by producing positive ions from an anode coated with a suitable salt of the element.   During the initial period of investigation by ASTON it was apparent that the masses of individual atoms were integral, but with increased resolving power it was found that there were slight but significant deviations from the integral values*. Thus chlorine, which was found to have atoms with masses of 35 and 37 with the instruments of low resolving power, was shown to have mass values of 34·983 and 36·980.

This type of instrument is particularly useful in the determination of the relative abundance of isotopes. This was first achieved by estimating the intensity of blackness of the lines on the photographic plates by means of a

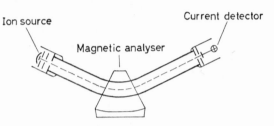

Figure 1.3. Nier's mass spectrometer

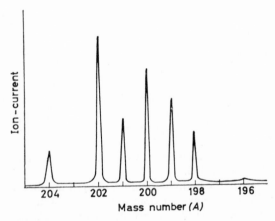

Isotopic abundance

A	204	202	201	200	199	198	196
%	6·85	29·80	13·22	23·13	16·84	10·02	0·146

Figure 1.4. Separation of the isotopes of mercury

microphotometer. Though this method was of some use it was not particularly accurate and it has been superseded by ion-current measuring devices or mass spectrometers. In these instruments the photographic plate has been replaced by a detector for current measurement; a typical arrangement is shown in *Figure 1.3* which is a diagrammatic representation of the spectrometer developed by NIER. A typical separation of isotopes using such an instrument is given in *Figure 1.4.*

* These integral values have been retained for brevity, and are referred to as mass numbers of the element.

5

Some selected examples of these physical atomic weights are given in *Table 1.2.*

Isotopic weights determined in this manner are expressed using the isotope of oxygen of atomic mass 16·0000 as a standard of comparison, this being the most abundant of the oxygen isotopes. The same element is used for a standard of comparison in chemical atomic weight determinations, but in this instance

Table 1.2. Some physical atomic masses

Entity	Mass (amu*)
$^1_0$n	1·00893
$^1_1$H	1·00813
$^2_1$H	2·01473
$^4_2$He	4·00387
$^{12}_6$C	12·00380
$^{14}_7$N	14·00753
$^{16}_8$O	16·00000†

The mass of the electron on the same scale is 0·0005486.

* These units of mass (amu) are mentioned later, p. 7.

†More recently it has been suggested that ^{12}C should be used as a standard for the determination of atomic masses. This makes only slight alterations in the above values. The atomic weights given on the inside of the front cover are based on the carbon standard.

the value of 16·0000 is assigned to oxygen gas which is a mixture of the three isotopes with mass numbers 16, 17 and 18 and with corresponding relative abundances of 99·76, 0·04 and 0·2 per cent. The mass of this average oxygen atom on the physical scale is 16·0044 and in order to obtain chemical isotopic weights from the physical values it is necessary to divide the latter by the factor (16·0044/16·0000) or 1·000275.

Except in the case of the hydrogen isotope of mass number one, the isotopic mass numbers of atoms are greater than the number of protons that are contained in the nucleus of the atom; this discrepancy is accounted for by the presence of other fundamental particles in the nucleus with masses approximately that of the proton but of zero charge; these are known as *neutrons* (see p. 16). In simple terms, a nucleus is composed of *protons* and *neutrons* and an atom of mass number (A) and atomic number (Z) contains Z protons and $A-Z$ neutrons. An isotope of the element is designated as ^A_ZM. If, however, a summation of the masses of the protons, electrons and neutrons in any one isotope (except $^1_1$H) is made, there is a noticeable difference between this value and that obtained from physical measurement. Thus in the case of the helium atom, which may be considered to be a composite nucleus of two protons and two neutrons, together with two extranuclear electrons, the physical atomic mass is 4·00387, whereas that from a summation of the mass of two protons, two neutrons and two electrons is 4·03412; this difference of 0·03025 is termed the *mass defect*. Mass defects may be accounted for by the relativity theory of EINSTEIN which proposes that mass and energy are interconvertible. The relationship between the two is given by the equation

$$E = mc^2 \qquad\qquad \cdots \quad \cdots \quad (7)$$

6

The energy (E) is given in ergs for mass (m) in grammes and the velocity of light (c) in cm/sec*.

Reverting to the case of the helium atom, the mass defect of 0·3025 represents an energy release of approximately 28·2 MeV when the atom is synthesized from its components. Such energy is termed the *binding energy*, being the energy required to break down the atom into its fundamental components. Estimates of the binding energies of other atoms have been made and are shown graphically in *Figure 1.5* as binding energy per particle. This figure shows that the elements of mass number around 60, namely iron, cobalt,

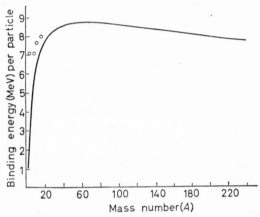

Figure 1.5. Binding energy curve. High values of B.E./A are obtained for ^{4}He, ^{8}Be, ^{12}C and ^{16}O, indicating some added stability of atoms with mass numbers that are integral multiples of four

nickel and copper, possess the most stable nuclei; those at both ends of the Periodic Table are less stable. Energy can accordingly be released by either of two nuclear reactions:

(*a*) the fusion of the lightest nuclei to form heavier particles, as in the hydrogen bomb,

(*b*) the breaking-down or fission of the heaviest nuclei into lighter ones as in the atomic bomb and nuclear reactors.

RADIOACTIVITY

At about the same time as Thomson's researches on the electron, the phenomenon of radioactivity was discovered; this is a spontaneous breakdown of the atomic nucleus which is unaffected by external conditions such as temperature

* A mass loss of one gramme means the release of energy equivalent to 9×10^{20} ergs taking the velocity of light as 3×10^{10} cm/sec. In the case of single atoms, masses are measured in terms of an atomic mass unit (amu) where 1 amu $= 1/N$ g $= 1·66 \times 10^{-24}$ g, N being the Avogadro number. The loss of such a mass is equivalent to $1·49 \times 10^{-3}$ ergs. An energy unit frequently employed in this field is the million electron volt (MeV). The electron-volt (eV) is the energy that an electron acquires when it falls through a potential difference of one volt; the charge on the electron is approximately $4·8 \times 10^{-10}$ esu and one volt is 1/300 esu. Hence the electron-volt is equivalent to $4·8 \times 10^{-10}/300$ ergs and one MeV is equivalent to $1·6 \times 10^{-6}$ ergs.

The loss of one amu is therefore equivalent to 931 MeV.

and pressure. During the course of some work concerned with x-rays and phosphorescence, BECQUEREL accidentally placed a uranium compound in close contact with some photographic plates; later it was found that although these plates had been wrapped in protective paper, exposure of the plates had occurred. The conclusion reached was that the uranium salt had been emitting some form of radiation that could penetrate materials normally opaque to light. Further work by the CURIES led to the discovery that the same radiation ionized air.

The CURIES demonstrated that the phenomenon was also characteristic of other substances; in particular they isolated two new elements—polonium and radium—in the form of certain salts by careful separation from the uranium ore pitchblende.

In contrast to x-rays, which also ionize air and affect photographic plates, the radiations from radioactive materials were found to be capable of sub-division into various categories. This subdivision was made after a study of the deflections experienced by the radiations in strong magnetic fields when three groups were characterized α, β and γ. Two sets were found to be deflected in opposite directions, one to a greater extent than the other. Those more deflected (β) were shown from the direction of deflection to be negatively charged and quantitative studies indicated that they were electrons, often with high velocities*. The second group (α) were examined by measuring e/m and were found to be positively charged particles with an e/m almost exactly half that of the proton. Verification of their identity came when experiments by RUTHERFORD and ROYDS showed these particles to be ionized helium atoms. The final set of radiations were undeflected by the applied magnetic fields and are known to be electromagnetic radiation of short wavelength. These γ-rays are formed as a consequence of the readjustment of energy levels within the nucleus after the emission of alpha or beta particles has taken place.

The property common to all three types of radiation, that of ionization of air, has been used in instruments for their detection; the property of excitation of fluorescence in phosphors, originally used by RUTHERFORD and CROOKES, has also been incorporated in scintillation counters. In the instruments based upon ionization, detection of the radiations is effected by the amplification and recording of the change in the potential across two electrodes caused by the presence of ionizing radiation. In scintillation counting, the scintillations excited in phosphors are detected by photoelectric cells and converted to electrical impulses. A further device that was of use during initial investi-gations—the Wilson Cloud Chamber—depended upon the condensation of water vapour on charged particles when air saturated with water vapour was adiabatically expanded within the chamber. The water droplets thus formed

---

* Measurement of the value of e/m for electrons emitted from radioactive materials gives a value that is generally less than that found for electrons from conventional sources. Because the electrons are emitted with high energies their mass is significantly different from the rest mass. The relationship between mass at high speeds and rest mass (m_0) is

$$ m = \frac{m_0}{\sqrt{1 - (v^2/c^2)}} $$

where v is the velocity of the particle and c is the velocity of light. As the particle velocity increases and approaches that of light the mass will also increase; thus with a velocity of $0\cdot1c$ the mass m is approximately $1\cdot005m_0$ and with a velocity $0\cdot9c$ the mass is approximately $2\cdot294m_0$. Values of e/m will therefore decrease as the particle energy increases.

left distinctive trails which were further examined under a microscope or recorded photographically. It was in such a chamber that the positive analogue of the electron—the *positron*—was first identified.

Radioactive Transformations

The emission of an alpha or beta particle causes a chemical change in the radioactive atom and the activity of the parent atom decays exponentially with time. The exponential decay is plotted in *Figure 1.6* and for N radioactive nuclei the variation with time of the activity may be expressed as

$$\frac{dN}{dt} = -\lambda N \qquad \qquad \cdots \quad \cdots \quad (8)$$

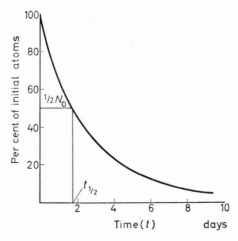

Figure 1.6. Decay curve for a radioactive material

where λ is a transformation constant or the proportion of the atoms in the sample that decay in unit time. Integration of equation (8) leads to

$$N = N_0 e^{-\lambda t} \qquad \qquad \cdots \quad \cdots \quad (9)$$

N_0 being the number of radioactive atoms at time $t=0$. From equation (9) an extremely important constant of the radioactive atom—the half-life $(t_{1/2})$—may be evaluated. The radioactive half-life of the element is the time required for one half of the atoms to decay, thus

$$N = \tfrac{1}{2}N_0$$
$$\text{or} \quad \tfrac{1}{2} = e^{-\lambda t_{1/2}}$$
$$\text{and} \quad t_{1/2} = (\log_e 2)/\lambda \qquad \qquad \cdots \quad \cdots \quad (10)$$

Values of this constant vary between millionths of a second to about 10^{10} years.

The naturally occurring radioactive isotopes or nuclides of the heavy elements are found to belong to one of three decay series, which are named after the most stable nuclide in each series. These series are given in *Figures 1.7, 1.8* and *1.9*, the parent elements being [232]Thorium, [238]Uranium

9

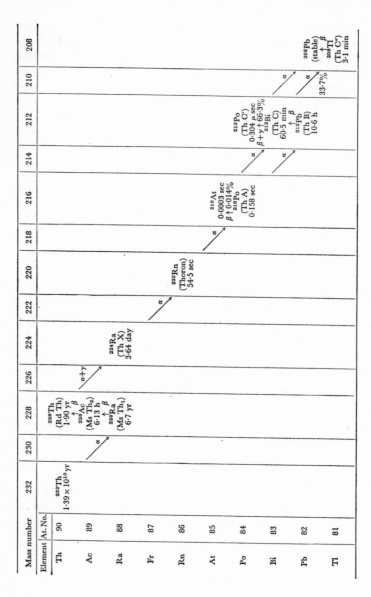

Figure 1.7. Thorium decay series

and ^{235}Uranium* with respective half-lives of $1{\cdot}4 \times 10^{10}$, $4{\cdot}5 \times 10^9$ and $7{\cdot}8 \times 10^8$ years. An alternative nomenclature is the 4n, (4n+2) and the (4n+3) series, indicating that all the members of the 4n series have mass numbers that are integral multiples of four and those in the other two have mass numbers divisible by four with remainders of two and three respectively.

The emission of an alpha particle results in the formation of an atom with mass number four units less and atomic number two units less than the parent atom. The emission of a beta particle causes isobaric change or the formation of an atom with identical mass number but one greater in atomic number than the decaying atom; this type of change is also characteristic of positron emission and K-capture† (see p. 17 and p. 22) which yield isobars with atomic numbers one less than the decaying atom. In the case of the heavy elements this process of radioactive decay is a series of successive ejections of particles and frequent adjustment of energy within the nucleus until an element is reached that is no longer unstable; this occurs with each of the three series at element 82.

Table 1.3. *Some naturally occurring radioactive isotopes not in the disintegration series*

Isotope	Type of decay	Product	Half-life (years)
$^3_1$H	beta	$^3_2$He	12·5
$^{14}_6$C	beta	$^{14}_7$N	$5{\cdot}7 \times 10^3$
$^{40}_{19}$K	beta+gamma K-capture†	$^{40}_{20}$Ca $^{40}_{18}$Ar	$1{\cdot}4 \times 10^9$
$^{87}_{37}$Rb	beta+gamma	$^{87}_{38}$Sr	$6{\cdot}0 \times 10^{10}$
$^{152}_{62}$Sm	alpha	$^{148}_{60}$Nd	$2{\cdot}5 \times 10^{11}$

A fourth radioactive decay series exists for elements with mass numbers divisible by four with a remainder of one (4n+1) and atomic numbers greater than 83. This is the Neptunium series which contains isotopes that do not occur naturally but arise from the decay of ^{241}Plutonium prepared by alpha bombardment of ^{238}Uranium. The end product of this series is ^{209}Bismuth as shown in *Figure 1.10* (p. 14).

In addition to the isotopes of elements with atomic number greater than 82, a number of naturally occurring isotopes of elements of lower atomic number exist that are also radioactive; these are characterized by long half-lives and weak activity. Some examples are given in *Table 1.3*.

Scattering of Alpha Particles

In 1911, RUTHERFORD carried out experiments on the effect of placing extremely thin sheets of metal foil in the paths of streams of alpha particles.

*The Actinium series takes its name from the original name *Actino*uranium (^{235}U).

†K-capture signifies the capture of an orbital electron by the nucleus. This electron generally comes from the K shell and the vacancy left by it is filled by an electron from a higher energy level, giving rise to the formation of a spectral line in the x-ray region.

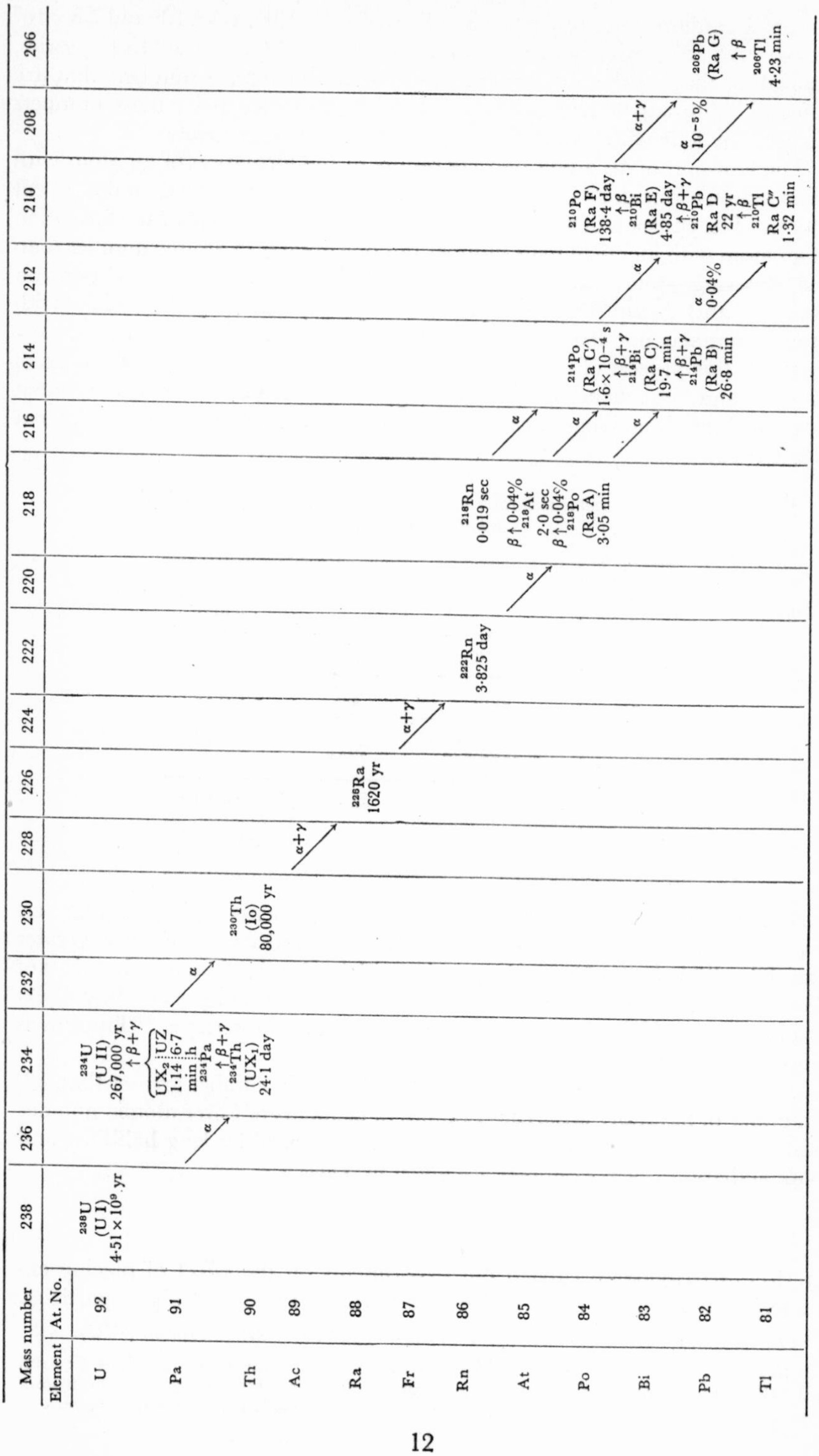

Mass number	238	236	234	232	230	228	226	224	222	220	218	216	214	212	210	208	206
Element	At. No.																
U	92	^{238}U (U I) $4 \cdot 51 \times 10^9$ yr		^{234}U (U II) 267,000 yr $\uparrow \beta + \gamma$													
Pa	91			UX$_2 \overset{\cdot \cdot}{\cdot \cdot}$UZ $1 \cdot 14 \overset{|}{|} 6 \cdot 7$ min$\overset{|}{\downarrow}$h ^{234}Pa $\uparrow \beta + \gamma$	α												
Th	90		α	^{234}Th (UX$_1$) $24 \cdot 1$ day		^{230}Th (Io) 80,000 yr											
Ac	89						$\alpha + \gamma$										
Ra	88							^{226}Ra 1620 yr	$\alpha + \gamma$								
Fr	87																
Rn	86									^{222}Rn $3 \cdot 825$ day	α	^{218}Rn $0 \cdot 019$ sec						
At	85											$\beta \uparrow 0 \cdot 04\%$ ^{218}At $2 \cdot 0$ sec						
Po	84											$\beta \uparrow 0 \cdot 04\%$ ^{218}Po (Ra A) $3 \cdot 05$ min	α	^{214}Po (Ra C') $1 \cdot 6 \times 10^{-4}$ s	α	^{210}Po (Ra F) $138 \cdot 4$ day	$\alpha + \gamma$	
Bi	83												α	$\uparrow \beta + \gamma$ ^{214}Bi (Ra C) $19 \cdot 7$ min	α $0 \cdot 04\%$	$\uparrow \beta$ ^{210}Bi (Ra E) $4 \cdot 85$ day	α $10^{-5}\%$	
Pb	82													$\uparrow \beta + \gamma$ ^{214}Pb (Ra B) $26 \cdot 8$ min		$\uparrow \beta + \gamma$ ^{210}Pb Ra D 22 yr		^{206}Pb (Ra G)
Tl	81															^{210}Tl Ra C'' $1 \cdot 32$ min		$\uparrow \beta$ ^{206}Tl $4 \cdot 23$ min

Figure 1.8. Uranium-238 decay series

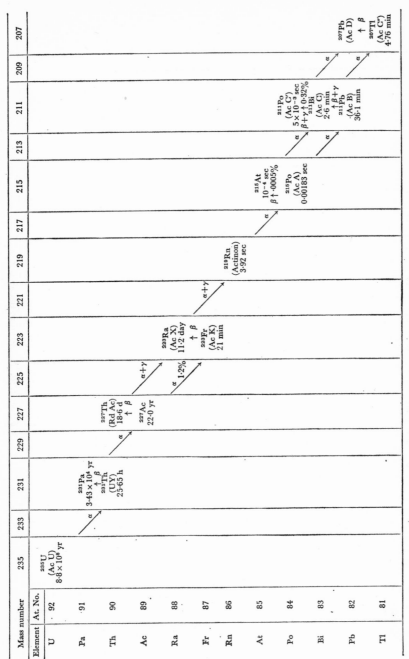

Figure 1.9. Actinium decay series

13

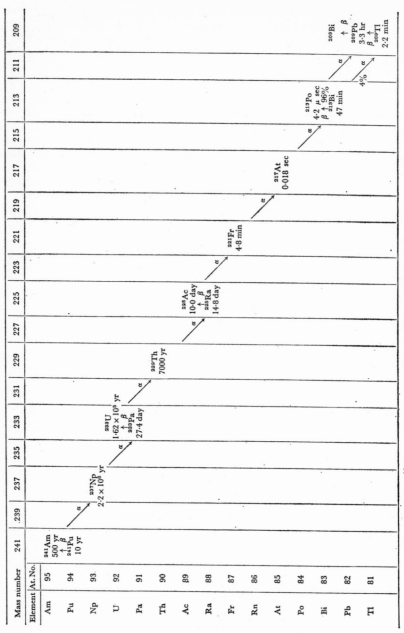

Figure 1.10. Neptunium decay series

The majority of the particles, detected by scintillations produced on a zinc sulphide screen, passed through the foils suffering little or no deflection but a few underwent deflections through wide angles (*Figure 1.11*). From these observations he concluded that the atoms of which the metal foils were composed possessed a positively charged body of finite mass occupying but a small fraction of the total atomic volume. Since the majority of alpha particles were not deflected to any great extent the proposal was made that the remainder of the atomic volume was a void but that in this space there were sufficient electrons to keep the atom electrically neutral. A quantitative examination of the results indicated that the particles within the atom in fact only occupy about 10^{-12} of the total volume and that the value of the positive charge on the nucleus was numerically equal to approximately one half the atomic weight of the metal of which the foil was composed. In 1913 VAN DEN BROEK proposed that the atomic number of the element, itself approximately one half the atomic weight in many instances, was in fact identifiable with the number of

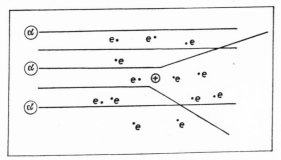

Figure 1.11. Alpha particle bombardment of atoms in metal foils

positive charges on the nucleus. This was verified shortly afterwards by MOSELEY from studies upon the x-ray spectra of elements of known atomic number.

RUTHERFORD, in addition, investigated the action of alpha particles upon various gases. Using nitrogen, he observed from Cloud Chamber experiments that occasionally collision occurred between an alpha particle and a nitrogen atom resulting in the formation of a proton (*Figure 1.12*). This reaction is represented as

$$^{14}_{7}N + ^{4}_{2}He \longrightarrow ^{1}_{1}H + ^{17}_{8}O$$

and is an artificial disintegration of the atomic nucleus. It may be considered generally as a two-stage process; firstly the coalescence of the alpha particle and the nitrogen nucleus with the formation of a compound nucleus and secondly the transformation of this nucleus, which is nearly always unstable, to a stable state by the emission of either a particle or gamma radiation.

This initial discovery was quickly followed by those of other workers in the same field and reactions such as

$$^{19}_{9}F + ^{4}_{2}He \longrightarrow ^{1}_{1}H + ^{12}_{10}Ne$$
$$^{23}_{11}Na + ^{4}_{2}He \longrightarrow ^{1}_{1}H + ^{26}_{12}Mg$$

were found to occur with elements of low atomic number.

The capture of an alpha particle did not lead unequivocally to the ejection of a proton by the compound nucleus. Thus in the case of the bombardment of beryllium, Bothe and Becker found a particularly penetrating type of radiation was emitted that caused protons to be ejected from paraffin wax placed in its path. This particular type of radiation was identified by Chadwick (1932) as characteristic of a particle of unit mass and zero charge—the *neutron*.

$$^9_4\text{Be} + ^4_2\text{He} \longrightarrow ^1_0\text{n} + ^{12}_6\text{C}$$

The bombardment of a positively charged nucleus by a positively charged particle, such as the alpha particle, immediately poses experimental problems. A potential barrier is set up by electrostatic repulsion and if a disintegration reaction is to be achieved this potential barrier must be overcome. In order to overcome this repulsion the particle must possess a high kinetic energy; that

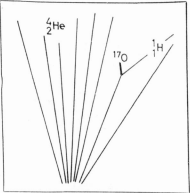

Figure 1.12. Representation of formation of the ^{17}O isotope by bombardment of ^{14}N by alpha particles

of the naturally produced alpha particles is in the range of 4–8 MeV and is sufficient only for reaction with the lightest elements.

Particles with the required kinetic energies are obtained by means of accelerating devices. The first success in this field was by Cockcroft and Walton (1932) who devised an instrument capable of producing high energy protons by accelerating them through a potential difference of the order of 500,000 volts. These protons achieved disintegrations of the lithium isotope, mass number seven, into two alpha particles:

$$^7_3\text{Li} + ^1_1\text{H} \longrightarrow 2\,^4_2\text{He}$$

Further research led to the development of the linear accelerator, the cyclotron and the synchrocyclotron enabling the production of protons with energies in excess of 400 MeV and alpha particles with energies greater than 50 MeV. Using these instruments, a large variety of induced disintegrations has been accomplished by bombardment of atoms with particles such as the proton, the deuteron (the ionized atom of hydrogen with mass number 2) and the alpha particle.

Neutrons, on the other hand, have no energy barrier to overcome and consequently are extremely useful in the field of radiochemistry. In particular, they are employed to a large extent for the production of artificially radioactive isotopes in the atomic pile.

Typical reactions induced by positively charged particles and yielding stable isotopes are given below:

(a) Proton induced

$$^{19}_{9}F + ^{1}_{1}H \longrightarrow ^{16}_{8}O + ^{4}_{2}He \quad \text{otherwise} \quad ^{19}_{9}F \ (p, \alpha) \ ^{16}_{8}O$$
$$^{27}_{13}Al + ^{1}_{1}H \longrightarrow ^{24}_{12}Mg + ^{4}_{2}He \qquad\qquad\quad ^{27}_{13}Al \ (p, \alpha) \ ^{24}_{12}Mg$$

(b) Deuteron induced

$$^{16}_{8}O + ^{2}_{1}H \longrightarrow ^{14}_{7}N + ^{4}_{2}He \quad \text{otherwise} \quad ^{16}_{8}O \ (d, \alpha) \ ^{14}_{7}N$$

(c) Alpha induced

$$^{27}_{13}Al + ^{4}_{2}He \longrightarrow ^{30}_{14}Si + ^{1}_{1}H \quad \text{otherwise} \quad ^{27}_{13}Al \ (\alpha, p) \ ^{30}_{14}Si$$

Artificial Radioactivity

The nuclear reactions dealt with above result in the formation of stable isotopes. This does not occur with every nuclear reaction. In many instances the nuclei first formed exhibit radioactivity. This production of radioactivity artificially was originally recognized by CURIE–JOLIOT during the bombardment of boron, magnesium and aluminium with alpha particles. This resulted in the formation of neutrons and positrons, the emission of the former being terminated by the removal of the bombarding source but not the positron emission which could still be detected and was observed to decay exponentially with time.

Taking aluminium as an example, this phenomenon was explained by the initial production of an unstable isotope that decayed by positron emission to a stable isotope of silicon. This hypothesis was confirmed (i) by dissolving the aluminium, after alpha bombardment, in hydrochloric acid. Evaporation to dryness gave a residue that had no activity, but the gas evolved during this chemical treatment, i.e. phosphine, was active; (ii) by dissolving the aluminium in aqua regia to give phosphoric acid which could be precipitated as radioactive phosphate.

The three nuclear reactions above were found to be as follows:

$$^{10}_{5}B + ^{4}_{2}He \longrightarrow ^{13}_{7}N \quad + \quad ^{1}_{0}n$$
$$\downarrow \quad t_{1/2} = 10 \text{ min}$$
$$^{13}_{6}C \quad + \quad ^{0}_{+1}e$$

$$^{24}_{12}Mg + ^{4}_{2}He \longrightarrow ^{27}_{14}Si \quad + \quad ^{1}_{0}n$$
$$\downarrow \quad t_{1/2} = 7 \text{ min}$$
$$^{27}_{13}Al \quad + \quad ^{0}_{+1}e$$

$$^{27}_{13}Al + ^{4}_{2}He \longrightarrow ^{30}_{15}P \quad + \quad ^{1}_{0}n$$
$$\downarrow \quad t_{1/2} = 3 \text{ min}$$
$$^{30}_{14}Si \quad + \quad ^{0}_{+1}e$$

Other transmutations effected include:

$$^{7}_{3}\text{Li} + ^{4}_{2}\text{He} \longrightarrow ^{10}_{4}\text{Be} + ^{1}_{1}\text{H}$$

$$\downarrow \quad t_{1/2} = 2 \cdot 7 \times 10^{6} \text{ yr}$$

$$^{10}_{5}\text{B} + _{-1}^{0}e$$

$$^{25}_{12}\text{Mg} + ^{4}_{2}\text{He} \longrightarrow ^{28}_{13}\text{Al} + ^{1}_{1}\text{H}$$

$$\downarrow \quad t_{1/2} = 2 \text{ min}$$

$$^{28}_{14}\text{Si} + _{-1}^{0}e$$

The positron or electron emission may produce a stable nucleus without further changes but frequently an excited nuclide is first formed and this loses energy by emission of gamma radiation.

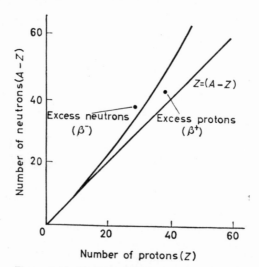

Figure 1.13. Nuclear stability curve. At low atomic numbers, the number of protons is approximately equal to the number of neutrons in stable nuclei. Radioactive nuclei are represented by points to the right and the left of the curve. (β^{-}) and (β^{+}) indicates electron and positron emitters respectively.

Neutron irradiation is particularly important for production of radioactive isotopes. This irradiation is carried out in an atomic pile where the neutrons are of two types (i) slow and (ii) fast, *i.e.* they have low or high kinetic energies. The reactions induced are (n, γ) and (n, α) respectively and the isotopes obtained are predominantly electron emitters. Types of reaction that may take place are (n, γ), (n, α), (n, p) and $(n, 2n)$ and examples of these are

$$^{23}_{11}\text{Na } (n, \gamma) \ ^{24}_{11}\text{Na} \longrightarrow ^{24}_{12}\text{Mg} + _{-1}^{0}e \quad (t_{1/2} = 15 \text{ h})$$

$$^{19}_{9}\text{F } (n, \alpha) \ ^{16}_{7}\text{N} \longrightarrow ^{16}_{8}\text{O} + _{-1}^{0}e \quad (t_{1/2} = 7 \cdot 4 \text{ sec})$$

$$^{14}_{7}\text{N } (n, p) \ ^{14}_{6}\text{C} \longrightarrow ^{14}_{7}\text{N} + _{-1}^{0}e \quad (t_{1/2} = 5600 \text{ yr})$$

$$^{31}_{15}\text{P } (n, 2n) \ ^{30}_{15}\text{P} \longrightarrow ^{30}_{14}\text{Si} + _{+1}^{0}e \quad (t_{1/2} = 3 \text{ min})$$

Whether the radioactive nucleus so produced is an electron or positron emitter may be deduced from *Figure 1.13* which is a plot of the number of protons against neutrons for stable nuclei of the elements. For the light elements this line has a slope of one, but with increasing atomic number the neutrons are in excess and the slope consequently is greater than one for the heavy nuclei. Nuclei with more protons than the stable nuclei lie to the right of this stability curve and decay by positron emission; those with excess neutrons lie to the left of the curve and decay by electron emission.

NUCLEAR FISSION

A study of the binding energy curve reveals that large quantities of energy are released when heavy nuclei are broken down into lighter ones. Spontaneous fission is only a rare phenomenon, but in 1939 it was found that fission could

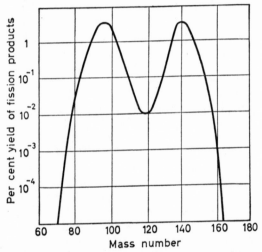

Figure 1.14. Distribution of fission products from ^{235}U. The fission products which are produced in greatest quantity are those of mass numbers in the region of 90 and 140

be induced in uranium by bombardment with neutrons, with the formation of a barium isotope as one of the products. Under such bombardment fission of ^{235}U occurs when the neutrons have relatively low velocities and fission of ^{238}U occurs with high velocity neutrons. In addition to the fission of the lighter isotope of uranium, slow neutrons also cause ^{233}U and ^{239}Pu to undergo fission.

The break-up of the compound nucleus into primary fission products occurs almost always into particles of unequal mass as indicated by *Figure 1.14* for the fission of ^{235}U by slow neutrons; concentration of the fission products occurs in the region of mass numbers 90 and 140 as indicated by the two maxima. The fission products in general have an excess of neutrons and decay by electron emission; also formed by the fission process are a number of neutrons. A possible mode of decay may be

$$^{235}_{92}U + ^{1}_{0}n \longrightarrow {}^{236}_{92}U \longrightarrow {}^{94}_{38}Sr + {}^{140}_{54}Xe + 2\,{}^{1}_{0}n + \gamma$$

19

and the two nuclei undergo electron emission to yield eventually $^{94}_{40}$Zr and $^{140}_{58}$Ce respectively.

The fact that two or more neutrons which may cause further fission are produced for every neutron consumed suggested that a *chain reaction* might be established which could be used as a source of large amounts of energy. Calculations show that a critical size of fissile material is required for a self-sustaining chain reaction to occur. When this size is exceeded the reaction can, in the absence of efficient neutron absorbers, proceed at a rate which is uncontrollable and terminate in an explosion. When pure ^{235}U is used in the atomic pile or nuclear reactor it is necessary to control the reaction by the introduction of neutron absorbers such as boron or cadmium. These make it possible to maintain a steady neutron level. Natural uranium contains only 0·7 per cent of this lighter isotope, the remainder being ^{238}U, and if used in the pile without separation from the latter, proves inefficient. Some of the heavy isotope is converted via neutron capture to ^{239}U and thence by electron emission to ^{239}Np and finally to ^{239}Pu, which is itself fissionable. In the pile, therefore, the fissile material gradually becomes converted to fission products which can absorb neutrons and cause the reaction to be no longer self-sustaining. The fuel rods are removed from time to time, stored for approximately 100 days to allow the short-lived fission products to decay, and then chemically treated by dissolution in nitric acid. Separation procedures are then applied; thus uranium and plutonium may be separated by solvent extraction (see p. 188).

Neutrons produced in such reactors are used, as already mentioned, for the production of radioactive nuclides, particularly by the (n, γ) type of reaction and also by (n, α) and (n, p) reactions. In the last two instances the product is non-isotopic with the target material and has to be separated from it; this may be achieved by methods such as solvent extraction, ion exchange, precipitation and high temperature distillation.

These radioactive isotopes are useful as *tracers*; that is, their activity may serve in the detection of the element concerned. Applications of such isotopes are numerous; thus ^{24}Na, ^{131}I and ^{32}P are useful in biological work; ^{60}Co is used in the treatment of cancer; others are used in the study of diffusion and corrosion and many are employed for elucidating the nature and mechanism of chemical reactions.

Since the fission of the fuel in the reactor produces a vast amount of energy in the form of heat, cooling is necessary. This is accomplished by circulating a suitable fluid through the reactor; such fluids must have high thermal conductivities, high specific heats and should not significantly capture or be affected by neutrons. Typical coolants include water, air, carbon dioxide and molten sodium. The conversion of this energy via a heat exchanger to electrical power, thereby supplementing the present world supplies, is one of the major peacetime applications of nuclear fission.

NUCLEAR FUSION

The second source of nuclear power is from the fusion of lighter elements into heavier nuclei. This process is the source of energy from the sun and also the basis of the hydrogen bomb.

Various reactions have been proposed for the production of stellar energy. One, involving six steps and known as the carbon cycle (a), is thought to be responsible for the energy of the brightest stars. With the cooler stars the energy is thought to arise from a smaller cycle that involves proton–proton reaction (b).

(a)

$$^{12}_{6}C + ^{1}_{1}H \longrightarrow ^{13}_{7}N$$
$$^{13}_{7}N \longrightarrow ^{13}_{6}C + ^{0}_{+1}e$$
$$^{13}_{6}C + ^{1}_{1}H \longrightarrow ^{14}_{7}N$$
$$^{14}_{7}N + ^{1}_{1}H \longrightarrow ^{15}_{8}O$$
$$^{15}_{8}O \longrightarrow ^{15}_{7}N + ^{0}_{+1}e$$
$$^{15}_{7}N + ^{1}_{1}H \longrightarrow ^{12}_{6}C + ^{4}_{2}He$$

(b)

$$^{1}_{1}H + ^{1}_{1}H \longrightarrow ^{2}_{1}H + ^{0}_{+1}e$$
$$^{2}_{1}H + ^{1}_{1}H \longrightarrow ^{3}_{2}He$$
$$^{3}_{2}He + ^{1}_{1}H \longrightarrow ^{4}_{2}He + ^{0}_{+1}e$$

These reactions suffer from the disadvantage that they are realized only at extremely high temperatures (about 10^6 to 10^7 °C). Such temperatures are difficult to obtain on earth and as yet have been obtained only momentarily by a fission process which is used to promote the fusion process in the hydrogen bomb.

TRANSURANIC ELEMENTS

The discovery of elements beyond uranium in the Periodic Table arose from nuclear bombardment experiments. Thus the bombardment of ^{238}U by fairly fast neutrons produces an extremely unstable isotope of uranium that decays by emission of an electron to an isotope of element 93, named neptunium

$$^{238}_{92}U + ^{1}_{0}n \longrightarrow ^{239}_{92}U \xrightarrow{t_{1/2} = 23 \text{ min}} ^{239}_{93}Np + ^{0}_{-1}e$$

The isotope of neptunium so obtained is itself unstable and decays further by electron emission to element 94, named plutonium

$$^{239}_{93}Np \xrightarrow{t_{1/2} = 2 \cdot 3 \text{ day}} ^{239}_{94}Pu + ^{0}_{-1}e + \gamma$$

This isotope of plutonium has a long half-life $(2 \cdot 4 \times 10^4$ years) decaying by alpha emission to ^{235}U.

Element 95, americium, is produced by several methods:

(a) bombardment of ^{238}U by accelerated alpha particles (40 MeV)

$$^{238}_{92}U + ^{4}_{2}He \longrightarrow ^{241}_{94}Pu + ^{1}_{0}n$$

$$^{241}_{94}Pu \xrightarrow{t_{1/2} = 10 \text{ yr}} ^{241}_{95}Am + ^{0}_{-1}e$$

and (b) by the process ^{239}Pu (n, γ) $\rightarrow$ ^{240}Pu (n, γ) $\rightarrow$ ^{241}Pu which then decays as in (a).

The decay of ^{241}Am occurs by alpha particle emission of half-life 5000 years.

Isotopes of element 96 (curium) have been obtained by alpha particle

2+M.A.I.C.   21

bombardment of ^{239}Pu (α, n) and by the reaction ^{241}Am $(n, \gamma) \rightarrow {}^{242}$Am which decays by electron emission to ^{242}Cm.

Accelerated alpha particles have also been used in the production of element 97, berkelium, and element 98, californium. The reactions involved are

$$^{241}_{95}\text{Am} + {}^{4}_{2}\text{He} \longrightarrow {}^{243}_{97}\text{Bk} + 2\,{}^{1}_{0}\text{n}$$

$$^{243}_{97}\text{Bk} \underset{t_{1/2}=4\cdot5\,\text{h}}{\overset{K\text{-capture}}{\longrightarrow}} {}^{243}_{96}\text{Cm}$$

and

$$^{242}_{96}\text{Cm} + {}^{4}_{2}\text{He} \longrightarrow {}^{244}_{98}\text{Cf} + 2\,{}^{1}_{0}\text{n}$$

Bombardment with heavy ions* has also been of use in effecting transmutations of this type. Thus accelerated stripped carbon atoms (C^{6+}) have enabled the 246 isotope of californium to be prepared by the reaction

$$^{238}_{92}\text{U} + {}^{12}_{6}\text{C} \longrightarrow {}^{246}_{98}\text{Cf} + 4\,{}^{1}_{0}\text{n}$$

Eleven isotopes have been reported for this element.

Element 99, einsteinium, has been prepared as follows

$$^{238}_{92}\text{U} + {}^{14}_{7}\text{N} \longrightarrow {}^{248}_{99}\text{Es} + 4\,{}^{1}_{0}\text{n}$$

and element 100, fermium, has been prepared by a similar technique using accelerated oxygen ions. These two elements have also been obtained by irradiation of ^{239}Pu in an intense neutron flux when repeated neutron capture and electron emission occurs. Eleven isotopes of the former and eight of the latter have been made.

The preparation of element 101, mendelevium, was achieved in 1955 by bombarding small amounts of ^{253}Es with 41 MeV alpha particles; this resulted in the formation of ^{256}Md by an (α, n) reaction, the product decaying by spontaneous fission.

Various reports of the synthesis of element 102, nobelium, have been forthcoming but some have not been capable of repetition. A short-lived isotope ^{254}No has been prepared by the bombardment of ^{246}Cm with accelerated ^{12}C ions.

Recently the transmutation of an isotope of californium by bombardment with accelerated ^{10}B ions has been reported. This resulted in the production of an isotope of the final element in the actinide series, element 103, for which the suggested name is lawrencium.

SUGGESTED REFERENCES FOR FURTHER READING

ASTON, F. W. *Mass Spectra and Isotopes*, 2nd edn, Arnold, London, 1941.
GLASSTONE, S. *Sourcebook on Atomic Energy*, 2nd edn, Van Nostrand, Princeton, 1958.
TOLANSKY, S. *Introduction to Atomic Physics*, 4th edn, Longmans Green, London, 1961.

* The process of bombardment with heavy ions is useful in that it allows an element of much higher atomic number to be synthesized by a single step; otherwise a process such as repeated neutron capture would have to be used.

ATOMIC STRUCTURE — 2

QUANTUM THEORY AND ATOMIC SPECTRA

Towards the end of the nineteenth century the introduction of a wave theory of light by Huygens enabled explanations for certain properties of light such as diffraction and interference to be given; these phenomena had been previously inexplicable on the Newtonian corpuscular theory. In addition to this, scientists became aware of certain inadequacies in other branches of classical theory; thus both Wien and Rayleigh were unable to give completely satisfactory interpretations of the phenomenon of 'black-body radiation'. In 1900, however, Planck derived an empirical relationship that completely satisfied the data from experiments on 'black-body radiation' and by introducing a concept of 'quantization of energy' he was able to justify the relationship theoretically. It had been shown that at a specific temperature the spectrum of radiation from a 'black body' was unique in its characteristics and that the energy varied throughout the spectrum and possessed a maximum

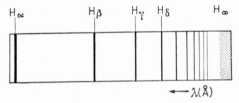

Figure 2.1. Visible spectrum of atomic hydrogen

value at one particular wavelength for one temperature of emission. Planck proposed that the 'black body' was composed of many vibrating bodies or oscillators that were emitting or absorbing energy in packets or 'quanta' of energy. Such quanta had energy values dependent on the frequency of radiation ν and were emitted as photons of energy E, where

$$E = h\nu \qquad \dots \quad (1)$$

in which h is Planck's constant, equal to $6 \cdot 6252 \times 10^{-27}$ erg sec.

An analysis of the radiation emitted by bodies, using a spectrometer, results in the production of a spectrum. Spectra of this type may be obtained by examination of atoms or molecules excited to states of higher energy by the application of heat, by electrical discharge or by bombardment with high speed electrons. A return of the system to its lower energy states results in the emission of energy as radiations of definite wavelengths. With gases these emission spectra take the form of a series of sharply defined lines distributed throughout the spectral region; for instance, the analysis of radiation emitted by hydrogen gas when subjected to an electrical discharge at low pressures results in just such a spectrum (*Figure 2.1*), some of the lines being visible to the naked eye. This spectrum of atomic hydrogen is the simplest one known but at first no satisfactory explanation of the spectral lines was forthcoming. Success at interpreting the lines was achieved by BALMER (1885) who showed that the wavelengths of certain lines in the spectrum were related by the equation

$$\lambda = 3645 \cdot 6 \frac{n^2}{n^2-4} \; \text{Å} \qquad \qquad \cdots \cdots \; (2)$$

where n is any integer from three upwards and $1 \; \text{Å} = 10^{-8}$ cm (*Table 2.1*).

Other lines have since been shown to be related by a general formula

$$\lambda = 3645 \cdot 6 \frac{n^2}{n^2-m^2} \; \text{Å} \qquad \qquad \cdots \cdots \; (3)$$

n and m being integers $(n > m)$. Different series of lines are recognized in the spectrum depending on the values of n and m. These are:

Lyman series	$m = 1$;	$n = 2, 3, 4$, *etc.*
Balmer series	$m = 2$;	$n = 3, 4, 5$, *etc.*
Paschen series	$m = 3$;	$n = 4, 5, 6$, *etc.*
Brackett series	$m = 4$;	$n = 5, 6, 7$, *etc.*
Pfund series	$m = 5$;	$n = 6, 7, 8$, *etc.*

Expression (2) may be rearranged to give the frequency of radiation emitted. Using the relationship $\nu = c/\lambda$, where c is the velocity of light and ν is the frequency of radiation, leads to the expression

$$\nu = \frac{c(n^2-4)}{3645 \cdot 6 n^2}$$

$$= Rc \left\{ \frac{1}{2^2} - \frac{1}{n^2} \right\} \qquad \qquad \cdots \cdots \; (4)$$

where R is known as the Rydberg constant.

Attempts to explain the line spectrum of hydrogen by means of the Rutherford concept of the atom proved unsuccessful. This model, it will be recalled,

Table 2.1. *Comparison of wavelengths of the first four lines of the Balmer series (i) observed and (ii) calculated from the Balmer formula*

Line	n	$\lambda_{observed}$ Å	$\lambda_{calculated}$ Å
H_α	3	6562·1	6562·08
H_β	4	4860·7	4860·8
H_γ	5	4340·1	4340·0
H_δ	6	4101·2	4101·3

consisted of a central positive nucleus surrounded by electrons sufficient in number to give electroneutrality to the atom; these were assumed to rotate about the nucleus in a manner resembling the motion of planets about the sun, similar forces being envisaged to maintain the electrons in orbit as keep the planets rotating. In the case of the hydrogen atom there is one electron and the picture is a reasonably simple one. When, however, this model was used in an attempt to interpret the atomic spectrum certain flaws became apparent; thus the uniform motion of the electron about the nucleus, with its acceleration, arising from centrifugal forces, towards the centre of the orbit, would according to the theory of MAXWELL require radiation to be emitted continuously. As we have already seen, the spectrum is discontinuous.

Bohr Theory of Atomic Spectra

In 1913, BOHR proposed his theory for the explanation of the spectrum of atomic hydrogen using as his foundation the quantum theory of PLANCK. In this theory two assumptions were made:

(a) that the electrons in any atom could exist in a number of orbits and rotate about the nucleus in these without emitting radiation. The energy is quantized by placing the electrons in orbits of constant energy or 'stationary states'. Furthermore, BOHR extended PLANCK's theory by postulating that the electrons had angular momenta equal in value to integral multiples of $h/2\pi$.

(b) that radiation was emitted only when an electron jumped from one stationary state to another of lower energy. In making such a transition, a quantum of energy equal to $h\nu$ would be emitted where

$$h\nu = E_n - E_m \qquad \cdot \quad \cdot \quad \cdot \quad \cdot \quad (5)$$

and $E_n > E_m$, these being the energies of the two quantized energy states.

Let us now consider the application of these two basic assumptions to the case in hand.

The angular momentum of an electron, mass m, travelling in a circular orbit of radius r about the nucleus, with velocity v, is mvr. Utilizing the first of the above assumptions,

$$mvr = nh/2\pi \qquad \cdot \quad \cdot \quad \cdot \quad \cdot \quad (6)$$

where n is any integer.

The total energy (E) of the electron is the sum of its kinetic and potential energies. The former is equal to $\frac{1}{2}mv^2$ and the latter at a distance r from the nucleus is $-e^2/r$, where e is the electronic charge. Hence

$$E = \tfrac{1}{2}mv^2 - e^2/r \qquad \cdot \quad \cdot \quad \cdot \quad \cdot \quad (7)$$

In order for the electron to remain in its orbit, the centrifugal force (mv^2/r) must be equal to the force of electrostatic attraction between the nucleus and the electron (e^2/r^2). Hence

$$\frac{mv^2}{r} = \frac{e^2}{r^2}$$

$$\text{or} \quad \tfrac{1}{2}mv^2 = \frac{e^2}{2r} \qquad \cdot \quad \cdot \quad \cdot \quad \cdot \quad (8)$$

Substituting in equation (7) leads to

$$E = -\tfrac{1}{2}mv^2 \qquad \qquad \cdots \cdots \quad (9)$$

but from equation (6) it can be seen that

$$\tfrac{1}{2}mv = \frac{nh}{4\pi r}$$

and substituting this in equation (8)

$$v = \frac{2\pi e^2}{nh}$$

Hence
$$E = \frac{-\tfrac{1}{2}m4\pi^2 e^4}{n^2 h^2}$$

$$= -\frac{2\pi^2 me^4}{n^2 h^2} \qquad \cdots \cdots \quad (10)$$

Alternatively it may be said that the energy required to remove the electron from its orbit to infinity is (10) but with a positive sign; the larger this value, the more stable the system, $i.e.$ the most stable system is found for $n=1$. Also the radii of various orbits are given by

$$r = \frac{n^2 h^2}{4\pi^2 me^2} \qquad \cdots \cdots \quad (11)$$

$$i.e. \quad r \propto n^2$$

For $n=1$ and 2, the values of the radii are respectively 0·53 Å and 2·12 Å (by substituting the values of m, e and h in equation (11)).
    Application of the second assumption allows us to calculate the energy of the emitted radiation. If the electron is excited to a state of principal quantum number (n) equal to n_2 and returns to one of lower energy where $n=n_1$, then a quantum of energy is emitted equal to the difference in energy between the two states, thus

$$h\nu = E_{n_2} - E_{n_1}$$

$$\text{or} \quad \nu = \frac{2\pi^2 me^4}{h^3}\left\{\frac{1}{n_1^2} - \frac{1}{n_2^2}\right\} \qquad \cdots \cdots \quad (12)$$

Equation (12) will be seen to be identical with the rearranged form of Balmer equation (4) where $R = 2\pi^2 me^4/h^3 c$.
    Substituting $\bar{\nu} = \nu/c$ in (12) gives the energy of emitted radiation in wavenumbers or reciprocal centimetres (cm^{-1})

$$\bar{\nu} = \frac{2\pi^2 me^4}{h^3 c}\left\{\frac{1}{n_1^2} - \frac{1}{n_2^2}\right\} \qquad \cdots \cdots \quad (13)$$

The energy values of various transitions are thus dependent upon the values of n_1 and n_2; these are shown in the energy level diagram (*Figure 2.2*) which also shows the origin of the various spectral lines. Agreement between experiment and theory proves to be close; thus the experimental value of the Rydberg constant is 109,677·58 cm^{-1} compared with the calculated value using equation (13) of 109,737·31 cm^{-1}. Though this is a small discrepancy, it is possible to account for it. The approach used above has been one based on a fixed nucleus, whereas in fact rotation about a common centre of gravity should have been considered. This leads to a readjustment of equation (13) which becomes

$$\bar{\nu} = \frac{2\pi^2\mu e^4}{h^3 c}\left\{\frac{1}{n_1^2} - \frac{1}{n_2^2}\right\} \qquad \cdots \cdots \quad (14)$$

where the electron mass has been replaced by a reduced mass μ given by

$$\mu = mM/(m+M)$$

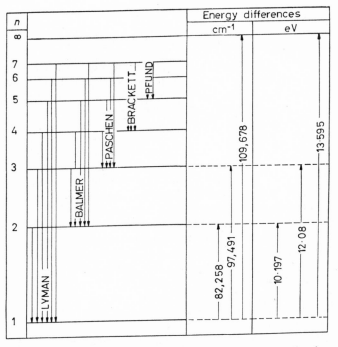

Figure 2.2. Energy level diagram for the hydrogen atom showing transitions responsible for the various spectral series

M being the mass of the hydrogen nucleus. The values of the Rydberg constant are thus dependent upon the nuclear mass, and the value of $R = 109,737·31$ cm^{-1} is therefore that of a nucleus of infinite mass and is written as R_∞. This variation of R with mass of the nucleus has important consequences. Thus the spectral investigation of residues from the evaporation of liquid hydrogen showed a faint spectral line close to the H_α line. This line may be accounted for by the presence of an isotope of hydrogen of mass number two which has a Rydberg constant of 109,707·42 cm^{-1}. This would give a line approximately 1·8 Å distant from the H_α line. This isotope effect is quite common in spectral observations.

The energy for any one level of the hydrogen atom may be written as

$$E_n = \frac{-R_{\mathrm{H}}hc}{n^2} \qquad \cdots \cdots \quad (15)$$

and thus the difference between the *ground state* and the first *excited state* is $\frac{3}{4}R_{\mathrm{H}}hc = \frac{3}{4}E_{n_1}$; this energy difference is referred to as the first *excitation potential* of the hydrogen atom. The ground state has an energy E_{n_1} which may be expressed in different units

e.g. $\quad E_{n_1} = 109{,}677 \cdot 58\ \mathrm{cm}^{-1} = -13 \cdot 595\ \mathrm{eV} = -313 \cdot 55\ \mathrm{kcal/g\ atom}$

Throughout this text energies will be quoted in kilocalories (1 eV = 23·06 kcal/g atom).

Modifications of the Bohr Theory

The first extension to the simple theory of BOHR was made by SOMMERFIELD who proposed the subdivision of the principal quantum levels into sets of sub-levels and introduced a second or subsidiary quantum number (k) which together with n defined a series of elliptical orbits. The orbits of different k but same n were shown to possess only slightly different energies; electron transitions involving these orbits gave rise to additional spectral lines. The ratio of n/k defined the ratio of the major to the minor axis of the elliptical orbit; thus $n=k$ would correspond to a circular orbit. The value of $k=0$ was excluded since it necessitated the oscillation of the electron through the nucleus. In more recent work this quantum number has been replaced by l, where $l=(k-1)$ and takes the values of 0, 1, 2, 3 to $(n-1)$. Not all transitions between energy states are possible; they are governed by a selection rule that states 'such transitions, either in emission or absorption spectra, are governed by the principle that n may change arbitrarily but l may change only by ± 1'.

Further spectral lines are produced when the atoms emitting the radiation are placed in a strong magnetic field (Zeeman effect) and in order to explain this splitting of energy levels a third quantum number was introduced which defined the possible orientations that the plane containing the electron orbit could assume with respect to the applied magnetic field. This quantum number can take the values $-l \rightarrow 0 \rightarrow +l$ and is designated m_l, the magnetic quantum number.

Finally a fourth quantum number, the spin quantum number m_s, was introduced to account for certain double lines in the spectra of alkali metals (UHLENBECK and GOUDSMIDT). The electron is regarded as spinning about some axis through its centre thereby possessing a magnetic moment. An electron in a particular energy level can, in fact, have two slightly differing energy values depending on the alternative orientations of this moment, that is, on the two possible directions of spin. This spin can be described in terms of m_s which has values $\pm\frac{1}{2}$.

The Bohr–Sommerfeld theory proved to be but temporarily successful in its interpretation of atomic spectra for, although it could be satisfactorily applied to hydrogen-like species or one-electron systems, inaccurate results were obtained when systems containing more than one electron were considered. It became obvious that if further advances were to be made an entirely new approach to the problem would be necessary.

WAVE MECHANICS

The new method originated in a hypothesis by DE BROGLIE (1924) who suggested that an electron in motion should have wave properties associated with it that could be described by the equation

$$\lambda = h/mv \qquad \qquad \cdots \cdots (16)$$

where λ is the wavelength of the associated wave property and v is the velocity of the electron. The wave nature of the electron was shown by DAVISSON and GERMER (1927) who succeeded in diffracting a beam of electrons by means of a crystal lattice in a manner similar to the diffraction of x-rays. The first application of this hypothesis to the problem of atomic structure was made by SCHRÖDINGER (1925) and later by DIRAC and by HEISENBERG. Their work laid the foundations of the methods of wave mechanics which is a more sophisticated approach than that of BOHR, though it may be shown quite readily that the Bohr theory is a special solution of this more general treatment. The basic assumption made is that the electron orbits can only exist where the waves associated with them reinforce one another, that is to say, a standing wave is set up. In an orbit of radius r therefore

$$n\lambda = 2\pi r \qquad \qquad \cdots \cdots (17)$$

Substituting from equation (16) gives

$$mvr = nh/2\pi$$

in other words quantization is a natural outcome of the wave theory.

The method of wave mechanics involves a reconciliation of the wave and particle properties of the electron and describes the system in terms of ψ, a function of the co-ordinates of the electron and time. Such a function is a solution of the wave equation that describes the amplitude of the electron as a wave. An integration of the square of this wave function over definite limits in space allows an estimate to be made of the probability of finding the electron within these limits. The idealized system of orbits envisaged by BOHR is now replaced by this probability concept. The dual nature of the electron means that any measurement of its position immediately places some uncertainty upon its momentum and vice versa. This point is embodied in the *Heisenberg Uncertainty Principle* which states that 'it is impossible to determine simultaneously with any degree of precision both the momentum and the position of an electron'. HEISENBERG showed that if Δx were the uncertainty in determining the position and Δp that in determining the momentum, then

$$\Delta x . \Delta p \geqslant h/2\pi$$

Instead of speaking of an electron moving in an orbit of fixed radius the wave-mechanical approach uses the term orbital to describe a certain volume within which the electron has a probability of being found.

The equation showing the variation of the amplitude, ψ, with space and time was first given by SCHRÖDINGER as

$$\nabla^2\psi + \frac{8\pi^2\mu}{h^2}(E-V)\psi = 0 \qquad \cdots \quad (18)$$

where $\nabla^2\psi$ is the sum $\partial^2\psi/\partial x^2 + \partial^2\psi/\partial y^2 + \partial^2\psi/\partial z^2$, E and V are the total and potential energies respectively of the electron.

Solutions to equation (18) are numerous, but for a standing wave only certain solutions are permissible, being rigorously governed by a set of boundary conditions that require solutions to be finite, continuous and single-valued. The equation may be solved by transforming to a system of spherical polar co-ordinates in place of the cartesian co-ordinate system of x, y and z. The wave equation then becomes a function of three variables, r (radial) and θ and ϕ (angular); this conversion allows the equation to be broken down into three simpler equations that depend on r, θ and ϕ separately. Solutions to these

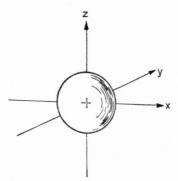

Figure 2.3. Boundary surface for $1s$ electron

equations may only be obtained by the introduction of certain constants, the values of which are determined by the boundary conditions. Although the mathematics is rather complex, it can be shown that these constants are integral and may be identified with the three previously defined quantum numbers n, l and m_l.

For the hydrogen atom in the ground state the solution of the Schrödinger equation gives a wave function that is dependent upon r only; it is in fact spherically symmetrical and the values of n, l and m_l are 1, 0 and 0 respectively. Various methods of representation of the nature of this wave function have been used, perhaps the simplest is that of drawing (*Figure 2.3*) a boundary surface or contour of constant ψ value such that the electron has a certain chance, say 95 per cent, of being found within this surface. This boundary surface represents the $1s$ atomic orbital. This type of representation proves sufficiently adequate for many purposes and will be used frequently in subsequent chapters.

Another useful approach is to plot the radial density or $4\pi r^2\psi^2 \cdot dr$ (the probability of the electron being found in a volume between r and $r+dr$ from the nucleus) against r. This is given in *Figure 2.4* for the ground state of the

30

hydrogen atom; it is interesting to note that the radial density reaches a maximum at a distance r_0 from the nucleus which is equal to the value of the radius of the first Bohr orbit.

Other solutions of the Schrödinger equation for the hydrogen atom may be obtained that represent excited states of the atom. For instance, a second solution occurs for $n=2$, $l=0$ and $m_l=0$; this again is dependent upon r only and represents a spherically symmetrical orbital in which the average electron density is further away from the nucleus than in the $1s$, the maximum radial

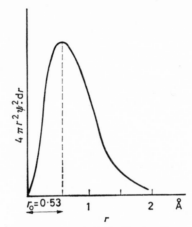

Figure 2.4. Radial distribution function of the $1s$ electron of hydrogen

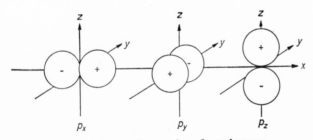

Figure 2.5. Boundary surfaces for p electrons

density occurring at $r=2\cdot16$ Å. This is the $2s$ orbital of the hydrogen atom. For $n=2$ there are also solutions where $l=1$ and $m_l=\pm1$ and 0; these depend upon the radial functions in addition to r and are unsymmetrical. Boundary surfaces are drawn for these in *Figure 2.5*, one lobe has a positive ψ while the other has a negative ψ; these three orbitals, referred to as the $2p$, are mutually perpendicular and are directed along the x, y and z axes respectively. Solutions for $n=3$ besides giving the $3s$ and $3p$ orbitals also give five d orbitals characterized by $l=2$, as shown in *Figure 2.6*. With $n=4$, in addition to s, p and d orbitals, seven f orbitals are formed, characterized by $l=3$.

31

Each orbital may accommodate a maximum of two electrons having spin quantum numbers of $+\frac{1}{2}$ and $-\frac{1}{2}$; such electrons are termed paired, having antiparallel spins. Electrons having parallel spins are termed unpaired and

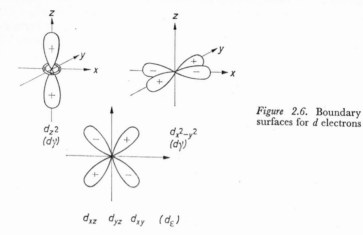

d_{z^2}
$(d\gamma)$

$d_{x^2-y^2}$
$(d\gamma)$

Figure 2.6. Boundary surfaces for *d* electrons

d_{xz} d_{yz} d_{xy} (d_ε)

Table 2.2 Quantum numbers for the various electrons in the first three shells

n	l	m_t	m_s	Nomenclature	
				Electron	Shell
1	0	0	$+\frac{1}{2}$	1s	K
1	0	0	$-\frac{1}{2}$		$\sum e=2$
2	0	0	$+\frac{1}{2}$	2s	
2	0	0	$-\frac{1}{2}$		
2	1	0	$+\frac{1}{2}$		
2	1	0	$-\frac{1}{2}$		L
2	1	+1	$+\frac{1}{2}$		$\sum e=8$
2	1	+1	$-\frac{1}{2}$	2p	
2	1	−1	$+\frac{1}{2}$		
2	1	−1	$-\frac{1}{2}$		
3	0	0	$+\frac{1}{2}$	3s	
3	0	0	$-\frac{1}{2}$		
3	1	0	$+\frac{1}{2}$		
3	1	0	$-\frac{1}{2}$		
3	1	+1	$+\frac{1}{2}$		
3	1	+1	$-\frac{1}{2}$	3p	
3	1	−1	$+\frac{1}{2}$		
3	1	−1	$-\frac{1}{2}$		M
3	2	0	$+\frac{1}{2}$		$\sum e=18$
3	2	0	$-\frac{1}{2}$		
3	2	+1	$+\frac{1}{2}$		
3	2	+1	$-\frac{1}{2}$		
3	2	−1	$+\frac{1}{2}$		
3	2	−1	$-\frac{1}{2}$	3d	
3	2	+2	$+\frac{1}{2}$		
3	2	+2	$-\frac{1}{2}$		
3	2	−2	$+\frac{1}{2}$		
3	2	−2	$-\frac{1}{2}$		

cannot be found in the same orbital. These concepts are of fundamental importance in the interpretation of the properties of chemical compounds. In the hydrogen atom itself there is only one electron in the $1s$ orbital. In elements of higher atomic number electrons are present in the other types of orbital. Energy levels where there are several equivalent orbitals are spoken of as degenerate orbital levels. The s levels are non-degenerate, p levels are threefold degenerate, the d levels are fivefold degenerate and the f levels are sevenfold degenerate.

Whereas, for the hydrogen atom, atomic orbitals with the same principal quantum number are of the same energy, shielding effects of the inner electrons with the heavier atoms cause distinct separations of the levels and the individual electron energies are affected by interelectronic repulsion. Exact

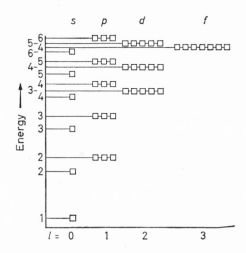

Figure 2.7. Approximate energy level diagram of orbitals in atoms. Each square represents one orbital into which two electrons with paired spins may be placed

solutions of the Schrödinger equation cannot be obtained and various approximations have to be introduced to enable the equation to be solved. This still leads to the electrons being defined by a set of quantum numbers and the shapes of the orbitals resemble those of the hydrogen atom but are of different size.

The number of electrons that may be accommodated in the various principal quantum shells and their notation for $n=1$, 2, 3 are given in *Table 2.2*.

Relative displacements of the energy levels have been determined from spectroscopic observations and for the elements of low atomic number $(Z<20)$ the ascending order of energy is

$$1s < 2s < 2p < 3s < 3p < 4s < 3d < 4p < 5s < 4d < 5p < 6s < 5d < 4f$$

as shown in *Figure 2.7*. With increasing atomic number the relative positions of the levels change until for the heaviest elements the order is as given in *Figure 2.8*.

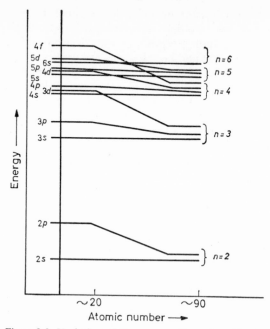

Figure 2.8. Variation of the energy of atomic orbitals with atomic number (adapted from HERZBERG, G. *Atomic Spectra and Atomic Structure*, Dover Publications, New York, 1944)

PERIODIC CLASSIFICATION AND ELECTRONIC CONFIGURATION

The way in which electrons arrange themselves in the atomic orbitals available is the key to the periodic classification of the elements. There are two fundamental rules relating to electronic configurations. The first is that electrons are accommodated in the orbitals of lowest energy first; combined with this rule is HUND's rule of *Maximum Multiplicity* which states that when electrons are present in a number of degenerate orbitals they occupy all the orbitals singly, with parallel spins, before pairing in any one orbital occurs. Thus if there are three electrons to be accommodated in the $2p$ level, the arrangement will be

1	1	1

and not

1↓	1	

The second principle is one of an empirical nature, deduced from a careful study of atomic spectra and correlation of the data with quantum theory. It was enunciated by PAULI (1925)—the *Pauli Exclusion Principle*—and states

34

that no two electrons in any one atom may be described by the same set of four quantum numbers. It is obvious from this principle that electrons with parallel spins cannot be accommodated in the same orbital and therefore those in the same orbital must have antiparallel spins.

Applying these principles to the electronic configuration of the elements, the simplest case is that of the single electron in the hydrogen atom, i.e. $Z=1$, where the electron enters the $1s$ orbital and the electronic configuration is written as $1s^1$.

For helium, where $Z=2$, the electrons are paired in the orbital of lowest energy with $m_s=+\frac{1}{2}$ and $-\frac{1}{2}$, $n=1$, $l=0$ and $m_l=0$. The electronic configuration is $1s^2$.

Table 2.3. Electronic configurations of the elements H to Ne

Element	Electronic configuration
H	$1s^1$
He	$1s^2$
Li	$1s^2 2s^1$
Be	$1s^2 2s^2$
B	$1s^2 2s^2 2p^1$
C	$1s^2 2s^2 2p^1 2p^1$ }Parallel spins
N	$1s^2 2s^2 2p^1 2p^1 2p^1$
O	$1s^2 2s^2 2p^2 2p^1 2p^1$
F	$1s^2 2s^2 2p^2 2p^2 2p^1$ }Pairing of spins
Ne	$1s^2 2s^2 2p^2 2p^2 2p^2$

This completes the K shell and for elements of higher atomic number the outer orbital levels start to fill up. For lithium the electronic configuration is written $1s^2 2s^1$. To obtain the electronic configuration of any element all that is required is to take that of the preceding element and to place the additional electron into the appropriate orbital with due regard for the two fundamental rules stated above. This process is termed the *Aufbau* or building-up process. Thus we may write down the electronic configurations of the first ten elements in the periodic table (*Table 2.3*). The electronic configurations from Na to Ca follow a similar pattern with the filling up of the $3s$, $3p$ and $4s$ orbitals. After Ca, $1s^2 2s^2 2p^6 3s^2 3p^6 4s^2$, the $3d$ orbitals are the nearest vacant ones and the $3d$ level starts to fill up. The series of ten elements ending at zinc, which are thereby obtained, constitute the *First Transition Series*. Within this series there is some irregularity in filling up; chromium and copper have the respective configurations $3d^5 4s^1$ and $3d^{10} 4s^1$ and not the expected $3d^4 4s^2$ and $3d^9 4s^2$. The half-filled or completely filled inner quantum level appears to have a certain added stability; this also shows itself in the stability of certain ions of the transition metals (p. 250). After zinc the $4p$ level starts to fill up and is complete at Kr. The *Second Transition Series* is found after Sr and the $5p$ level is complete at Xe.

In the next series of elements beginning at Cs an *Inner Transition Series* is observed. In the elements Cs and Ba the electrons enter the $6s$ level; La has the configuration $5d^1 6s^2$ but element 58 (cerium) does not, however, have the configuration $5d^2 6s^2$ but $4f^2 5d^0 6s^2$ and thereafter the $4f$ level continues to fill up. In such an inner transition series where the outer orbital configuration is unaltered and electrons are entering an inner quantum level, chemical resemblances are particularly noticeable. Here again the filling of the inner quantum level is not entirely regular and the $4f^7$ and $4f^{14}$ arrangements appear to be of added stability. The $6p$ level is filled up from Tl to Rn and the $7s$ level fills up as expected. With elements above atomic number 90, there is a

Table 2.4. Electron configurations for atoms in their ground states

Element	Z	1s	2s 2p	3s 3p	3d	4s 4p	4d 4f	5s 5p	5d	5f	6s 6p	6d 6f	7s
H	1	1											
He	2	2											
Li	3	2	1										
Be	4	2	2										
B	5	2	2 1										
C	6	2	2 2										
N	7	2	2 3										
O	8	2	2 4										
F	9	2	2 5										
Ne	10	2	2 6										
Na	11	2	2 6	1									
Mg	12			2									
Al	13		10	2 1									
Si	14		Ne Core	2 2									
P	15			2 3									
S	16			2 4									
Cl	17			2 5									
Ar	18			2 6									
K	19	2	2 6	2 6		1							
Ca	20					2							
Sc	21				1	2							
Ti	22				2	2							
V	23				3	2							
Cr	24				5	1							
Mn	25		18		5	2							
Fe	26		Ar Core		6	2							
Co	27				7	2							
Ni	28				8	2							
Cu	29				10	1							
Zn	30				10	2							
Ga	31				10	2 1							
Ge	32				10	2 2							
As	33				10	2 3							
Se	34				10	2 4							
Br	35				10	2 5							
Kr	36				10	2 6							
Rb	37	2	2 6	2 6 10		2 6		1					
Sr	38							2					
Y	39						1	2					
Zr	40						2	2					
Nb	41						4	1					
Mo	42						5	1					
Tc	43						(5)	(2)*					
Ru	44			36			7	1					
Rh	45			Kr Core			8	1					
Pd	46						10	0					
Ag	47						10	1					
Cd	48						10	2					
In	49						10	2 1					
Sn	50						10	2 2					
Sb	51						10	2 3					
Te	52						10	2 4					
I	53						10	2 5					
Xe	54						10	2 6					

Table 2.4. (contd.)

Element	z	1s	2s 2p	3s 3p 3d	4s 4p 4d	4f	5s 5p	5d	5f	6s 6p	6d 6f	7s
Cs	55	2	2 6	2 6 10	2 6 10		2 6			1		
Ba	56			46			8			2		
La	57							1		2		
Ce	58					(2)				(2)		
Pr	59					(3)				(2)		
Nd	60					(4)				(2)		
Pm	61					(5)				(2)		
Sm	62					6				2		
Eu	63					7				2		
Gd	64					7		(1)		2		
Tb	65					(8)		(1)		(2)		
Dy	66					(10)				(2)		
Ho	67					(11)				(2)		
Er	68					(12)				(2)		
Tm	69					13				2		
Yb	70			54 Xe Core		14				2		
Lu	71					14		1		2		
Hf	72					14		2		2		
Ta	73					14		3		2		
W	74					14		4		2		
Re	75					14		5		2		
Os	76					14		6		2		
Ir	77					14		7		2		
Pt	78					14		9		1		
Au	79					14		10		1		
Hg	80					14		10		2		
Tl	81					14		10		2 1		
Pb	82					14		10		2 2		
Bi	83					14		10		2 3		
Po	84					14		10		2 4		
At	85					14		10		2 5		
Rn	86					14		10		2 6		
Fr	87	2	2 6	2 6 10	2 6 10	14	2 6	10		2 6		1
Ra	88			78						8		2
Ac	89										(1)	(2)
Th	90										(2)	(2)
Pa	91								(2)		(1)	(2)
U	92								(3)		(1)	(2)
Np	93								(5)			(2)
Pu	94								(6)			(2)
Am	95			86 Rn Core					(7)			(2)
Cm	96								(7)		(1)	(2)
Bk	97								(7)		(2)	(2)
Cf	98								(9)		(1)	(2)
Es	99											
Fm	100											
Mv	101											
No	102											
Lw	103											

*Configurations shown in parentheses are uncertain.

limited amount of experimental data and the electronic configurations of some elements are not conclusively settled.

The configurations of the elements are given in *Table 2.4*. From these, four distinct types of element may be recognized; they are:

(a) *The Inert Gases:* In these elements all subsidiary levels are filled and except for helium they are characterized by the configuration ns^2np^6.

(b) *The Representative Elements:* These have incomplete s and p levels with all underlying levels filled and are characterized by the configurations ns^1 to ns^2np^5.

(c) *The Transition Elements:* These are characterized by an incompletely filled d level; they are generally extended to include the elements of subgroups I B and II B.

(d) *The Inner Transition Elements:* These are distinguished from the elements of type (c) by the filling up of the inner f level.

SUGGESTED REFERENCES FOR FURTHER READING

COULSON, C. A.   *Valence,* 2nd edn, Clarendon Press, Oxford, 1961.

HERZBERG, G.   *Atomic Spectra and Atomic Structure,* Dover Publications, New York, 1944.

RICE, O. K.   *Electronic Structure and Chemical Binding,* McGraw-Hill, New York, 1940.

3

VALENCY

THE concept of valency as essentially electrostatic in nature was first proposed in 1812 shortly after the discovery of the phenomenon of electrolysis. In his theory, BERZELIUS attributed positive or negative polarities to the elements and visualized molecules as built up by partial neutralization of electrical charges. Later work in the middle of the same century by FRANKLAND, who surveyed numerous compounds of different elements, suggested a combining power for the elements which was looked upon as a number, the valency, such that the atomic weight of the element was the multiple of that number and the equivalent weight.

Following the discovery of the electron and the development of theories of atomic structure, it was suggested that the electrons in shells round the nucleus were involved in the formation of chemical bonds with other atoms. The Bohr theory gave the first indication of the arrangement of the electrons around the nucleus in shells and it was soon realized that for many elements the number of outermost electrons was related directly to the valency*. Thus, the alkali metals with one electron in the outermost shell have a unipositive valency, the alkaline earth metals with two outermost electrons have a dipositive valency, etc. It is therefore customary to speak of the outermost electrons as valency electrons and, as we have seen, the division of elements into various groups, each of which exhibits a characteristic valency or valencies, arises from their electronic configurations. The discovery of the inert gases and their remarkable inability to enter into chemical combination led to the development of an electronic theory of valency. Three main types of bond were defined: (a) electrovalent, (b) covalent and (c) dative.

* Confusion often arises over the term valency when the student changes from elementary to more advanced chemistry. A simple example of this arises in the case of the ferricyanide ion $[Fe(CN)_6)]^{3-}$, where the iron atom, although in the ferric or tervalent state, is bonded to six cyanide groups. It is thus desirable, in the light of the complex nature of modern inorganic chemistry, to use a term that is likely to cause less confusion. It is common to refer to an atom as being in a particular *oxidation state*. Thus, ferric iron is said to be in the $+3$ oxidation state and cupric copper in the $+2$ oxidation state. These are frequently written as Fe^{III} and Cu^{II} or iron (III) and copper (II).

The oxidation state of an atom is worked out from certain elementary rules.

(i) Atoms in the elementary state are in the zero oxidation state.
(ii) Hydrogen, except in the ionic hydrides and the hydrogen molecule, is in the $+1$ oxidation state.
(iii) Oxygen, except in peroxides, oxygen difluoride and the oxygen molecule, is in the -2 oxidation state.
(iv) The halogens are in the -1 oxidation state in the halides.

The oxidation state of a particular atom in a compound or ion may be worked out by breaking down the species into its component atoms and equating the algebraic sum of the component oxidation states to the charge on that species.

Thus, in $KMnO_4$ the oxidation state of the manganese atom may be computed as follows:

$$\begin{array}{ccc} K & Mn & O_4 \\ +1 & +? & -8 \end{array} = 0. \quad \text{Hence} \quad Mn^{7+}$$

39

The electrovalent bond was first postulated by Kossel (1916) who suggested that the atoms of elements just before or just after the inert gases in the periodic classification could increase the stability of their electron arrangement by the gain or loss of electrons respectively until an inert gas configuration was attained. An element which gains electrons is described as *electronegative* and one which loses electrons as *electropositive*. For example, in the formation of sodium chloride the sodium atom loses an electron to form a positive ion with the configuration of neon; chlorine gains one electron to form a negative ion with the configuration of argon. This may be visualized pictorially as

$$\text{Na } (2.8.1) \longrightarrow \text{Na}^+ (2.8) + e^-$$
$$\text{Cl } (2.8.7) + e^- \longrightarrow \text{Cl}^- (2.8.8)$$

The sodium and chloride ions then form an electrovalent bond by the mutual attraction of their electrostatic charges. The electrovalent bond arises whenever atoms of one element gain electrons at the expense of the atoms of another.

In the case of the covalent bond, the essential feature of the proposal of Lewis (1916) is that electrons are shared between the atoms bonded together and that no transfer of electrons takes place. This type of bond is generally formed by the combination of two electronegative atoms with, again, the criterion of the attainment by both atoms of the electronic configuration of an inert gas. Thus the formation of a single covalent bond in the chlorine molecule may be represented as

$$\overset{\times\times}{\underset{\times\times}{\times}}\!Cl_\times + \cdot\overset{\cdot\cdot}{Cl}\!: \rightarrow \overset{\times\times}{\underset{\times\times}{\times}}\!Cl\!\boxed{\cdot}\!\overset{\cdot\cdot}{Cl}\!:$$

the shared pair of electrons constituting the covalent bond. Double and triple bonds as found for instance in ethylene and acetylene may be regarded as involving the sharing between two atoms of two and three pairs of electrons respectively:

$$\begin{matrix} \text{H} & & & \text{H} \\ {}^{\circ}_{\circ}\text{C} & \boxed{\cdot} & \text{C}{}^{\circ}_{\circ} & \text{or } H_2C{=\!=}CH_2; \end{matrix} \qquad H{}^{\times}_{\circ}C \boxed{\vdots} C{}^{\times}_{\circ}H \text{ or } HC{\equiv}CH$$

The dative or co-ordinate bond arises when a molecule or ion donates an electron pair to an atom or ion which requires electrons to complete its shell thereby attaining an inert gas arrangement. As examples here we may quote the cyanide ion and the ammonia molecule whose electron arrangements may be written as

$$\left[\overset{\cdot}{\underset{\cdot}{\circ}}|C \boxed{\vdots} N^{\times}_{\times}\right]^- \qquad \text{and} \qquad \boxed{\times}\overset{\text{H}}{\underset{\text{H}}{\times N_\circ^\times}}H$$

In each instance, there is an electron pair or lone pair which can be donated to an acceptor molecule or atom with the formation of the dative bond. Thus ferrocyanide may be visualized as ferrous ion accepting six lone pairs from cyanide ions to form a complex anion $[Fe(CN)_6]^{4-}$

i.e. $\quad$ Fe (2. 8. 8. 6. 2) $\longrightarrow$ Fe^{2+} (2. 8. 8. 6)

$\quad\quad$ Fe^{2+} + 6 CN$^-$ $\longrightarrow$ [Fe(CN)$_6$]$^{4-}$ (2. 8. 8. 18)

or $\quad$
$$\left[\begin{array}{c} \text{CN} \\ \text{NC} \;|\; \text{CN} \\ \text{Fe} \\ \text{NC} \;|\; \text{CN} \\ \text{CN} \end{array}\right]^{4-}$$

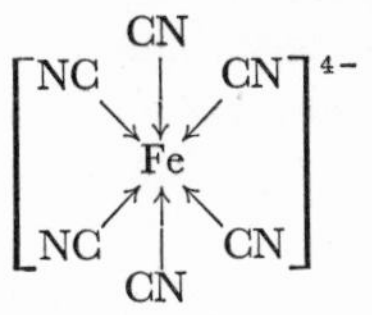

Likewise ammonia will donate its lone pair to B(CH$_3$)$_3$. The octet of the boron atom is thereby completed:

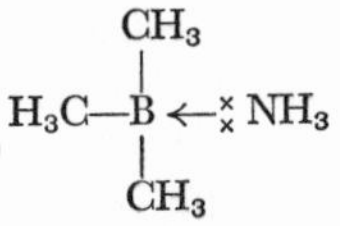

$$\text{H}_3\text{C}-\overset{\overset{\displaystyle\text{CH}_3}{|}}{\underset{\underset{\displaystyle\text{CH}_3}{|}}{\text{B}}}\leftarrow{}^{\times}_{\times}\text{NH}_3$$

In forming the co-ordinate bond there is effectively a partial transfer of electrons from one atom to the other; hence this bond is also referred to as a semi-polar bond. The complex between ammonia and trimethylboron can also be represented as

$$(\text{CH}_3)_3\overset{\ominus}{\text{B}}-\overset{\oplus}{\text{N}}\text{H}_3$$

THE ELECTROVALENT BOND

The discussion of the ionic bond in the résumé above has been restricted to ions possessing the configuration of inert gases. In the case of anions this is the only stable arrangement and the anions which occur are predominantly those with one or two charges. In the case of cations, however, there are configurations other than those of the inert gases that have stability.

Figure 3.1. Occurrence of the inert-pair effect

Group	II B	III B	IV B	V B
(Be)		B	C	N
(Mg)		Al	Si	P
Zn		Ga	Ge	As
Cd		In	Sn	Sb
Hg		Tl	Pb	Bi

For instance, many sub-group B elements that cannot form an inert gas configuration by electron loss can nevertheless form stable ions. Thus zinc forms a stable dipositive ion with the electron arrangement (2. 8. 18). In other cases such as the sub-group I B elements, the eighteen electron arrangement has not such great stability and variable valency is exhibited by the atoms; thus copper has the two ions Cu$^+$ and Cu^{2+}.

The atoms of certain other sub-group B elements, particularly those of high atomic number, possess two electrons that are characterized by a certain degree of inertness. This *inert-pair* effect shows up in the chemistry of these elements in the formation of ions other than the eighteen electron type and is associated with extra stability of the two *s* electrons of the highest quantum group. Examples of this are to be found in the chemistry of sub-groups II B to V B of the periodic table as indicated in *Figure 3.1*; the inert-pair effect is

41

found with elements below the dotted line. The inert-pair effect is demonstrated by the formation of ionic compounds in which the element shows a valency two units less than the maximum or group valency.

With the transition elements the stability of the half-filled shell has already been mentioned (p. 35); this also shows itself as a stable grouping in ion formation. This is discussed later (p. 250).

Ionization Potential and Electron Affinity

The ease with which an atom will form an ion depends upon the magnitudes of its *ionization potential* and its *electron affinity*.

In the Bohr theory of the hydrogen atom it was pointed out that a certain amount of energy was required to remove completely the electron from its orbit to infinity. This is termed the ionization potential of the hydrogen atom. The magnitude of the ionization potential of an atom depends on various factors:

(*i*) the distance of the electrons from the nucleus,
(*ii*) the effective nuclear charge, *i.e.* the actual nuclear charge less a correction for the screening effect of inner shells of electrons
and (*iii*) the type of electron that is being removed, *i.e.* whether it is an *s*, *p*, *d* or *f* electron.

In general, the further an electron is from the nucleus the less firmly it is held and hence the lower the value of the ionization potential. Exact comparisons are not possible here since the atoms of two different elements do not have the same electronic configurations in the ground states. Considerations of the ionization potentials of consecutive elements in a group, *e.g.* I A (*Table 3.1*) where (*ii*) is about the same for each element and the single *s* electron is being removed illustrates the effect of increased atomic radius.

The ease of removal of an electron depends also on the effective nuclear charge, for in general an increase in shielding effect, other factors remaining constant, produces a decrease in ionization potential and vice versa. This effect may be demonstrated by considering the successive ionization potentials for a particular atom where the electrons being removed are of the same type. Thus the removal of the first electron, although it has no effect on the nuclear charge, causes a decrease in screening effect as far as the next electron is concerned and consequently the second electron is harder to remove than the first; for instance, in the case of carbon the ionization potentials are 259·6; 562·2 and 1104 kcal/g atom for the first, second and third electrons respectively.

The *s* electrons approach the nucleus more closely and on average these experience less shielding than do the *p*, *d* or *f* electrons of any one quantum shell. The *s* electrons are thus the most tightly bound in any particular atom; correspondingly the *f* electrons are the least strongly held. If the successive ionization potentials of an atom such as oxygen be considered, there is a steady increase in the values for the first four electrons but a considerably larger difference between the ionization potential of the fourth and fifth electrons, the latter being an *s* electron (*Table 3.1*).

Table 3.1. Ionization potentials of the elements

Element	Ionization potential (kilocalories/gramme atom)						
	1st	2nd	3rd	4th	5th	6th	7th
H	313·6						
He	566·8	1254·5					
Li	124·3	1743·8	2822·5				
Be	214·9	419·9	3548·9	5020·2			
B	191·3	580·0	874·4	5797·9	7845		
C	259·6	562·2	1103·6	1486·9	9039	11294	
N	335·3	682·8	1093·7	1786·0	2256	12727	15376
O	313·8	810·6	1266·8	1784·6	2626	3185	17044
F	401·7	806·6	1444·7	2011·5	2633	3623	4628
Ne	497·2	947·1	1475·8	2240·5	2915	3641	
Na	118·4	1090·5	1652·2	2280·2	3196	3999	4806
Mg	176·3	346·6	1847·6	2520·5	3256	4310	5195
Al	138·0	434·0	655·8	2582·7	3547	4391	5578
Si	187·9	376·8	771·6	1040·7	3844	4730	4767
P	243·3	453·1	695·5	1184·1	1499	5082	6072
S	238·9	539·6	807·1	1090·5	1672	2030	6480
Cl	300·0	548·8	920·0	1233·7	1563	2230	2636
Ar	363·4	636·9	943·1	1378·9	1730	2105	2859
K	100·0	733·5	1060·6	1404·3		2299	2721
Ca	140·9	273·7	1180·9	1545·0	1946	2562	2952
Sc	151·3	295·2	570·7	1704·1	2121	2562	
Ti	157·5	312·9	648·9	997·1	2301	2767	3247
V	155·4	337·8	684·9	1106·9	1504	2972	3482
Cr	156·0	380·2	(714·9)	(1162)			
Mn	171·4	360·6	(738·0)	(1200)			
Fe	182·2	373·1					
Co	181·3	393·2					
Ni	176·0	418·5					
Cu	178·1	467·9	680·3				
Zn	216·6	414·2	922·3				
Ga	138·4	473·0	705·6	1471·2			
Ge	181·7	367·3	785·7	1049·2	2145		
As	226·2	465·8	645·7	1150·7	1441		
Se	224·8	495·8	781·7	985·1	1678	1877	
Br	273·0	498·1	592·6	(1153)			
Kr	322·8	566·4	848·6	(1568)			
Rb	96·3	634·2	(1084)	(1845)			
Sr	131·2	254·4					
Y	147·1	282·0	470·4				
Zr	157·6	297·9	553·4	779·4			
Nb	158·7	320·2	558·1				
Mo	164·4	352·1					
Tc	166·7	342·9					
Ru	169·8	382·6					
Rh	172·1	367·1					
Pd	192·1	447·8					
Ag	174·7	495·3	827·9				
Cd	207·3	389·7	876·3				
In	133·4	434·2	643·4	1332·9			
Sn	169·1	337·4	703·3	908·6	1859		
Sb	199·2	438·1	569·6	1014·6	1280		
Tl	207·7	495·8	703·3	869·4	1384	(1666)	
I	240·7	438·1					
Xe	279·7	489·1	737·9	(1061)	(1753)		
Cs	89·3	578·8	(807)	(1176)	(1337)		
Ba	120·1	230·6					
La	129·4	263·6	470·4				
Ce	(159·3)	341·3					
Pr	(132·8)						
Nd	145·3						

43

Table 3.1. (contd.)

Element	Ionization potential (kilocalories/gramme atom)						
	1st	2nd	3rd	4th	5th	6th	7th
Pm							
Sm	129·1	258·2					
Eu	130·8	259·2					
Gd	142·0	276·7					
Tb	(155·4)						
Dy	(157·3)						
Ho							
Er							
Tm							
Yb	143·3	279·0					
Lu	141·8	339·0					
Hf	126·8	343·6					
Ta	177·6						
W	184·0						
Re	181·5						
Os	200·6						
Ir	212·2						
Pt	207·5	428·0					
Au	212·6	472·7	(691·5)				
Hg	240·5	432·4	791·0	(1660)	(1891)		
Tl	140·8	470·9	684·9	1164·5			
Pb	171·0	346·0	(735·6)	971·1	1600		
Bi	168·0	445·0	586·2	1040·0	1284		
Po	194·4						
At							
Rn	247·9						
Fr							
Ra	121·7	233·8					
Ac			677·9				
Th							
Pa							
U	92·24						

The lowest ionization potentials are found with the alkali metals and a gradual increase is observed in traversing the Periodic Table to the inert gases. The increase is not continuous, however, for higher values are obtained for beryllium and nitrogen than would be expected by comparison with the other elements in the same period (*Figure 3.2*). These increases are attributed to the stability of the filled *s* and half-filled *p* levels respectively. In a transition or inner transition series the variation in first ionization potentials is not so great because the addition of an electron to an inner quantum shell gives a high shielding effect which virtually compensates for the increased nuclear charge. Values of ionization potentials are listed in *Table 3.1.*

The *electron affinity* of an atom is the energy associated with the formation of an anion from the gaseous atom; with the halogens this process is exoergic, that is energy is given out when the anion X^- is formed, but with the elements of Groups V and VI the addition of electrons to form the anions is an endoergic process, that is energy is absorbed. Thus oxygen forms the ion O^{2-}; the formation of O^- is associated with an energy change of approximately 34 kcal/g atom, the process being exoergic, but the addition of the second electron is an endoergic process and the total affinity is approximately 153 kcal/g atom. The magnitude of the electron affinity is dependent upon various factors.

In particular, the atomic size and effective nuclear charge are important; in general, the electron affinity decreases with increasing atomic radius and increases with decreased screening by inner electrons. Also the value will depend to a certain extent upon the type of orbital that the added electron enters; other things remaining constant, the affinity is greatest for an electron entering an *s* orbital and decreases for *p*, *d* and *f* orbitals. In fact in the common

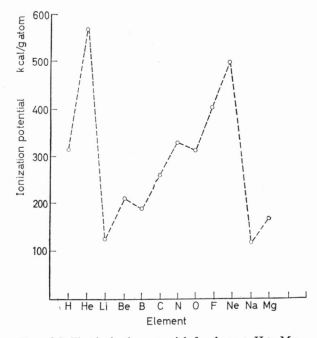

Figure 3.2. First ionization potentials for elements H to Mg

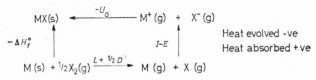

Figure 3.3. Born–Haber cycle for MX

monatomic anions the electrons enter a *p* orbital (except for H^- where the 1*s* orbital is occupied).

Electron affinities may be derived by indirect means involving thermodynamic data for binary compounds and the Born–Haber cycle. This cycle is shown in *Figure 3.3* for the compound MX where M may be any monovalent metal such as sodium and X is a halogen.

The cycle relates the heat of formation ΔH_f°, that is, the heat evolved or absorbed when 1 mole of the compound MX is formed from its elements in their physical states at 25°C, with the energy changes of the individual steps of such a reaction.

45

The reaction of a solid M with gaseous X_2 can be broken down into the following steps:

(a) Vaporization of the metal to give isolated metal atoms. The energy absorbed is L, the latent heat of vaporization.

(b) Dissociation of the X_2 molecule to form isolated halogen atoms. The energy for the formation of 1 g atom is $\frac{1}{2}D$, where D is the dissociation energy of the X_2 molecule.

(c) Conversion of M to M^+. The energy required is the ionization potential, I, of the metal.

(d) Conversion of X to X^-. The electron affinity, $-E$, is the energy evolved.

(e) The formation of 1 g molecule of MX as an ionic solid by bringing together, from infinite distance apart, in the gaseous phase 1 g ion of M^+ and 1 g ion of X^-. The energy given out is $-U_0$, the *lattice energy* of MX.

The cycle is therefore completed and hence

$$-\Delta H_f^\circ = -U_0 + I - E + L + \tfrac{1}{2}D$$

U_0 can be calculated (see the following section), ΔH_f°, I, L and D can be measured experimentally and so E, the only unknown, may be determined.

Table 3.2. Electron affinities of various elements

Element	Electron affinity (kcal/g atom)
F	−80·2*
Cl	−85·1*
Br	−79·5*
I	−72·6*
O	+152·9†
S	+94·5‡
Se	+101§

Note 1: Negative values indicate that the process $X \rightarrow X^-$ is exoergic.
  Note 2: The process for oxygen, sulphur and selenium is $X \rightarrow X^{2-}$ and is endoergic for the formation of X^{2-} since energy has to be expended in order to overcome the repulsion due to the first electron.
  * Data from Cubiciotti, D. *J. chem. Phys.*, 31 (1959) 1646.
  † Data from Morris, D. F. C. *Proc. roy. Soc.*, A-242 (1957) 116.
  ‡ Data from Morris, D. F. C. *Acta cryst.*, 11 (1958) 163.
  § Data from Bevan, S. C., and Morris, D. F. C. *J. chem. Soc.*, 106 (1960) 516.

An average value for the electron affinity is calculated from thermochemical data on a number of different compounds containing X^-. Typical values are given in *Table 3.2*.

Lattice Energy

In the Born–Haber cycle, the quantity U_0 was introduced as the lattice energy, that is the energy required to break down the crystal into its component ions at infinite distance apart in the gaseous phase.

The calculation of lattice energies has been made possible from the work of Born and Landé and others who developed a theory of the structure of crystalline solids from a consideration of the interaction of pairs of ions both in the gas and the solid phase. Between any two oppositely charged ions i, j in the gas phase there exists an attractive and repulsive potential. The attractive potential (U_{att}) is given by

$$U_{att} = \frac{z_i z_j e^2}{r} \qquad \cdots \quad (1)$$

where z_i and z_j are the charge numbers on the two ions and r their distance apart. The repulsive potential (U_{rep}) may be represented as

$$U_{rep} = \frac{b_{ij} e^2}{r^n} \qquad \cdots \quad (2)$$

where b_{ij} is a constant characteristic for the compound under consideration and n has the values between 5 and 14 depending upon the electron configurations of the ions (see *Table 3.3*).

Table 3.3. Values of n for different electronic configurations

Electronic configuration	n value
He	5
Ne	7
Cu$^+$ Ar	9
Ag$^+$ Kr	11
Au$^+$ Xe	12
Rn	14

Note: Where ions are not isoelectronic the average of the two values is used

Hence the energy of interaction (U) of two ions in the gas phase is given by

$$U = \frac{z_i z_j e^2}{r} + \frac{b_{ij} e^2}{r^n} \qquad \cdots \quad (3)$$

(*Note*: since either z_i or z_j is negative, the first term in (3) is always negative.)

The energy of an ion pair in the crystal is obtained by summation of the energies of interaction between all the isolated ion pairs. For any single ion pair in the crystalline state of a binary compound, this gives

$$U = \frac{A z^2 e^2}{r} + \frac{B e^2}{r^n} \qquad \cdots \quad (4)$$

where A is the Madelung constant, which has values dependent upon the type of crystal lattice and B is the repulsion coefficient. Values of A are given in *Table 3.4*.

Table 3.4. Values of the Madelung constant for different crystal structures

Madelung constant	Crystal structure
1·744	Sodium chloride
1·763	Caesium chloride
1·639	Zinc blende
1·641	Wurtzite
5·039	Fluorite
4·816	Rutile

B may be determined from the observed equilibrium interionic distance r_c in the crystal and equating dU/dr to zero. This gives

$$B = -\frac{r_c^{n-1}Az^2}{n} \qquad \qquad \ldots \ldots (5)$$

Hence

$$U = \frac{Az^2e^2}{r_c}\left\{1-\frac{1}{n}\right\} \qquad \qquad \ldots \ldots (6)$$

and the lattice energy, which refers to one mole, is obtained by multiplying (6) by the Avogadro number N.

Hence

$$U_0 = \frac{NAz^2e^2}{r_c}\left\{\frac{n-1}{n}\right\} \qquad \qquad \ldots \ldots (7)$$

Small corrections to this relationship may be made by including van der Waals forces between the ions and the zero point vibrational energy of the ions.

The lattice energies, calculated for different compounds assuming complete ionic character, show in many instances distinct deviations from the values calculated from thermodynamic data. The deviations indicate a departure

Table 3.5. Lattice energies of the alkali halides

Crystal	U_{exp} (kcal/mole)	U_{theor} (kcal/mole)	Δ
NaF	217	217	0
NaCl	184	182	+2
NaBr	176	173	+3
NaI	165	162	+3
KF	192	192	0
KCl	168	166	+2
KBr	161	159	+2
KI	152	150	+2
RbF	184	183	+1
RbCl	161	160	+1
RbBr	156	154	+2
RbI	147	145	+3
CsF	172	174	-2
CsCl	154	150	+4
CsBr	149	145	+4
CsI	141	137	+4

Data from MORRIS, D. F. C. *Acta cryst.*, 9 (1956) 197.

from purely ionic character in the bonding (see *Tables 3.5* and *3.6*). A qualitative approach to the transition between ionic and covalent bonding was made by FAJANS who considered the nature of the attraction between the cation and anion in a compound M^+X^-. In such a compound the cation exerts an attraction on the outermost electrons associated with the anion. If the cation exerts a strong enough pull on the anion charge cloud, this is polarized or distorted and partial sharing of electrons occurs between M and X. A

Table 3.6. Lattice energies of some metal halides

Crystal	U_{exp} (kcal/mole)	U_{theor} (kcal/mole)	Δ
CaF_2	624	622	+2
PbF_2	595	584	+11
HgF_2	655	626	+29
MgF_2	695	684	+11
$MgBr_2$	575	513	+62
MgI_2	549	476	+73
FeF_2	696	681	+15
CoF_2	708	688	+20
NiF_2	728	694	+34
CuF_2	727	627	+100
$FeBr_2$	607	530	+77
FeI_2	589	493	+96
AgF	231	219	+12
$AgCl$	219	203	+16
$AgBr$	217	197	+20
AgI	214	190	+24

Data from MORRIS, D. F. C., and AHRENS, L. H. *J. inorg. nuclear Chem.*, 3 (1956) 263 and MORRIS, D. F. C. *J. inorg. nuclear Chem.*, 4 (1957) 8.

number of general rules were suggested to determine whether there is likely to be appreciable covalent character. He suggested that polarization is large when:

(*a*) the anion or cation is highly charged. An anion with a charge of unity will exert less repulsion on its outer electrons than one with a higher charge; a cation with a charge greater than one will attract electrons more strongly than one with a charge of unity. Though little comparison is possible for the effect of anionic charges, since these are largely restricted to -1 and -2, the effect of increased cation charge is readily seen from the melting points of some anhydrous chlorides:

Cation	Radius (Å)	Melting point (°C)
Na^+	0·95	800
Mg^{2+}	0·65	712
Al^{3+}	0·50	180 (sublimes)

The decrease in melting point corresponds with increasing polarization of chloride ion and therefore of increasing covalent character.

(*b*) the cation is small and the anion is large. Since small cations may approach an anion more closely than large cations they are able to exert a stronger polarizing effect. With large anions the outermost electrons are more easily polarized than those of small anions since they are at a greater distance from the positive charge of the nucleus. The effect of size upon polarization is well illustrated by the Group II A halides (*Figures 3.4 and 3.5*).

(*c*) the cation has an electronic configuration other than that of an inert gas. This point may be demonstrated by a consideration of the corresponding compounds of the alkali metals and the coinage metals, in which the latter have the $18e$ configuration in the cation M^+. The univalent halides of copper,

49

silver and gold are water-insoluble and of lower melting point than the water-soluble halides of sodium, potassium and rubidium (*Figure 3.6*). This effect may be explained by the fact that the coinage metals in their univalent cations

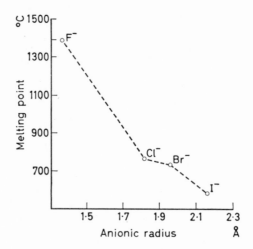

Figure 3.4. Melting points of the anhydrous calcium halides

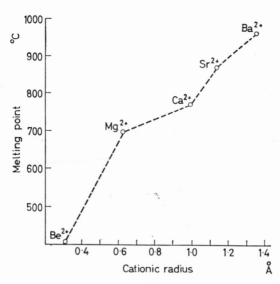

Figure 3.5. Melting points of the anhydrous chlorides of Group II A metals

possess *d* electrons which do not provide such an efficient screening of the nuclear charges as do the *s* and *p* electrons for the alkali metals. The univalent cations of the coinage metals are thus able to exert a stronger polarizing effect on an anion. A similar effect is observed for the transition metals in general as shown by the differences between calculated and experimental lattice energies (*Table 3.6*).

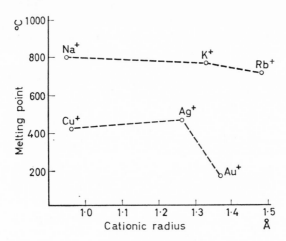

Figure 3.6. Melting points of the chlorides of the Group I A and I B metals

Solubility of Ionic Compounds

The process of solution of an ionic compound must involve the breakdown of the crystal lattice to produce solute species. In polar solvents, these species are the individual solvated ions. The energy needed for lattice breakdown is provided by that released in the solvation process.

Polar solvents are effective for the dissolution of ionic compounds because their high dielectric constants lead to diminished attractive forces between the ions*.

The process of solution of an ionic halide MX can be described in terms of a Born–Haber cycle. The lattice breaks up to give the isolated, gaseous ions and then solvation takes place:

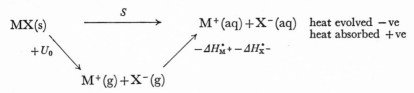

The heat of solution (S) is related to the lattice energy (U_0) and the solvation energies $-\Delta H^{\circ}_{M^+}$, and $-\Delta H^{\circ}_{X^-}$ by the equation

$$U_0 - \Delta H^{\circ}_{M^+} - \Delta H^{\circ}_{X^-} = S$$

S may be positive or negative depending on the relative magnitudes of the other quantities in the equation.

* The force between two charges q_1 and q_2, a distance l apart *in vacuo* is $q_1 q_2 / l^2$; in a medium of dielectric constant ϵ the force is reduced to $q_1 q_2 / \epsilon l^2$.

Most ionic compounds show positive heats of solution in water, that is heat is absorbed in the solution process and consequently the solubility in water generally increases with rising temperature. The solvation energies and the lattice energy are greater for increasing ionic charge. The lattice energy usually shows the larger increase and for example, the alkaline earth metal salts are less soluble than the corresponding salts of the alkali metals.

Electronegativity and Partial Ionic Character

Attempts to put partial ionic character on a more quantitative basis have been made by various workers. These have all involved the electronegativity of the atoms concerned. This is defined as the tendency of an atom to attract an electron to itself. MULLIKEN related the electronegativity to the ionization potential and the electron affinity by defining it as the mean of the ionization potential and electron affinity of the element. Difficulties arise here through inadequate knowledge of accurate values of electron affinities for all but a few elements.

A second and more successful approach was made by PAULING. In it he determined the differences between the actual bond energies, $D_{AB(expt)}$, of molecules and those calculated for pure covalent bonds in compounds of the type AB on the assumption that $D_{AB(calc)} = \frac{1}{2}(D_{AA} + D_{BB})$, where the D terms are the dissociation energies of the bonds indicated by the subscripts. The difference Δ_{AB} is given by

$$\Delta_{AB} = D_{AB(expt)} - \frac{1}{2}(D_{AA} + D_{BB})$$

It is of necessity always positive and results from the resonance energy contributed by ionic forms (A^+B^- or A^-B^+). Pauling's electronegativity scale is based on the equation

$$\Delta_{AB} = 23 \cdot 06(x_A - x_B)^2 \qquad \cdot \quad \cdot \quad \cdot \quad \cdot \quad (8)$$

where x_A and x_B are the electronegativities of the elements A and B, and $23 \cdot 06$ is the conversion factor from electron-volts to kcal. This, however, only gave a value for the difference in electronegativities for the elements and in order to obtain comparative electronegativities of the elements the arbitrary value of $2 \cdot 1$ was assigned to hydrogen, giving the elements from carbon to fluorine values of $2 \cdot 5$ to $4 \cdot 0$. This method enabled values for the more electronegative elements, *e.g.* F, O, Cl, N, Br, S, C, I, Se, P, As and Si to be determined; those for other elements were obtained from thermochemical data for compounds formed between the element, whose electronegativity value was required, and one of the elements whose electronegativity value was known.

The values derived by PAULING are quoted in *Table 3.7* and it will be seen that the values are highest for the element fluorine and lowest for caesium. Ionic bonding is favoured when the difference in electronegativity between the atoms is high and conversely covalent bonding is favoured by small differences in electronegativity values.

Attempts to relate difference in electronegativity to percentage ionic character in the bonding have also been made. Empirical relationships have been derived that agree with the data for the hydrogen halides in which the

Table 3.7. Electronegativity values for selected elements (after PAULING)

			H 2·1			
Li 1·0	Be 1·5	B 2·0	C 2·5	N 3·0	O 3·5	F 4·0
Na 0·9	Mg 1·2	Al 1·5	Si 1·8	P 2·1	S 2·5	Cl 3·0
K 0·8	Ca 1·0	Sc 1·3	Ge 1·8	As 2·0	Se 2·4	Br 2·8
Rb 0·8	Sr 1·0	Y 1·2	Sn 1·8	Sb 1·9	Te 2·1	I 2·5
Cs 0·7	Ba 0·9					

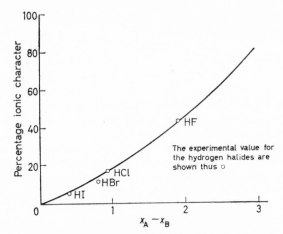

Figure 3.7. Percentage ionic character as a function of electronegativity difference $x_A - x_B$ plotted from Hannay and Smyth's formula (9)

ionic character is determined from dipole moments*. Work by HANNAY and SMYTH showed that

$$\text{Percentage ionic character} = 16(x_A - x_B) + 3.5(x_A - x_B)^2 \quad . \quad . \quad . \quad (9)$$

and its relation with electronegativity difference is shown in *Figure 3.7*. In

---

* *Dipole Moments*—In a diatomic molecule a dipole arises through unequal sharing of electric charge between the two atoms and as a consequence the molecule has a positive and negative end similar to a small magnet. Polyatomic molecules also possess dipoles except in certain instances such as CCl_4 and CO_2 where the bonds are symmetrical about the central atom. This charge displacement is measured by the dipole moment of the molecule (μ). If two charges $+\delta$ and $-\delta$ are separated by a distance r, the dipole moment is given by $\mu = \delta.r$. Dipole moments have been determined experimentally (p. 280) for the hydrogen halides and compared with the theoretical values derived from the observed internuclear distance in the hydrogen halide and the value of the electronic charge 4.8×10^{-10} esu. The ratio of these two dipole moments can be regarded as the fraction of ionic character in the bond assuming that the covalent bonding contributes nothing to the dipole moment. The values for the experimental and calculated dipole moments of the hydrogen halides are given in *Table 3.8*.

Figure 3.7 it is apparent that when the difference in electronegativity is above about 2·1 then the bonding is more than 50 per cent ionic.

Table 3.8. *Dipole moments and electronegativity differences for the hydrogen halides*

Hydrogen halide	$\overset{r}{(\text{Å})}$	μ_{ionic} (Debyes)	μ_{obs} (Debyes)	μ_0/μ_1	$x_A - x_B$
HF	0·92	4·41	1·91	0·43	1·9
HCl	1·28	6·07	1·03	0·17	0·9
HBr	1·43	6·82	0·78	0·11	0·8
HI	1·62	7·74	0·38	0·05	0·4

THE COVALENT BOND

The simple Lewis theory of the covalent bond envisaged the sharing of electrons between atoms forming the bond but gave no indication as to how or why this sharing occurred. The more modern picture of covalent bond formation considers the energy changes taking place when two atoms approach one another. The condition for the formation of the stable bond is that, at a certain interatomic distance, the potential energy of the system reaches a minimum.

A clear idea of the concept of resonance is essential to the understanding of the energy changes which occur on bonding. In describing a molecule in terms of covalent bonds it is possible to write down more than one formula that satisfies the requirements of the Lewis theory. The molecule is said to have various resonance forms. These are all involved in the structure of the molecule, which is itself energetically more stable than any of the component forms. The resonance forms at no time have an independent existence and so the concept is quite different from that of tautomerism where the individual forms may be isolated by chemical or physical means. Resonance simply involves the rearrangement of electrons between the various forms whilst maintaining the same number of unpaired electrons in each of the structures and the same relative positions of the nuclei.

Thus in the case of the hydrogen molecule, we may write down the following four resonance forms:

$$^{1}\text{H}_a\!-\!^{2}\text{H}_b \qquad ^{2}\text{H}_a\!-\!^{1}\text{H}_b \qquad \text{H}_a^{+} \,^{1,2}\text{H}_b^{-} \qquad ^{1,2}\text{H}_a^{-} \ \text{H}_b^{+}$$
$$\text{(I)} \qquad\qquad \text{(II)} \qquad\qquad \text{(III)} \qquad\qquad \text{(IV)}$$

where the two hydrogen nuclei are designated H_a and H_b and the two electrons are 1 and 2. Resonance form (I) represents H_a and H_b joined by a covalent bond, electron 1 being more closely associated with H_a and electron 2 with H_b. Form (II) is a second covalent structure with the positions of the electrons interchanged. Forms (III) and (IV) are ionic contributions with both electrons associated with either H_b or H_a respectively.

Similarly, for a more complex molecule such as CO_2, we may write different resonance formulations such as:

$$\overset{\times\times}{\underset{\times\times}{_\times^\times\text{O}_\times^\times\text{C}_\times^\times\text{O}_\times^\times}} \qquad \overset{-}{\underset{\times\times}{_\times^\times\text{O}_\times^\times}}\overset{\times\times}{\text{C}}\overset{+}{\underset{}{\text{O}_\times^\times}} \qquad \overset{+}{\underset{}{_\times^\times\text{O}}}\overset{}{\text{C}}\overset{-}{\underset{\times\times}{\text{O}_\times^\times}}$$
$$\text{(V)} \qquad\qquad\qquad \text{(VI)} \qquad\qquad\qquad \text{(VII)}$$

Each of the resonance forms on the wave-mechanical approach has a definite energy and may be described by an approximate wave function ψ_I, ψ_II, etc. We may now apply one of the general principles of wave mechanics, namely that if a certain system can be described by a set of approximate wave functions then a linear combination of these is also a satisfactory description of the system. The linear combination that gives the lowest energy is taken to be the best description of the system in its normal state.

If we consider a system such as nitromethane (CH_3NO_2) where two resonance forms can be written

$$CH_3\text{—}\overset{+}{N}\overset{\displaystyle O}{\underset{\displaystyle O^-}{}} \quad \text{(A)} \quad \text{and} \quad CH_3\text{—}\overset{+}{N}\overset{\displaystyle O^-}{\underset{\displaystyle O}{}} \quad \text{(B)}$$

then the actual structure is more stable than either of these by an amount of energy ΔE, termed the *resonance energy* of the molecule, this being the difference

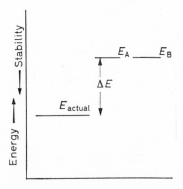

Figure 3.8. Representation of the energies of resonance forms of a molecule such as nitromethane where both forms are of equal energy. The nitromethane molecule is more stable than either of these forms [(A) and (B) above] by the resonance energy ΔE.

in energy between that of the actual molecule and that of the most stable of the resonance forms (*Figure 3.8*).

Where multiple bonds are present, the existence of resonance forms may be deduced from the measurements of bond distances within the molecule and of heats of formation. Thus in the case of CO_2 the carbon–oxygen bond length is 1·15 Å for both bonds and this is intermediate between the values predicted for C=O and C≡O; none of the three resonance forms in itself accounts for this observation. The measured heat of formation of carbon dioxide is 383 kcal compared with that of 346 kcal predicted theoretically for the simple formulation $O{=}C{=}O$, indicating a resonance energy of 37 kcal/mole.

The Nature of the Covalent Bond

Two theories have been put forward to explain the formation of a covalent bond. The first of these is the valence-bond approach (HEITLER, LONDON, PAULING and SLATER) which treats the bond formation from the standpoint of the pairing of electron spins and the maximum overlapping of atomic orbitals containing these electrons to give a region of common electron density to the combining atoms. The second approach, known as the molecular-orbital approach, considers the molecule as a whole and allocates electrons to a set of

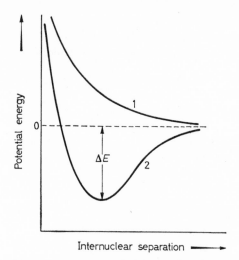

Figure 3.9. Energy variation as a function of internuclear separation for the hydrogen molecule

molecular orbitals in a manner similar to the allocation of electrons in an atom to a set of atomic orbitals (HUND and MULLIKEN). Unfortunately neither of the methods is applicable to all systems. They are both extreme cases and both therefore have their limitations.

The valence-bond approach may be illustrated qualitatively by considering the hydrogen molecule. In this case, we consider the possibility of interchange of the electrons between the two atoms. There are two possible equivalent structures which are indistinguishable once the bond has been formed. These are given by (I) and (II) of the resonance forms (p. 54). As the two hydrogen nuclei approach each other from an infinite distance the weak attractive forces are gradually opposed by strong repulsive forces at short interatomic distances. Interaction between the wave functions of the electrons occurs, for their spins may be parallel or opposed. If the electrons have parallel spins then the energy continues to rise as the atoms get closer together (line 1 in *Figure 3.9*) and no bond is formed. If, however, the spins are opposed the energy curve possesses a definite minimum which corresponds to the formation of a stable molecule (line 2, *Figure 3.9*).

This approach stresses the importance of electron spin, since in order for bonding to occur each atom must have an unpaired electron available for pairing up with the unpaired electron on the other atom.

The molecular-orbital method of HUND and MULLIKEN differs basically from the valence-bond approach in that it takes into consideration all the electrons of the combined atoms and considers these to be jointly held by the molecule in a set of polynuclear orbitals.

This method may be illustrated by reference to diatomic molecules. The molecular orbitals are obtained by a process known as the linear combination of atomic orbitals (LCAO). Thus the electron, when it is in close association with any one of the nuclei, may be described by a wave function that is approximately that of an atomic orbital. The wave function of a molecular orbital is then formed by taking a linear combination of the separate atomic orbital wave functions. From each pair of atomic orbitals so combined a new

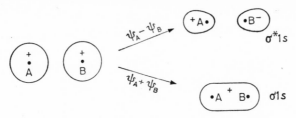

Figure 3.10. Formation of the $\sigma 1s$ and σ^*1s molecular orbitals

pair of molecular orbitals is formed. One of these is of higher energy than the other and the combination may be represented as

$$\Psi = c_1\psi_1 \pm c_2\psi_2$$
$$= \psi_1 \pm \lambda\psi_2$$

For homonuclear diatomic molecules each makes an equal contribution to the wave function of the molecular orbital and so $\lambda=1$.

In the case of the combination of the two $1s$ wave functions, on the atoms A and B respectively, the two molecular orbitals are given by

$$\Psi_{bonding} = \psi_{A,1s} + \psi_{B,1s}$$

and
$$\Psi_{antibonding} = \psi_{A,1s} - \psi_{B,1s}$$

The first of these is of lower energy than the component atomic orbitals and is termed a bonding molecular orbital; the second is of higher energy and is termed an antibonding molecular orbital. Pictorially they may be represented as in *Figure 3.10*. Both of these molecular orbitals have symmetry about the bond axis and are designated as σ orbitals. The bonding orbital is termed the $\sigma 1s$ and the antibonding orbital the σ^*1s.

With p atomic orbitals, two different types of molecular orbital may be formed. If the bond is formed along the x axis, the two p_x atomic orbitals will give rise to a σp and a σ^*p molecular orbital which are, again, symmetrical about the bond axis. The p_y and p_z orbitals, however, overlap to form orbitals that do not have symmetry about the bond axis. The molecular orbitals formed in this instance are termed π molecular orbitals. The combination is shown (*Figure 3.11*) for the $2p_y$ atomic orbitals where both bonding and anti-bonding orbitals are formed (π and π^* respectively).

We may go one step further and consider what happens if the two nuclei coalesce into a united atom. The correlation between the atomic orbitals on the separated atoms and those on the united atom is given in *Figure 3.12*.

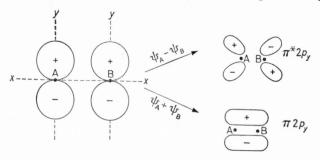

Figure 3.11. Formation of the $\pi 2p$ and $\pi^* 2p$ molecular orbitals

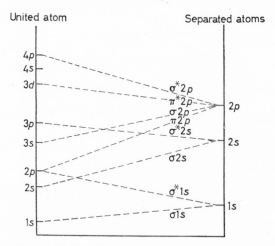

Figure 3.12. Relation between the energy levels in the separated atoms and in the united atoms

The formation of the united atom orbitals is easily seen from the diagrams of the formation of the molecular orbitals; thus the $\pi^* 2p$ become of similar shape to the interaxial atomic d orbitals as the internuclear distance decreases, hence these molecular orbitals become correlated with the $3d$ level on the united atom.

The energies of the various molecular orbitals of the homonuclear diatomic molecules formed by the elements in the first row of the periodic table are arranged in the following order:

$$\sigma 1s < \sigma^* 1s < \sigma 2s < \sigma^* 2s < \sigma 2p < \pi_y 2p = \pi_z 2p < \pi_y^* 2p = \pi_z^* 2p < \sigma^* 2p$$

The molecular orbitals are filled up in exactly the same manner as atomic orbitals, *i.e.* two electrons to an orbital and in order of increasing energy with due regard for the possible degeneracy of the orbitals.

We may therefore write down the molecular orbital description of some simple diatomic molecules:

(*i*) H_2 $(\sigma 1s)^2$

(*ii*) He_2 $(\sigma 1s)^2 (\sigma^* 1s)^2$

In the case (*ii*) the energy of the antibonding electrons exceeds that of the bonding electrons and the molecule is therefore unstable. Effectively, whenever the number of bonding and antibonding electrons is the same there is no stable bond formed between the atoms. Excited states of the molecule may, however, be obtained by exciting one of the antibonding electrons to a higher bonding orbital. Thus the excited states of the helium molecule have been observed in discharge tubes.

(*iii*) Li_2 $(\sigma 1s)^2 (\sigma^* 1s)^2 (\sigma 2s)^2$

The lithium molecule exists in lithium vapour. The $(\sigma 2s)$ pair is the bonding pair, for the inner $1s$ electrons are very little affected by bonding and remain virtually as they are in the isolated atoms. These electrons are non-bonding and the configuration of the lithium molecule is commonly written as

$$Li_2 \quad KK (\sigma 2s)^2$$

(*iv*) N_2 $KK (\sigma 2s)^2 (\sigma^* 2s)^2 (\sigma 2p)^2 (\pi_y 2p)^2 (\pi_z 2p)^2$

The bond in nitrogen is a triple one arising from one σ- and two π-type bonds.

(*v*) O_2 $KK (\sigma 2s)^2 (\sigma^* 2s)^2 (\sigma 2p)^2 (\pi_y 2p)^2 (\pi_z 2p)^2 (\pi_y^* 2p)^1 (\pi_z^* 2p)^1$

This description of the oxygen molecule tells us that there are two unpaired electrons in the doubly degenerate $\pi^* 2p$ molecular orbital level. On the valence-bond approach all electrons would be paired. The molecular-orbital approach is superior to the valence-bond description in this case as it can account for the observed paramagnetism of the oxygen molecule.

(*vi*) F_2 $KK (\sigma 2s)^2 (\sigma^* 2s)^2 (\sigma 2p)^2 (\pi_y 2p)^2 (\pi_z 2p)^2 (\pi_y^* 2p)^2 (\pi_z^* 2p)^2$

In this molecule, although several pairs of bonding and antibonding electrons are present, the fluorine atoms are joined effectively by a single bond, the $(\sigma 2p)$ pair.

For heteronuclear diatomic molecules such as CO and NO the situation becomes a little more complicated. In the linear combination of atomic orbitals, we must write

$$\Psi = \psi_1 \pm \lambda \psi_2$$

where λ is not equal to one, for in such cases the separate atomic wave functions no longer contribute equally to the molecular orbital. The energies of the orbitals of the separate atoms are not the same and a different nomenclature for the molecular orbitals is preferable. The nomenclature used is that evolved by MULLIKEN who suggested that the molecular orbitals from the $(\sigma 2s)$ to the $(\sigma^* 2p)$ should be designated

$$z\sigma < y\sigma < x\sigma < w\pi < v\pi < u\sigma$$

This avoids the association, which arises in the case of the homonuclear diatomic molecules, of the molecular orbitals with the particular atomic orbitals.

The molecular orbital configurations of CO and NO can be written as

CO $KK\,(z\sigma)^2\,(y\sigma)^2\,(x\sigma)^2\,(w\pi)^4$

NO $KK\,(z\sigma)^2\,(y\sigma)^2\,(x\sigma)^2\,(w\pi)^4\,(v\pi)^1$

The bond in CO is effectively a triple bond (one σ and two π bonds). In NO there is an additional electron present in the antibonding orbital; this accounts for the observed paramagnetism of the nitric oxide molecule.

POLYATOMIC MOLECULES AND HYBRIDIZATION

The formation of the covalent bond may be considered as the pairing of electron spins by approach and overlap of atomic orbitals of suitable energy and symmetry. Because the combining atoms have orbitals of definite

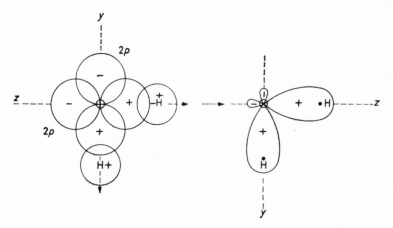

Figure 3.13. Predicted shape of H_2O by overlap of $2p$ orbitals on oxygen with $1s$ orbitals on hydrogen

geometric shape the bonds will be directed in space, the strength of the bond depending upon the extent to which overlapping occurs. The strongest bonds are formed when a maximum admixture of electron density is effected.

In the case of the water molecule, which is one of the simplest polyatomic molecules, we may consider bond formation as taking place by σ overlap, in the plane of the two oxygen orbitals containing the unpaired p electrons, between the hydrogen $1s$ orbital and the oxygen $2p$ orbitals. Strong overlap occurs between the $1s$ and $2p$ as illustrated in *Figure 3.13*, but effectively no other overlap is obtained. In such a case we speak of a localized molecular orbital, *i.e.*

one formed over only two atoms in the molecule. According to this simple pictorial approach the expected bond angle in water is 90°; an angle of 104° 30' is found. From a similar treatment of the formation of ammonia we would predict three N—H bonds at 90° to each other in a pyramidal arrangement formed by overlapping of the three $2p$ orbitals on the nitrogen atom with three $1s$ orbitals on hydrogen. The observed bond angle is 106° 45'.

The simple theory thus appears to be inadequate to explain the observed shapes of polyatomic molecules.

A consideration of the electronic configurations of beryllium, boron and carbon suggests that these elements should be inert, monovalent and divalent respectively. The elements are, however, typically divalent, trivalent and tetravalent respectively. It is impossible to explain the valencies of these elements on the basis of the number of unpaired electrons in the atoms and the overlap of atomic orbitals. In such cases it becomes necessary to suggest that electrons from the $2s$ level are unpaired and one promoted to the $2p$ level with the formation of excited states of the atom.

The promotions for the three elements above are

Be $(1s^2 2s^2)$ to   Be $(1s^2 2s^1 2p^1)$

B $(1s^2 2s^2 2p^1)$ to   B $(1s^2 2s^1 2p^1 2p^1)$

C $(1s^2 2s^2 2p^1 2p^1)$ to   C $(1s^2 2s^1 2p^1 2p^1 2p^1)$

Figure 3.14. Process of digonal hybridization

and in these excited states the number of unpaired electrons corresponds with the observed valencies of the atoms. However, this still does not account for the fact that all bonds are equivalent in a molecule such as BCl_3 or CCl_4. For example, if the carbon atom used three pure p orbitals and one pure s orbital in binding four atoms, one would expect in CCl_4 three fairly strong bonds directed at right angles to one another and a fourth weaker bond with no special orientation in space relative to the other three. It is necessary, therefore, to introduce a further concept, that of *hybridization* (or mixing) of atomic orbitals to form exactly equivalent hybrid orbitals which have characteristic directions in space.

The simplest case is that of *digonal* hybridization where two orbitals from an s and a p atomic orbital form two sp hybrid orbitals. This occurs in the beryllium atom wherein each hybrid orbital contains one electron and is capable of overlapping with a half-filled orbital on another atom to form a covalent bond. This type of hybridization is shown in *Figure 3.14*. The bonds that digonal hybrids make are at 180° to each other so that molecules such as $BeCl_2$ in the gas phase are linear.

In a similar manner the $2s$ and two $2p$ orbitals may undergo *trigonal* hybridization to give three equivalent sp^2 hybrid orbitals which are at an angle of 120° to each other in a plane (*Figure 3.15*).

3*

The hybridization of the 2s and three 2p orbitals produces four sp^3 hybrid orbitals that are directed towards the four corners of a regular tetrahedron as shown in *Figure 3.16*.

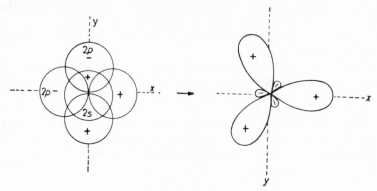

Figure 3.15. Process of trigonal hybridization

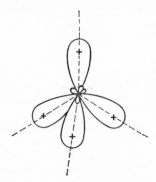

Figure 3.16. sp^3 Hybrid orbitals

The sp^2 hybridization accounts for the shape of molecules such as BCl_3 and the sp^3 hybridization for the *tetrahedral* arrangement of bonds in CCl_4.

Hybridization of Carbon Orbitals—The Formation of Double and Triple Bonds

The organic molecules methane, ethylene and acetylene serve a useful purpose in demonstrating the three types of hybridization above and help to illustrate the formation of double and triple bonds by orbital overlap.

(a) *Methane* (CH_4)—In this molecule the carbon orbitals are sp^3 hybridized and bonding occurs by overlap of the four hybrid orbitals with four $1s$ atomic orbitals on hydrogen. This results in a regular tetrahedral distribution of σ-bonds (*Figure 3.17*).

(b) *Ethylene* (C_2H_4)—Here the orbitals of the two carbon atoms are sp^2 hybridized. Overlap of one of these hybrid orbitals from each carbon atom gives rise to a σ-bond between the carbon atoms. The remaining hybrid orbitals on each carbon overlap with hydrogen $1s$ orbitals to give four σ-type carbon–hydrogen bonds as shown. Each carbon atom also has one electron located in a $2p$ orbital, the axis of which is perpendicular to the plane of the hybrid orbitals. These $2p$ orbitals add to the stability of the molecule by overlapping laterally to form a π-type carbon–carbon bond. This overlap is greatest when the carbon–hydrogen bonds are all coplanar and gives rise to

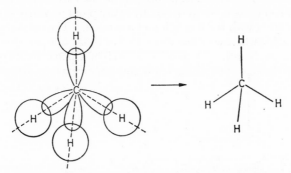

Figure 3.17. Formation of methane by overlap of carbon sp^3 hybrid orbitals with $1s$ atomic orbitals of hydrogen

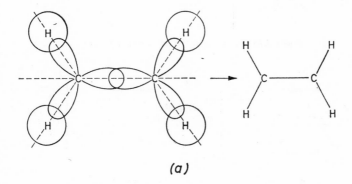

(a)

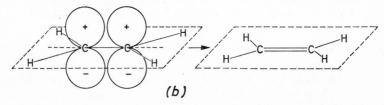

(b)

Figure 3.18. Bonding in the ethylene molecule, showing (a) formation of σ-bonds and (b) formation of π-bonds

a π molecular orbital as shown in Figure 3.18. This molecular orbital contains two electrons and takes the form of extended lobes, one above and one below the plane of the molecule.

The overlap of the two atomic p orbitals is less than the overlap of the two sp^2 hybrid orbitals and hence the π-bond is weaker than the σ-bond. This lower stability of the π-bond accounts for the reactivity of ethylene; the two carbon atoms tend to form a more stable σ-bond with other atoms. The presence of a π-bond means that the two carbon atoms are bound more strongly than by a single σ-bond; as a result of this the interatomic distance is shorter than would be obtained if only a single bond were present.

(c) *Acetylene* (C_2H_2)—In this molecule the orbitals of the carbon atoms are *sp* hybridized and the remaining 2*p* orbitals on each are unaffected. Bonding between the two carbon atoms occurs by overlap of an *sp* hybrid orbital from each carbon atom with the formation of a σ-bond. The remaining *sp* hybrid orbital on each carbon overlaps with the 1*s* orbital of hydrogen to form the carbon–hydrogen bonds. The *p* orbitals, each of which contains one electron, overlap, as in the case of ethylene, but in this instance two π-orbitals are formed

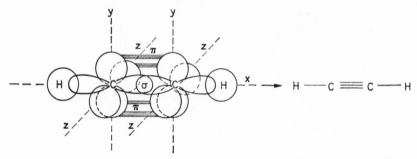

Figure 3.19. Bonding in the acetylene molecule

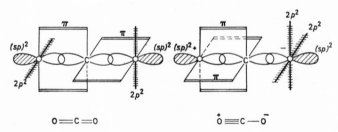

$$O = C = O \qquad \overset{+}{O} = C - \overset{-}{O}$$

Figure 3.20. Bonding in resonance forms of carbon dioxide. (2*p* orbitals are drawn as lines to avoid confusion. Shading indicates unshared electron pairs)

(*Figure 3.19*). The superposition of these π-orbitals leads to cylindrical symmetry about the carbon–carbon axis.

In systems where more than one double bond occurs, as in conjugated molecules such as butadiene and benzene, the π-electrons may be associated with more than two nuclei and are said to be delocalized. Thus in CO_2 the resonance forms may be written as

$$O{=}C{=}O \qquad {}^+O{=}C{-}O^- \qquad {}^-O{-}C{\equiv}O^+$$

Since the molecule is linear we may postulate *sp* hybridization for carbon and oxygen, giving the configurations

$$C \; = \; 1s^2 (sp)^1 (sp)^1 2p^1 2p^1 \qquad O \; = \; 1s^2 (sp)^2 (sp)^1 2p^2 2p^1$$
$$O^- = 1s^2 (sp)^2 (sp)^1 2p^2 2p^2 \qquad O^+ = 1s^2 (sp)^2 (sp)^1 2p^1 2p^1$$

The resonance hybrids may therefore be pictured as in *Figure 3.20.* Delocalization of the π-electrons occurs here.

The concept of hybridization gives a better picture of the structure of ammonia and water. If sp^3 hybridization is invoked for the nitrogen and oxygen atoms, the tetrahedral distribution of electron pairs would be as for methane, but for nitrogen one of these is a lone pair and for oxygen two are lone pairs. In such cases the lone pairs take up a larger volume than the bond pairs around the nitrogen and oxygen nucleus and this causes a decrease of the inter-bond angle in ammonia and water to below the tetrahedral value of 109° 28' *(Figure 3.21).* The presence of lone pairs therefore affects the bond angles of molecules; this is discussed further below.

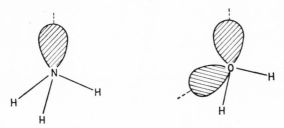

Figure 3.21. Bonding in ammonia and water showing lone-pair orbitals

When *d* orbitals are available, other types of hybridization may occur. Some examples of hybridization involving *d* orbitals are tabulated below.

Hybridization	Arrangement of hybrid orbitals
dsp^2	Square planar
sp^3d	Trigonal bipyramidal
d^2sp^3	Octahedral
d^4sp^3	Dodecahedral

SHAPES OF INORGANIC MOLECULES AND IONS

A useful qualitative approach to the shapes of inorganic molecules and ions was made by SIDGWICK and POWELL in 1940, who considered the shape to be dictated by the number of lone pairs and bonding pairs of electrons associated with the central atom. The basis of this premise is that these electron pairs arrange themselves so that the least repulsion occurs between them. Thus the shape of a molecule containing a multicovalent atom is related to the size of the valency shell of electrons on that atom. Accordingly, two pairs of electrons are arranged linearly, three pairs in a trigonal plane, four pairs tetrahedrally, five pairs as a trigonal bipyramid and six pairs as an octahedron. Regular molecular shapes are obtained only when all the electron pairs are used in bonding to identical atoms. If some of the atoms are different, departures from the ideal shape occur. When the central atom carries one or more lone-pairs the shape of the molecule or ion can be explained by postulating that the repulsion between electron-pairs decreases in the order:

lone pair–lone pair > lone pair–bond pair > bond pair–bond pair.

This makes it possible to account for the observed bond angles in molecules

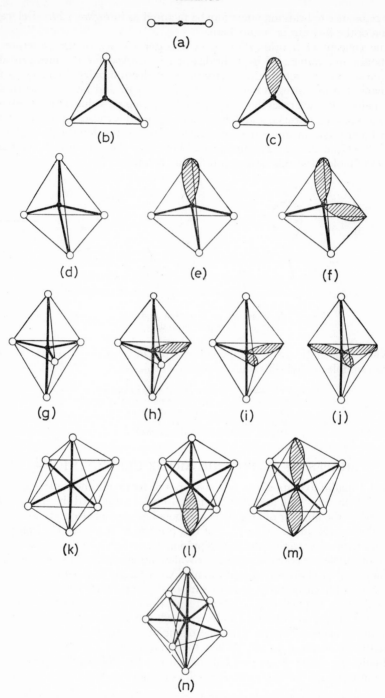

Figure 3.22. Shapes of simple molecules (adapted from GILLESPIE, R. J., and
NYHOLM, R. S. *Quart. Rev. chem. Soc., Lond.,* 11 (1957) 339)

where bond pairs are successively replaced by lone pairs, *e.g.* the series CH_4, NH_3 and H_2O. In the first molecule we have bonding to four hydrogen atoms and the bond angle is regular tetrahedral, *i.e.* 109° 28′. The replacement of one of the bonding pairs by a lone pair in ammonia causes the bond angle to decrease to 106° 45′ since the lone pair has a greater repulsive effect upon the remaining three bond-pairs. In water the replacement of a further bond pair by a lone pair causes even greater repulsion and the bond angle decreases further to 104° 30′. The decrease in bond angle observed for the hydrides of Group VI B and V B as the atomic number increases can also be interpreted by the simple Sidgwick–Powell approach (p. 230 and p. 220).

The shapes for simple inorganic molecules and ions of the non-transitional elements are given in *Figure 3.22* and an example is given for each shape.

The shapes of molecules and ions containing multiple bonds may also be explained if it is assumed that the multiple bond occupies only one position in space. The shapes for various molecules and ions are given in *Table 3.9*.

ONE- AND THREE-ELECTRON BONDS

Although the covalent bond that is most common is of the electron-pair type, two other related bonds are encountered in certain compounds. These are the one- and the three-electron bond.

The classic example of the first of these is the hydrogen molecule ion H_2^+ which has been detected spectroscopically. Two resonance forms of equal stability may be written for this species:

$$H.H^+ \quad \text{and} \quad {}^+H.H$$

It has a bond energy of 61 kcal/mole. On the molecular orbital approach the electron will be accommodated in the $\sigma 1s$ molecular orbital.

The three-electron bond is found in certain odd-molecules which it is impossible to describe in terms of completed octets. Such molecules are generally formed between atoms that are quite close in electronegativity. Typical examples are NO, NO_2 and ClO_2, for which we may write down the following conventional formulae:

$$:N{\overset{\cdot\cdot}{\equiv}}O:$$

Key to Figure 3.22

Shape	Electron pairs	Lone pairs	Molecular shape	Example
(a)	2	0	Linear	$HgCl_2$
(b)	3	0	Trigonal planar	BCl_3
(c)	3	1	V-shape	$SnCl_2$ (gas)
(d)	4	0	Tetrahedral	CH_4
(e)	4	1	Trigonal pyramid	NH_3
(f)	4	2	V-shape	H_2O
(g)	5	0	Trigonal bipyramid	PCl_5 (gas)
(h)	5	1	Irregular tetrahedral	$TeCl_4$
(i)	5	2	T-shape	ClF_3
(j)	5	3	Linear	ICl_2^-
(k)	6	0	Octahedral	SF_6
(l)	6	1	Square prism	IF_5
(m)	6	2	Square planar	ICl_4^-
(n)	7	0	Pentagonal bipyramid	IF_7

Table 3.9. The shapes of molecules containing multiple bonds

Total number of bonds and lone pairs	Arrangement	Number of bonds	Number of lone pairs	Shape	Examples
2	Linear	2	0	Linear	$O{=}C{=}O$; $H{-}C{\equiv}N$
3	Triangular	3	0	Trigonal planar	
	Planar	2	1	V-shaped	
4	Tetrahedral	4	0	Tetrahedral	
		3	1	Trigonal pyramidal	
		2	2	V-shaped	
5	Trigonal bipyramidal	5	0	Trigonal bipyramidal	
		4	1	Irregular tetrahedral	
6	Octahedral	6	0	Octahedral	

From GILLESPIE, R. J., and NYHOLM, R. S. 'Inorganic stereochemistry' *Quart. Rev. chem. Soc., Lond.* 11 (1957) 339.

Nitric oxide, as we have already seen, is alternatively described in terms of the molecular orbital theory as having a single electron in the $v\pi$ molecular orbital giving rise to paramagnetism characteristic of one unpaired electron. The other odd-molecules are paramagnetic and the odd electron may be considered as spread over the whole molecule in a molecular orbital.

ELECTRON DEFICIENT MOLECULES

Elements of Group III B, in particular boron and aluminium, show a great tendency to form 4 co-ordinate compounds, although the number of valency electrons is only three; when electron donor molecules are not present to form a 4 co-ordinate compound, the molecules of the Group III B elements may themselves dimerize. Thus aluminium chloride dimerizes to Al_2Cl_6 forming two electron bonds by bridging through chlorine. With other molecules of similar formulae, *e.g.* B_2H_6 and $Al_2(CH_3)_6$, there are insufficient electrons to write satisfactory structures involving electron-pair bonds. Such molecules are termed electron deficient and their structures are explained in terms of *multicentre* orbitals (see p. 207).

HYDROGEN BONDING

There is a great deal of evidence to show that when hydrogen is bonded to the very electronegative elements—fluorine, oxygen and nitrogen—there is a strong tendency for molecular association to occur. Thus hydrogen fluoride in the gas phase has a molecular weight far greater than that corresponding to

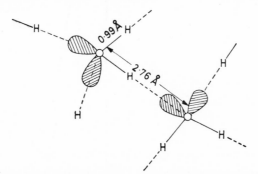

Figure 3.23. Hydrogen bonding in ice (after FOWLES, G. W. A. *J. chem. Educ.*, 34 (1957) 187)

the monomer HF. Association takes place in this and other compounds by hydrogen bonding. Compared with the strength of a normal covalent bond, the hydrogen bond is quite weak.

This type of bond can be explained in electrostatic terms. The bonding between hydrogen and the electronegative element has a large dipole and the electrostatic attraction between the positive end of one dipole on one molecule and the negative end of another dipole on a second molecule gives rise to molecular association. It has been suggested that this occurs by interaction between the positive end of the dipole and a lone pair of electrons on the electronegative atom. This situation in ice is shown in *Figure 3.23*. In ice (I), a form stable at low temperatures, the structure is similar to wurtzite for each oxygen is tetrahedrally surrounded by four other oxygens at distances of 2·76 Å and the hydrogens are positioned between the oxygen atoms, two at a distance of 0·99 Å (the normal O—H bond distance) and two at a distance of 1·77 Å. This wurtzite type structure (*Figure 3.24*) is an 'open' one and accounts for the low density of ice. In melting, this structure starts to break

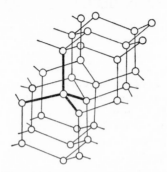

Figure 3.24. Section of the crystal structure of ice (I) showing the tetrahedral arrangement of the oxygen atoms

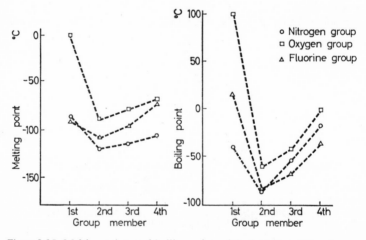

Figure 3.25. Melting points and boiling points of the hydrides of the nitrogen, oxygen and fluorine sub-groups

down causing a decrease in the volume which continues until 4°C. At this temperature, the expansion arising from the increase in thermal vibrations starts to outweigh this decrease in volume and water shows a maximum density at 4°C.

For hydrogen fluoride in the vapour phase, short zig-zag chains of polymeric molecules up to $(HF)_5$ exist below a temperature of about 60°C. In the solid state, infinite chains of HF molecules bonded via the hydrogens are found.

As a consequence of hydrogen bonding, certain other anomalous physical properties arise. The presence of hydrogen bonding is responsible for the deviations in melting points, boiling points, heats of vaporization and heats of fusion of the simple covalent hydrides of the most electronegative elements. The values of these physical properties for hydrogen fluoride, water and ammonia are all unexpectedly high compared with those of the other elements in the respective groups, due to molecular association. The variations in melting points and boiling points are shown in *Figure 3.25*.

The structures of certain organic molecules, *e.g. ortho*-hydroxybenzaldehyde and *ortho*-nitrophenol, are such that intramolecular rather than intermolecular hydrogen bonding may take place. The *meta* and *para* isomers of these compounds do not possess structures where hydrogen bonds can be formed within the molecules but they do form intermolecular hydrogen bonds. The *ortho* isomers are therefore of higher volatility than either the *meta* or *para* isomers.

o-hydroxybenzaldehyde   *o*-nitrophenol

Hydrogen bonds are to be found in many crystalline compounds, for instance H_3BO_3 and $NaHCO_3$. In many compounds hydration of the anion occurs; thus in copper sulphate pentahydrate one of the water molecules is hydrogen-bonded to the sulphate ion:

SUGGESTED REFERENCES FOR FURTHER READING

CARTMELL, E., and FOWLES, G. W. A. *Valency and Molecular Structure*, 2nd edn, Butterworths, London, 1961.

COULSON, C. A. *Valence*, 2nd edn, Clarendon Press, Oxford, 1961.

PAULING, L. *The Nature of the Chemical Bond*, 3rd edn, Cornell University Press, New York, 1960.

SANDERSON, R. T. *Chemical Periodicity*, Rheinhold, New York, 1960.

4

THE STRUCTURES OF THE ELEMENTS AND THEIR COMPOUNDS

THE CLASSIFICATION OF CRYSTALS

CRYSTALS were first studied systematically by examining their external shape and optical properties. It was recognized by STENSEN in 1669 that quartz crystals, however they originated, always had the same interfacial angles. The study of crystals by the contact and reflecting goniometers, instruments capable of measuring interfacial angles, amply confirmed this observation.

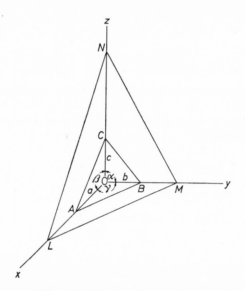

Figure 4.1. The crystallographic axes

One of the first laws of crystallography to be formulated stated the constancy of the angle between certain related faces of a crystal.

Crystals are classified into seven systems on the basis of their external shapes. The geometrical properties of a crystal are conveniently described in terms of its *crystallographic axes*. These are three, or sometimes four, lines meeting at a point. They are chosen so as to bear a definite relationship with characteristic features of the crystal, for example, the axes may coincide with or be parallel to the edges between principal faces. Where possible, the axes are chosen to be at right angles to each other. This is illustrated in *Figure 4.1. Ox, Oy* and *Oz* are the crystallographic axes and the interaxial angles, α, β and γ, are all equal to 90°. Next, a particular plane, say *ABC*, of the crystal is chosen as a standard or unit plane, in terms of which the crystal faces may be described.

This plane must cut all three crystallographic axes, and is often a fourth face of the crystal. The intercepts where this plane cuts the axes, $OA=a$, $OB=b$, $OC=c$, are known as the crystal *parameters*. Their lengths are purely relative but their ratios are important and are used to describe the crystal. The choice of axes and unit plane is such that the measured intercepts of any other face of the crystal such as LMN on these axes may be written as la, mb, nc, where l, m and n are simple whole numbers (2, 2 and 3 respectively in *Figure 4.1*). This is a statement of another crystallographic relationship, the law of rational indices.

Every crystal possesses certain elements of symmetry. Externally, this appears as a repetition of the crystal faces and their angles. A crystal is said to have an *n*-fold axis of symmetry when a rotation of $360°/n$ about this axis produces an orientation which cannot be distinguished from the first. 1-, 2-,

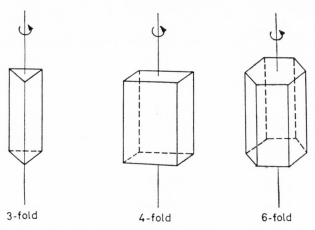

3-fold   4-fold   6-fold

Figure 4.2. Rotation axes of symmetry

3-, 4- and 6-fold axes are found for crystals and some of these are illustrated in *Figure 4.2*.

Another possible symmetry operation is inversion. This may be visualized in terms of the normals to the crystal faces. If these are imagined to be a set of vectors with a common origin, then on inversion the vectors are reversed. Therefore, rotation inversion axes, denoted $\bar{1}$, $\bar{2}$, $\bar{3}$, $\bar{4}$ and $\bar{6}$, may also be used to describe the symmetry of a crystal. A 1-fold inversion axis, $\bar{1}$, means that in effect there is a centre of symmetry present and for each face on the crystal there will be one parallel on the opposite side. The seven classes of crystal are summarized in *Table 4.1*.

The external crystal form, closely limited by the rigid rules of symmetry, can give only a restricted expression to the structure of a crystal and many crystalline compounds are classified together although their chemical and physical properties may vary enormously.

Insight into the internal structure of crystals quickly followed the classical experiment of FRIEDRICH and KNIPPING (1912) in which it was shown for the first time that x-rays were diffracted by a crystalline solid. Crystals act like a

73

diffraction grating towards x-rays (p. 275) and this fact provides very strong support for the concept of a crystal as an assembly of atoms or ions arranged in an ordered pattern with a three-dimensional periodicity. In 1913, W. L. BRAGG published the first crystal analysis, of sodium chloride, and many other structures were worked out within a short time. The crystal structures of very many solids have now been elucidated and it is quite clear that it is the internal pattern of atoms or ions which determines the external form and optical

Table 4.1. The classification of crystals

Class	Lattice constants	Examples	Essential symmetry
Cubic	$\alpha = \beta = \gamma = 90°$ $a = b = c$	NaCl, CaCl, CaF$_2$, ZnS, diamond, *etc.*	Four 3-fold axes
Tetragonal	$\alpha = \beta = \gamma = 90°$ $a = b \neq c$	TiO$_2$, SnO$_2$, NiSO$_4$	One 4-fold or 4-fold inversion axis
Hexagonal	Three axes at 120°; a fourth at right angles $a_1 = a_2 = a_3 \neq b$	HgS, graphite, AgI	One 6-fold or 6-fold inversion axis
Rhombo-hedral (Trigonal)	$\alpha = \beta = \gamma \neq 90°$ $a = b = c$	NaNO$_3$, Al$_2$O$_3$, CaCO$_3$ (calcite)	One 3-fold or 3-fold inversion axis
Orthorhombic	$\alpha = \beta = \gamma = 90°$ $a \neq b \neq c$	PbCO$_3$, BaSO$_4$, α-sulphur	Three mutually perpendicular 2-fold axis (either rotation or rotation inversion)
Monoclinic	$\alpha = \gamma = 90°$ $\beta \neq 90°$ $a \neq b \neq c$	CaSO$_4$.2H$_2$O, β-sulphur	One 2-fold or 2-fold inversion axis
Triclinic	$\alpha, \beta, \gamma \neq 90°$ $a \neq b \neq c$	CuSO$_4$.5H$_2$O, K$_2$Cr$_2$O$_7$	One 1-fold or 1-fold inversion axis

properties of a crystal. A crystal is made up of an infinite number of repeating groups. Each group constitutes a *unit cell*, this being the smallest portion of the crystal which possesses all the various kinds of symmetry which characterize the crystal as a whole.

A study of the elements and their compounds from the structural aspect is one important avenue of approach to the understanding of modern inorganic chemistry. A number of simple concepts have been applied to the correlation of structural data so that even the structures of complex, naturally occurring minerals such as the silicates are now well-established.

THE STRUCTURE OF THE ELEMENTS

Atomic Radii

From results of x-ray diffraction studies on solids and from electron diffraction or spectroscopic examination of gaseous molecules, a large amount of information is now available on the interatomic distances in the elements and their compounds.

Many elements, including the inert gases and most metals, are monatomic. Discrete atoms, not chemically bound to one another, are present in the solid state. On the simple picture of atoms as spheres of a definite radius which pack together so that adjacent atoms touch, the measured interatomic distance corresponds with twice the atomic radius. This concept of a fixed size for an atom conflicts with the wave-mechanical viewpoint which regards the electronic density in an atom as extending indefinitely from the nucleus and approaching zero asymptotically. Strictly speaking, it is impossible to define the size of an atom. Nevertheless, it is helpful in discussing the structure of the elements (and their covalent compounds) to assign a consistent set of radii which represent the relative sizes of the atoms. Atomic radii were assigned by PAULING from the interatomic distances observed in a number of elements. For many non-metals, where covalent bonds are present in the crystalline state, the atomic radii are determined from the measured interatomic distances. For a few non-metals such as nitrogen or oxygen, the atomic radius is calculated from interatomic distances in compounds containing a single covalent bond between non-metallic atoms, for example, the radius of the nitrogen atom is derived from the N—N distance in hydrazine, H_2N—NH_2. Values for the radii of metal atoms are half the interatomic distances in the solid state.

Values of atomic radii are given in *Table 4.2*. A study of these reveals a number of regularities:

(a) In a group, the atomic radius increases with the atomic number.

(b) This increase becomes more gradual as the atomic number becomes larger.

Table 4.2. The atomic radii of the elements (excluding the rare earths and actinides) in Ångstrom units

Group	I A	II A	III B	IV B	V B	VI B	VII B	0
								He 0·93
	Li 1·23	Be 0·89	B 0·80	C 0·77	N 0·74	O 0·74	F 0·72	Ne 1·12
	Na 1·57	Mg 1·36	Al 1·25	Si 1·17	P 1·10	S 1·04	Cl 0·99	Ar 1·54
	K 2·03	Ca 1·74	Ga 1·25	Ge 1·22	As 1·21	Se 1·17	Br 1·14	Kr 1·69
	Rb 2·16	Sr 1·91	In 1·50	Sn 1·41	Sb 1·41	Te 1·37	I 1·33	Xe 1·90
	Cs 2·35	Ba 1·98	Tl 1·55	Pb 1·54	Bi 1·52	Po 1·52		

Group	III A	IV A	V A	VI A	VII A	VIII			I B	II B
	Sc 1·44	Ti 1·32	V 1·22	Cr 1·17	Mn 1·17	Fe 1·16	Co 1·16	Ni 1·15	Cu 1·17	Zn 1·25
	Y 1·61	Zr 1·45	Nb 1·34	Mo 1·29	Tc —	Ru 1·24	Rh 1·25	Pd 1·28	Ag 1·34	Cd 1·41
	La 1·69	Hf 1·44	Ta 1·34	W 1·30	Re 1·28	Os 1·26	Ir 1·26	Pt 1·29	Au 1·34	Hg 1·44

Note: The atomic radius quoted for gold (1·34 Å) is less than the ionic radius given (Au$^+$ = 1·37 Å) in *Table 4.4*. For other elements, as we would expect, the positive ion radius is less than the radius of the atom. The example of gold serves to emphasize that although atomic radii are of significance relative to one another and similarly ionic radii are of significance relative to one another, the two sets of radii are not perfectly consistent with each other and the values assigned for one particular element cannot be regarded as absolute.

(c) In a period, there is a general decrease in radius from left to right as the atomic number increases.

(d) This decrease is less marked the higher the atomic number.

Considering the atom as a sphere of fixed size, the structure of the elements can be discussed from the viewpoint of the possible packing arrangements for spheres of equal size.

The Close-Packing of Spheres

In a plane, spheres pack together in such a way that their centres are at the corners of equilateral triangles with each sphere touching six others (*Figure 4.3*). A second layer can be superimposed on the first so that each sphere is in

Figure 4.3. The close-packing of spheres, showing the super-imposition of one layer upon another

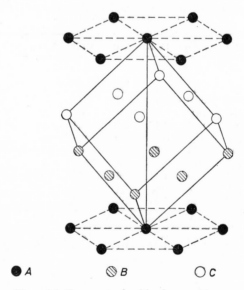

Figure 4.4. Face-centred cubic close-packing

contact with three spheres of the first layer. *A* and *B* represent the first and second layers respectively in the figure. A third similar layer of spheres may now be added in one of two ways, either so that the spheres in it are centred

76

immediately above those in the first or so that they are over holes in the first layer which are not occupied by second-layer spheres. In the first arrangement the structure is repeated after two layers and represents *hexagonal close-packing* ($ABABABABABAB\ldots\ldots$). In the second, the structure is repeated after three layers and represents *cubic close-packing* ($ABCABCABCABC\ldots\ldots$). This is, in fact, an assemblage of spheres at the corners and face centres of a cubic unit cell (*Figure 4.4*).

In both these close-packed structures each sphere is in contact with 12 neighbours; in other words its co-ordination number is 12. The two systems are very similar energetically and some metals are dimorphic, crystallizing in either the cubic (*A 1*) or the hexagonal (*A 3*) close-packed structure under different conditions. For perfect hexagonal packing the axial ratio $c/a = 1\cdot633$. However, in almost all cases of *A 3* packing c/a is found to be slightly less than

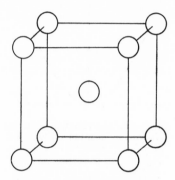

Figure 4.5. Body-centred cubic packing. This is the *A 2* arrangement for certain metals. It also represents the caesium chloride structure with caesium at the centre of the cube and the eight chloride ions at the corners

$1\cdot633$ and hence the six neighbours of one atom all in the same plane are slightly further from it than the three in the plane above and the three in the plane below. The axial ratio is observed to increase with temperature, thus tending to equalize the interatomic distances.

A third structure found with some metals is the *body-centred cubic arrangement* (*A 2*) in which the atoms are located at the corners and centre of a cube. The co-ordination number of the metal atom is therefore 8 (*Figure 4.5*).

BONDING IN THE CRYSTALLINE STATE

In the case of the elements, we can distinguish three types of bond in the solid state. These are the *metallic, covalent* and *residual* (or *van der Waals*) bonds.

The Metallic Bond

Most metals resemble one another chemically, for example in their tendency to form positive ions and to displace hydrogen from certain acids. They also

have many physical and mechanical properties in common including good conduction of heat and electricity, paramagnetism, a high tensile strength, malleability and ductility. Two or more metals can be melted together to form
alloys which differ profoundly in their properties from other chemical compounds. Particularly associated with alloys is the wide range possible in their
chemical composition. These characteristic properties of metals and alloys
are explicable in terms of the modern 'zone' theory of the metallic state.

A few properties of a metal were explained, at least qualitatively, by
LORENTZ in terms of a metal lattice consisting of positive ions with the valency

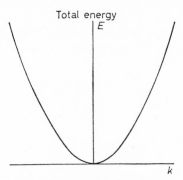

Figure 4.6. The variation of energy
(*E*) with momentum (*k*) for a free
electron

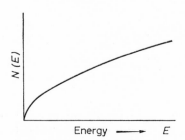

Figure 4.7. The variation of electron
density, *N(E)*, with *E* for a free
electron

electrons free to move within the body of the metal. SOMMERFELD extended
the simple theory by the application of quantum mechanics and concluded
that the mobile electrons were restricted to sets of permitted energy levels.
Even at the absolute zero of temperature the energies of electrons are spread
over a range of values, all the low-lying quantum states being fully occupied.

The energy of an electron, *E*, is related to its momentum, *k*, by the equations

$$E = \tfrac{1}{2}mv^2 = \frac{k^2}{2m}$$

where *m* is the mass, and *v* the velocity of the electron. *Figure 4.6* illustrates
the parabolic relationship between *E* and *k* and *Figure 4.7* shows how the electron

density (the number of electron pairs, $N(E)$, for any value of E) increases continuously with E.

BLOCH pointed out that the electron should more properly be regarded as a wave moving in the periodic field of the lattice of positive ions. In these circumstances, he showed that the energy no longer varies continuously with its momentum and that there are energy discontinuities at certain critical momenta values. This is shown in *Figure 4.8*, where ΔE_1, ΔE_2 and ΔE_3 represent ranges of energy that are completely forbidden to the electron. Electrons are accordingly restricted to certain permitted bands or zones of energy. In some respects this situation is analogous to that in the isolated atom where each electron has a certain energy, corresponding with a particular quantum level, and can only move to other permitted energy levels by the gain or loss of definite quantities of energy.

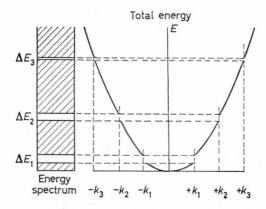

Figure 4.8. The variation of E with k for an electron moving in the periodic field of a lattice of positive ions

This simple approach is concerned with the relation between the energy and momentum of an electron in one dimension. The extended theory deals with the behaviour of electrons in a three-dimensional periodic field. It cannot be discussed here but it is interesting to note one of the conclusions of the complete theory—namely that electron densities in crystals can vary with E in one of two ways: in these, overlap may or may not be possible between permitted energy zones. *Figures 4.9(a)* and *4.9(b)* illustrate these alternatives.

The zone theory can account for many metallic properties. For example, electrical conductivity is associated either with an incompletely filled zone or two overlapping zones with vacant energy levels in the upper zone. In both cases electrons can take up energy and move to higher levels. If, however, one zone is completely filled and there is an appreciable gap between this and the next zone, which is completely vacant, the electrons cannot take up energy because there are no higher permitted energy levels within reach. As a result, the material is an insulator.

The characteristic behaviour of a semi-conductor can also be explained.

This is a substance whose electrical conductivity is greatly increased by a rise in temperature or by the addition of certain impurities. Single crystals of extremely pure germanium or silicon are the most commonly used semi-conductors. Compounds such as gallium arsenide, GaAs, and indium antimonide, InSb, are being increasingly employed because of their more favourable electrical properties. One way in which semi-conductivity can arise is when the lower filled zone is separated from a completely empty higher zone by a small energy gap. Then it may be possible to excite thermally an electron from the first to the second zone. The material is an insulator at low temperatures but shows conductivity when heated. Alternatively, the presence of an

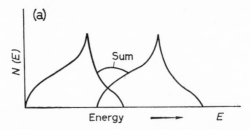

Figure 4.9(a). Overlapping between adjacent energy zones. Electrical conductivity is shown whenever the electrons available are insufficient to fill both zones completely

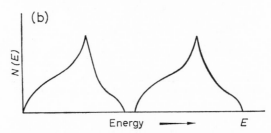

Figure 4.9(b). No overlap between adjacent zones. When the first zone is filled and the second completely empty, the substance is an insulator

impurity may introduce a new zone which lies between and possibly overlaps the two zones which are separated by a large gap in the pure material. The introduction of this extra zone may thus lead to conductivity in the impure material.

The Covalent Bond

In contrast to the close-packed structures of many elements, with their high co-ordination number of 12, some elements, especially the non-metals, have very low co-ordination numbers because of the formation of a small number of covalent bonds by each atom. The number of bonds formed depends on the number of valency electrons in the atom, that is, on the periodic group of the element, and is equal to $(8 - N)$ where N is the ordinal number of the group.

The $(8-N)$ rule is valid for many of the non-transitional elements in Groups VII to IV inclusive and the structures found are determined by the formation by each atom of one, two, three or four covalent bonds respectively.

The Residual Bond

This is the name given to the attraction which must exist between all atoms and molecules irrespective of whether or not they are joined by other bonds; it is often called the van der Waals bond. It is responsible for the cohesion between inert gas atoms in the liquid and solid states and for the attraction between molecules such as oxygen, nitrogen and hydrogen. Since these elements are solid only at very low temperatures and their heats of sublimation are very small (of the order of 0.5–2 kcal/mole), this type of bond is very weak compared with the metallic or covalent bond. The strength of the metallic bond, for example, is indicated by the high temperature usually necessary to break down the solid structure and cause the metal to melt or vaporize.

Before the advent of quantum mechanics, no description of the residual bond could be given. However, quantum mechanics shows that it is necessary to consider the dispersion forces, as they are called, between atoms or molecules. In very simple terms, molecules are regarded as having quickly fluctuating dipoles so that when two molecules approach one another, the dipoles at that instant come into phase and there is always a resultant attractive force. There is no permanent dipole moment, however, because the moments continue to vary rapidly in phase. A similar process is visualized as leading to inter-atomic attraction.

THE CLASSIFICATION OF THE ELEMENTS ACCORDING TO THEIR STRUCTURE

Six main types of structure exist, and each will be considered in turn.

1. The Inert Gases

The elements are monatomic and the bonding is exclusively residual. Ne, Ar, Kr and Xe have the $A\ 1$ arrangement, whereas He has the $A\ 3$.

2. Hydrogen, Nitrogen, Oxygen and the Halogens

These form stable diatomic molecules. In the case of oxygen, the paramagnetic O_2 molecules dimerize to O_4 molecules which rotate to give cubic symmetry and the $A\ 1$ structure for solid oxygen above 43°K. The structure below this temperature is uncertain. In H_2 $(A\ 3)$ and N_2 $(A\ 1$ below and $A\ 3$ above 35°K), the molecules again achieve spherical symmetry by rotation. The halogens Cl_2, Br_2 and I_2 are orthorhombic with the diatomic molecules oriented as shown in *Figure 4.10*.

3. The Representative Elements of Groups VI, V and IV

The structures of these exemplify the $(8-N)$ rule. The units may be small molecules, chains or layers of atoms, or three-dimensional networks. The bonding within the units is covalent with fairly weak residual forces between them. For some elements, notably those in Groups VI and V, there

81

is more than one way in which the atoms can combine covalently and satisfy the $(8-N)$ rule. As a result, the element shows allotropy, that is, several different solid modifications are known.

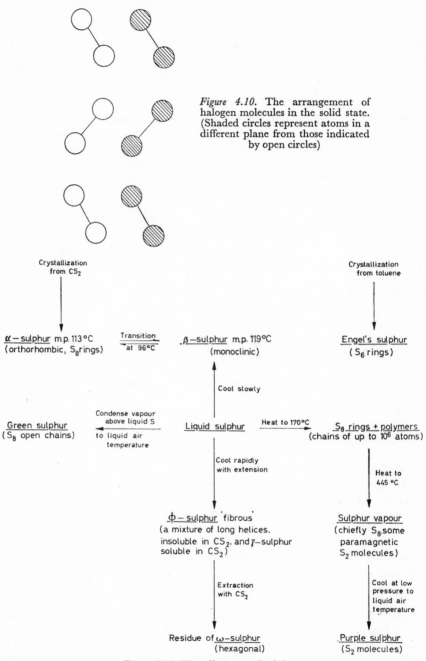

Figure 4.10. The arrangement of halogen molecules in the solid state. (Shaded circles represent atoms in a different plane from those indicated by open circles)

Figure 4.11. The allotropes of sulphur

Sulphur is well known for its many solid forms. The interrelation between the various allotropes is summarized in *Figure 4.11*. In several of these, the puckered S_8 ring (*Figure 4.12*) is the structural unit. Each sulphur atom forms two covalent bonds; the S—S distance is 2·04 Å and the bond angle is 107° 30', close to the tetrahedral angle (109° 28'). The existence of a puckered S_6 ring in Engel's sulphur has been established. Zig-zag chains of high molecular weight are also formed. In these, the sulphur atoms, except the two terminal ones, again form two covalent bonds. These polymers are found, for instance, in fibrous sulphur and their formation is believed to account for the remarkable viscosity increase and colour change observed when liquid sulphur is heated over the range 160–200°C. Finally, it is worth noting that the paramagnetic S_2 molecule, analogous to O_2, appears to be present in sulphur vapour and in the purple allotrope.

Two non-metallic crystalline forms of selenium are formed. These are the red monoclinic allotropes which are usually designated α and β. They are obtained from solutions of the element in carbon disulphide. Slow evaporation produces Se_α: rapid removal of solvent gives Se_β. Puckered Se_8 rings are present in both allotropes and the difference between them is probably

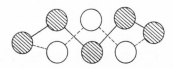

Figure 4.12. S_8 puckered ring

associated with the packing of the rings in the solid state. Metallic selenium is an opaque grey solid prepared by the crystallization of molten selenium. The small electrical conductivity of this allotrope is enhanced greatly by exposure to light, hence the use of this element in photocells. It is of the hexagonal class and contains zig-zag chains of great length packed together with their axes parallel. Metallic tellurium is similar to metallic selenium and amorphous varieties of both elements are also known.

The different allotropes of phosphorus are given in *Figure 4.13*. Molecular-weight determinations on solutions of white phosphorus in organic solvents have shown the presence of the P_4 molecule. Density measurements on phosphorus vapour show that this molecule is also present there. In the P_4 molecule (*Figure 4.14*) each phosphorus atom is located at the corner of a tetrahedron and is bound covalently to the three other atoms. Red phosphorus is believed to have a polymeric structure in which chains of phosphorus atoms are joined by random cross-linking (*Figure 4.15*). Each atom has three nearest neighbours at 2·29 Å, the next being at a distance of 3·48 Å. The scarlet and violet modifications are also believed to be polymeric. Black phosphorus has a metallic lustre and shows some electrical conductivity. It has a characteristic orthorhombic 'double-layer' structure (*Figure 4.16*) wherein each atom has two neighbours in the same layer at a distance of 2·17 Å and a third in the next layer at 2·20 Å. Although difficult to prepare, black phosphorus appears to be thermodynamically the most stable allotrope of this element.

The most stable allotrope of arsenic, antimony and bismuth is the metallic

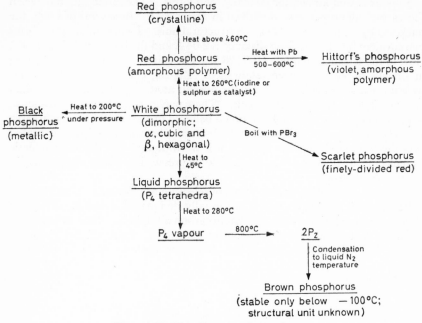

Figure 4.13. The allotropes of phosphorus

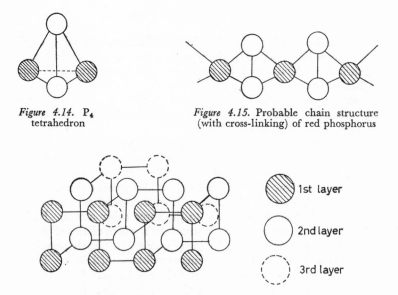

Figure 4.14. P₄
tetrahedron

Figure 4.15. Probable chain structure
(with cross-linking) of red phosphorus

Figure 4.16. Layer structure of black phosphorus

modification in each case and is in fact the only form known for bismuth.
The metallic allotrope has a layer structure (*Figure 4.17*) with each atom having
three nearest neighbours and three more somewhat further away. The

difference between the distances of these two sets of neighbours becomes relatively smaller as the metallic character of the element increases from arsenic to bismuth:

	Nearest atoms (Å)	*Next nearest atoms* (Å)
Arsenic	2·51	3·15
Antimony	2·87	3·37
Bismuth	3·10	3·47

These three elements in their metallic allotropes are evidently intermediate between the non-metals of low co-ordination number, and the metallic structures of high co-ordination number. The yellow non-metallic allotropes

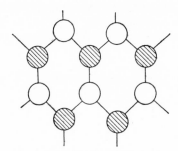

Figure 4.17. Layer structure of arsenic, antimony and bismuth

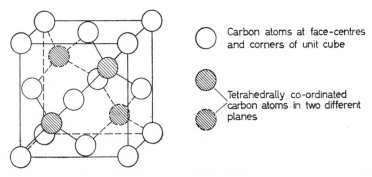

Carbon atoms at face-centres and corners of unit cube

Tetrahedrally co-ordinated carbon atoms in two different planes

Figure 4.18. The structure of diamond

of arsenic and antimony are metastable solids which have cubic symmetry. Yellow arsenic consists of tetrahedral As_4 units and probably yellow antimony is similar in structure. These readily change over to the more stable metallic modifications. Black amorphous forms of both arsenic and antimony are also known.

Two allotropes are known for carbon. Here the allotropy arises because the carbon atom can either form four single covalent bonds or one double and two single bonds.

In diamond, each carbon is tetrahedrally bound to four others (*Figure 4.18*). The C—C distance is 1·54 Å and the three-dimensional network of strong covalent bonds confers extreme hardness on the structure and is responsible for the very high melting point (3570°C).   Diamond is more stable than the second allotrope, graphite, under conditions of high temperature and pressure.   It was first successfully synthesized from carbon in the United States in 1954. Carbon, dissolved in a molten mixture of iron sulphide and iron, in the presence of a second metal such as Cr, Ni or Mn as catalyst, was induced to crystallize as diamonds by the application of high pressure at a high temperature.   Diamonds made in this way are individually small, usually coloured and so find their main uses in industrial cutting and abrading machinery.

Graphite possesses a layer lattice (*Figure 4.19*) in which each atom has three nearest neighbours in the same plane at a distance of 1·45 Å.   Each layer is composed of hexagons of carbon atoms.   Each atom forms three coplanar σ-bonds and the remaining valency electron enters a non-localized π-orbital. The presence of 'mobile' electrons makes the structure electrically conducting. The inter-layer distance is large (3·35 Å) and so the binding forces between

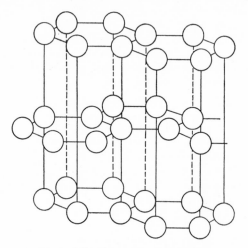

Figure 4.19. The structure of graphite

the layers are weak.   The attribution of the good lubricating properties of graphite to the weakness of these forces appears, however, to be an over-simplification, for it has recently been shown that the presence of substances such as water, ammonia, acetone, benzene, *etc.*, is essential for good lubrication. The cause of the lubricating action of graphite is not fully understood at present.

A number of derivatives of graphite, named *intercalation compounds*, are known in which foreign atoms are inserted between the carbon layers.   For example, a number of homogeneous compounds of composition between $CF_{0.68}$ and $CF_{0.995}$ have been prepared by direct reaction between fluorine and graphite between 420 and 460°C.   The fluorine atoms in these, situated between the graphite layers, are bound covalently to the carbon atoms.   In pure graphite, the planar arrangement of atoms may be attributed to sp^2 hybridization. In the carbon–fluorine intercalation compounds, the majority of carbon atoms form four single bonds.   The carbon atoms are therefore to be regarded as sp^3 hybridized; this accords well with the experimental observation that in these compounds the carbon layers are puckered and are no longer planar.   A number of other intercalation compounds are known, for example, the compounds of formulae C_8M and $C_{24}M$ which are prepared by direct reaction between alkali metal vapours and graphite.

The common form of graphite is hexagonal. Metastable rhombohedral graphite has been produced by mechanical deformation of the hexagonal allotrope. Here the packing is of the type $ABCABCABCABC\ldots\ldots$, where every fourth layer is vertically above the first. In hexagonal graphite, the packing of the layers is $ABABABABAB\ldots\ldots$ (*Figure 4.19*). Other forms of carbon such as charcoal and soot appear to be microcrystalline with the hexagonal graphite structure.

In the case of silicon and germanium, both these elements crystallize in the diamond structure. However, the very much reduced melting points, 1414°C and 958°C respectively, reflect the much weaker covalent bonds present compared with those in carbon (diamond allotrope).

Tin has two well-known allotropes. Grey tin is stable below 13·2°C and has the diamond structure. The four nearest neighbours to an atom are at a distance of 2·80 Å. White tin, the metallic form stable above 13·2°C, has a tetragonal lattice with each tin atom surrounded by six neighbours centred at the corners of a distorted octahedron, four at 3·016 Å and two at 3·175 Å. Lead has a typically metallic structure, *A 1*.

4. The Transition Metals

Their structures are summarized in *Table 4.3*. This includes a number of polymorphic forms which are observed at elevated temperatures. The transition metals which are noted for their malleability and ductility have the *A 1* structure. This class includes Ni, Cu, Ag, Au and Pt. Those, like Ti, V, Mo and W, which crystallize in the *A 2* or *A 3* structure, are less malleable and more brittle. There is an important difference between the two forms of close-packed structures which is responsible for the marked contrast in the

Table 4.3. The crystal structures of the transition metals

Group	III A		IV A		V A	
Sc	*A 3*	Ti	*A 3*	V	*A 2*
	A 1		*A 2* > 900°C		
Y	*A 3*	Zr	*A 3*	Nb	*A 2*
			A 2 > 850°C		
La	*A 3*	Hf	*A 3*	Ta	*A 2*
	A 1				

Group	VI A		VII A		VIII	
Cr	*A 2*	Mn	complex	Fe	*A 2*
	A 1 > 1850°C				*A 1* (916–1396°C)
Mo	*A 2*	Tc	*A 3*	Ru	*A 3*
W	*A 2*	Re	*A 3*	Os	*A 3*

Group	VIII		VIII		I B	
Co	*A 1/A 3*	Ni	*A 1*	Cu	*A 1*
	A 3 > 500°C				
Rh	*A 1*	Pd	*A 1*	Ag	*A 1*
Ir	*A 1*	Pt	*A 1*	Au	*A 1*

physical properties shown. In hexagonal close-packing, *A 3*, there is only one direction in which the atoms are arranged in close-packed sheets whereas in the cubic close-packed structure, *A 1*, the atoms are close-packed in no less than four directions, these being normal to the four body-diagonals of a cube (one of these diagonals is shown in *Figure 4.4*, p. 76). The ductility and malleability of metals depend largely on the ease with which adjacent planes of atoms can slip or glide over one another. Gliding occurs most readily between planes of close-packed atoms; there are more of these planes in the cubic close-packed than in the hexagonal close-packed structure and so the former is the more malleable and ductile.

Manganese has three crystalline forms; two of these are complex with 58 and 20 atoms respectively in the unit cell; the third modification has a distorted *A 3* structure. Cobalt is of interest because below 500°C it has a structure consisting partly of *A 1* packing and partly of *A 3* packing, with a random distribution of these two types of packing throughout the structure.

5. The Metals of Groups II B and III B, Boron and Aluminium

The structures of zinc and cadmium are sometimes quoted as extreme examples of the $(8 - N)$ rule. They both have distorted hexagonal structures in which each atom has six co-planar nearest neighbours and a further six, three above and three below the plane. In mercury, which has a rhombohedral lattice, the converse is the case for the six coplanar neighbours are further away than three atoms above and three below the plane.

At least three crystalline forms of boron are known. Two are rhombohedral, containing 12 and 108 atoms respectively in the unit cell. The third, containing 50 atoms in the unit cell, is tetragonal. Their structures are very complex and will not be considered here. Aluminium has the *A 1* structure. Gallium, its neighbour in the same group, has a unique arrangement for a metal in that each atom has one nearest neighbour, at 2·44 Å, and six more at distances between 2·7 and 2·8 Å. Indium has a tetragonal structure which is a distortion of cubic close-packing. Four nearest neighbours to each atom are located at a distance of 3·25 Å and a further eight are at 3·37 Å. Thallium is dimorphic, having the *A 3* structure at ordinary temperatures and the *A 2* structure above 262°C.

6. The Alkali and Alkaline-Earth Metals

Lithium, sodium, potassium, rubidium, caesium and barium all have the *A 2* structure. The softness and low density of these metals compared with those having the *A 1* or *A 3* structures is closely related to the lower co-ordination number of 8 compared with 12. Beryllium and magnesium have the *A 3* arrangement. Calcium and strontium are trimorphic and can show any of the three structures, depending on the temperature.

THE STRUCTURE OF INORGANIC COMPOUNDS

Bonding

In many inorganic compounds, the bonding is either predominantly ionic or chiefly covalent and characteristic properties are associated with each type of crystal. As in the case of the elements, residual forces will always be present.

An ionic compound may be visualized as an assemblage of positive and negative ions which extends indefinitely in three dimensions. Its chemical formula indicates the relative numbers of the different ions present in the crystal as a whole. For example, in the sodium chloride crystal (p. 96), six ions of one charge are octahedrally situated around one ion of the opposite charge. The chemical formula, NaCl, indicates that equal numbers of Na^+ and Cl^- ions are present but there exists no unit of Na^+Cl^- in which one chloride ion is more closely associated with one sodium ion than with any others. The strong Coulombic attractions between the oppositely charged ions result in lattice energies of appreciable magnitudes (p. 48). Accordingly, ionic structures usually have a characteristic hardness and are of high melting point and boiling point.

Other typical properties include very poor electrical conductivity in the solid state which generally improves near the melting point and becomes good in the fused state. The increase in electrical conductivity with temperature, particularly marked at the melting point, is due to the breaking up of the lattice. The ions become mobile and can transport an electric current. The cause of electrical conductivity is therefore different here from that shown by metals which is due to the presence of mobile electrons. The conductivity shown in the fused state is exploited in the extraction of metals from their molten ionic compounds by electrolysis (p. 179). It should be noted that electrical conductivity in the fused state does not necessarily mean that ions are present in the solid state. For instance, some of the interhalogens (p. 244) can be used as ionizing solvents because of the formation of ions in the liquid state from the discrete molecules which exist in the solid state. Ionic compounds are generally insoluble in non-polar solvents such as benzene, carbon tetrachloride, *etc.*, but are frequently very soluble in polar solvents like water, ammonia, *etc.* (p. 126).

Covalent compounds are of two main types: firstly, the molecular compounds in which the molecules are held together in the solid state by comparatively weak forces; and, secondly, the substances wherein covalent bonding extends throughout the crystal lattice.

The first type, exemplified by the halides of non-metals and of some metals in their high valency states, have soft crystals and low melting and boiling points. Strong covalent bonds are present within the molecule only. The solubility of this type of compound is usually much greater in non-polar than in polar solvents unless, of course, chemical reaction with the solvent (solvolysis) occurs. Another property typical of many molecular compounds is the absence of electrical conductivity in the fused state, provided that ionization does not occur on melting.

Compounds of the second class, typified by silicon carbide (SiC), silica (SiO_2), *etc.*, are hard, infusible and insoluble substances. The three-dimensional network of strong covalent bonds present in such substances requires a great deal of energy to destroy it.

A purely ionic and a completely covalent bond represent the two extremes of structure which are rarely observed in practice and the vast majority of compounds contain bonds that are intermediate in character. Fajans' Rules (p. 49) are of value in predicting significant departures from purely ionic bonding. For example, layer lattices (p. 100) are observed when polarization

89

of the anion by the cation is considerable and they can be regarded as structurally intermediate between a three-dimensional array of ions and a molecular lattice.

Ionic Crystals

In many compounds the bonding between the atoms is largely electrostatic and their structures in the solid state can be described in terms of an ionic model in which the ions are treated as charged compressible spheres. This approach provides a valuable starting point for the structural study of inorganic compounds.

Univalent and Crystal Radii

In ionic crystals the ions may be regarded as in contact with one another and so the measured interatomic distance corresponds with the sum of the radii of the cation and anion. As in the case of atomic radii, it is advantageous to have some idea of the relative sizes of ions and several attempts have been made to arrive at a suitable set of ionic radii.

The set most widely used is that due to PAULING. He took the experimental values of the interionic distance in a number of crystals—namely NaF, KCl, RbBr and CsI—and deduced from them a set of ionic radii which closely reproduce the observed interionic distances in many other compounds.

The four alkali halides have the following equilibrium interionic distances: NaF, 2·31 Å; KCl, 3·14 Å; RbBr, 3·43 Å; CsI, 3·85 Å. The first three have the same crystal structure, namely that of sodium chloride, whereas CsI has that of caesium chloride (p. 95). In each case, the compound is composed of a pair of isoelectronic ions.

The size of an ion is determined by the force of attraction between the nucleus and the outermost electrons. PAULING assumed this to be inversely proportional to the effective nuclear charge, defined as the actual nuclear charge, Ze, from which has been subtracted a screening correction, Se, to allow for the effect of electrons in the intervening shells. The screening constants, S, are variously obtained by theoretical calculation and from molecular refraction and x-ray experimental data.

The ionic radius, r, is given by

$$r = \frac{C_n}{Z-S}$$

where C_n is a constant for a particular isoelectronic sequence. For ions having the neon structure, PAULING assigned the value of 4·52 to S: the effective nuclear charges for Na^+ $(Z=11)$ and F^- $(Z=9)$ are then $6·48\,e$ and $4·48\,e$ respectively.

The observed Na—F distance of 2·31 Å is split up in the inverse ratio of these charges:

$$\frac{r_{Na^+}}{r_{F^-}} = \frac{4·48}{6·48}$$

and so the values $r_{Na^+} = 0·95$ Å and $r_{F^-} = 1·36$ Å are obtained.

Similarly, the radii of the other ions, $r_{K^+} = 1\cdot33$ Å, $r_{Cl^-} = 1\cdot81$ Å, $r_{Rb^+} = 1\cdot48$ Å, $r_{Br^-} = 1\cdot95$ Å, $r_{Cs^+} = 1\cdot69$ Å and $r_{I^-} = 2\cdot16$ Å, are calculated.

The calculations may be extended to ions carrying multiple charges which also have the inert-gas configurations (such as Ca^{2+}, S^{2-}, etc.) by using the above equation for r and the values for the constants, C_n, given by the radii of the alkali metal and halide ions. In this way the *univalent radii* of these multi-charged ions are estimated and these represent correctly their relative sizes compared with the alkali and halide ions. They cannot, however, be added to give the observed interionic distances in crystals containing multi-valent ions, since univalent radii, because of the way in which they are derived, are 'the radii the multivalent ions would possess if they were to retain their electronic distribution but to enter into Coulombic interaction as if they were univalent' (PAULING).

The *crystal radii* of multivalent ions, so-called because the sum of two crystal radii is equal to the actual interionic distance in a crystal containing the ions, are calculated from the univalent radii as follows:

The total potential energy, U, of an ion pair in a crystal is given by

$$U = -\frac{Ae^2z^2}{r} + \frac{Be^2}{r^n}$$

where the ions have charges of $+ze$ and $-ze$ respectively, A is the Madelung constant and B is the Born coefficient*.

Hence

$$\frac{dU}{dr} = \frac{Ae^2z^2}{r^2} - \frac{nBe^2}{r^{n-1}}$$

At the equilibrium distance, r_c, the forces of attraction and repulsion are equal, $dU/dr = 0$ and $Ae^2z^2/r_c^2 = nBe^2/r_c^{n-1}$ or

$$r_c = (nB/Az^2)^{1/n-1}$$

If the Coulombic forces corresponded with those of univalent ions, that is $z = 1$, with an unchanged value for B, the equilibrium interionic distance r_1 would be

$$r_1 = \frac{nB^{1/n-1}}{A}$$

The univalent and crystal radii are therefore related to one another by

$$r_c = r_1 z^{-2/n-1}$$

Approximate values for the Born exponent, n, can be calculated from the results of experiments on the compressibility of crystals and so R_c values can be determined.

Values of crystal radii are given in *Tables 4.4* and *4.5*. These include data for ions which have an outer shell of 18 electrons (Cu^+, Ag^+, Au^+, Zn^{2+} and so on), the values being calculated by using the same values for C_n as for

* B is a term expressing the repulsion between the ions and it varies with co-ordination number. Consequently, the crystal radius also changes. The values of crystal radii given in *Table 4.4* are calculated for a co-ordination number of 6 and must be decreased by about 5 per cent if tetrahedral and not octahedral radii are required.

argon-, krypton- and xenon-like ions with the appropriate screening constants. Other empirical radii for transition metal ions have been deduced from experimental results on crystals assumed to be essentially ionic in character using, as a basis, the value $O^{2-} = 1.40$ Å.

Table 4.4. Crystal radii according to Pauling (in Ångstrom units)

I		II		III		IV		V		VI		VII	
Li^+	0·60	Be^{2+}	0·31	B^{3+}	0·20			N^{3-}	1·71	O^{2-}	1·40	F^-	1·36
Na^+	0·95	Mg^{2+}	0·65	Al^{3+}	0·50	Si^{4+}	0·41	P^{3-}	2·12	S^{2-}	1·84	Cl^-	1·81
K^+	1·33	Ca^{2+}	0·99	Sc^{3+}	0·81	Ti^{4+}	0·68						
Rb^+	1·48	Sr^{2+}	1·13	Y^{3+}	0·93	Zr^{4+}	0·80						
Cs^+	1·69	Ba^{2+}	1·35	La^{3+}	1·15	Hf^{4+}	0·81						
Cu^+	0·96	Zn^{2+}	0·74	Ga^{3+}	0·62	Ge^{4+}	0·53			Se^{2-}	1·98	Br^-	1·95
Ag^+	1·26	Cd^{2+}	0·97	In^{3+}	0·81	Sn^{4+}	0·71			Te^{2-}	2·21	I^-	2·16
Au^+	1·37	Hg^{2+}	1·10	Tl^{3+}	0·95	Pb^{4+}	0·84						

Table 4.5. Empirical crystal radii of transition metal ions (based on $O^{2-} = 1.40$ Å)

M^{2+}		M^{3+}		M^{3+}		M^{3+}		M^{4+}	
Ti	0·90	Ti	0·76	Ce	1·11	Ac	1·18	U	0·93
V	0·88	V	0·74	Pr	1·09	Th	1·14	Np	0·92
Cr	0·84	Cr	0·69	Nd	1·08	Pa	1·12	Pu	0·90
Mn	0·80	Mn	0·66	Pm	1·06	U	1·11	Am	0·89
Fe	0·76	Fe	0·64	Sm	1·04	Np	1·09	Cm	0·88
Co	0·74	Co	0·63	Eu	1·03	Pu	1·07		
Ni	0·72	Ni	0·62	Gd	1·02	Am	1·06		
				Tb	1·00				
				Dy	0·99				
				Ho	0·97				
				Er	0·96				
				Tm	0·95				
				Yb	0·94				
				Lu	0·93				

The ionic radii show a number of interesting trends:

(*a*) In moving from left to right across a period, a sequence of isoelectronic cations or anions shows a marked decrease in radius, for example from Na^+ to Si^{4+} and from N^{3-} to F^-. As the atomic number increases the increasing nuclear charge acts on the same number of electrons and so the radius of the ion decreases.

(*b*) In moving down a group of non-transitional elements, the ionic radius increases both for cations and anions. When passing from one element to the next of higher atomic number, an extra shell of electrons is interposed between the nucleus and the outermost valency electrons. The nuclear charge also increases in the same direction but evidently the effect of this is more than offset by the additional screening effect of the extra electrons.

The combination of (*a*) and (*b*) results in a close similarity between the ionic radii of elements having a diagonal relationship to one another in the Periodic Table. This is most apparent for the electropositive metals of low atomic number as shown by the chemical resemblances between lithium and magnesium and between beryllium and aluminium.

(c) For the sequence of transition metals titanium to nickel, an increase in atomic number of one unit is accompanied by a small decrease in ionic radius. This suggests that the extra electron in the d sub-shell is more firmly held by the increased nuclear charge. The smallness of the decrease accounts for the similarities observed in the chemical and physical properties of the compounds formed by these metals in the oxidation state of $+2$ or $+3$.

(d) With the elements from cerium to lutetium, the $4f$ sub-shell is filling up and there is a concomitant decrease in ionic radius known as the *lanthanide contraction*. The decrease from one element to the next is very small and as a result these metals are related very closely to one another in their properties. The lanthanide contraction has important consequences outside Group III. For example, the ionic radius of Hf^{4+} is very near to that of Zr^{4+}, the effect of the lanthanide contraction being to counterbalance almost exactly the increase in ionic radius with atomic number normally found in a group. This accounts for the great chemical similarity between hafnium and zirconium. The effect of the lanthanide contraction extends to some of the later groups of transition metals so that niobium and tantalum resemble one another very closely and molybdenum and tungsten have many properties in common.

An analogous *actinide contraction* is shown by the elements from actinium onward and again results in marked similarities between them.

FACTORS WHICH DETERMINE THE OCCURRENCE OF SIMPLE IONIC STRUCTURES

In a simple approach to ionic structures we make use of the following concepts:

(a) Ions are spherical and have a definite size.

(b) Each ion tends to surround itself with as many ions of opposite charge as possible. This co-ordination number will depend on the relative sizes of the anion and cation and on the requirement that for the arrangement to be stable, the central ion must be in contact with each of its neighbours. Anions are generally larger than cations and so there will be a limit to the number which can surround and touch one cation. As a result, the co-ordination number of the cation will determine the type of structure found. In a simple binary compound AX, the co-ordination numbers of the cation and anion must be the same to ensure electroneutrality.

(c) The arrangement of anions about a central cation will usually be the most symmetrical in space. The electrostatic repulsion between the anions is then at a minimum. This concept leads us to expect that when the co-ordination number of the cation A is 2 with respect to the anion X, then the grouping AX_2 will be linear with an X ion on either side of A. For a co-ordination number of 3, least repulsion occurs when A is at the centre of an equilateral triangle, the vertices of which are occupied by X ions. In the case of co-ordination number 4, symmetry considerations require a tetrahedral arrangement of X about A for the greatest stability. For co-ordination number 6, the arrangement is octahedral. For 8 co-ordination, the electrostatic repulsion is minimal in a square anti-prismatic arrangement (*Figure*

4.20). This is not found, however, in ionic structures, the alternative cubic arrangement (*Figure 4.21*), with A at the centre and X at the corners of a cube, being preferred. The reason for this is that cubic co-ordination can extend indefinitely in three dimensions but such an extension is not possible for a square anti-prismatic arrangement, despite the fact that this is the more stable for an isolated AX_8 group.

The co-ordination number found in practice depends largely on the requirements of (*b*). The relative sizes of two ions is expressed in their radius

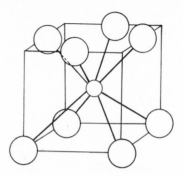

Figure 4.20. Square anti-prismatic
co-ordination

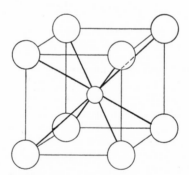

Figure 4.21. Cubic co-ordination

ratio, r_{A^+}/r_{X^-}, and the magnitude of this will determine the co-ordination number.

For example, in 3 co-ordination, a stable structure obtains when the three X ions are in contact with the central A^+ ion. If A^+ now becomes smaller relative to X^-, *i.e.* the radius ratio decreases, a stage is reached at which the three X^- ions also touch each other. Below this limiting lower value for the radius ratio, the structure is unstable because all three anions can no longer touch A^+. *Figure 4.22* illustrates the limiting situation. From this, the minimum radius ratio may be calculated for which this structure is stable. The three anions centred at *A*, *B* and *C* touch the cation centred at *D* and also touch one another.

94

In the triangle BDE,

$$\frac{BE}{BD} = \cos 30°$$

$$\frac{r_X}{r_A + r_X} = \frac{\sqrt{3}}{2}$$

$$2r_X = \sqrt{3}\, r_A + \sqrt{3}\, r_X$$

$$\frac{r_A}{r_X} = \frac{0·268}{1·732} = 0·1547$$

In a similar way, the radius ratio limits for other co-ordination numbers may be found. These are given in *Table 4.6* for the arrangements which occur most commonly in ionic crystals.

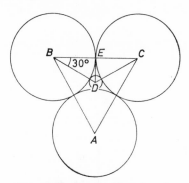

Figure 4.22. The limiting situation for 3 co-ordination

Table 4.6. Radius ratio limits for different co-ordination numbers

Co-ordination number	Shape	Radius ratio limits
3	Plane triangular	0·155 to 0·225
4	Tetrahedral	0·225 to 0·414
6	Octahedral	0·414 to 0·732
8	Cubic	> 0·732

The structures of a number of simple crystals are described in the following pages.

Sodium Chloride and Caesium Chloride

The compounds which should be most nearly ionic in character are those between the most electropositive metals and the most electronegative non-metals—namely the alkali halides. For simple binary compounds of formula AX, two structures are found: sodium chloride (*Figure 4.23*) in which each cation is octahedrally surrounded by 6 anions and each anion by 6 cations; and caesium chloride (*Figure 4.5*) in which the co-ordination number of cation and anion is 8 and the arrangement about each ion is cubic.

All the alkali metal halides except CsCl, CsBr and CsI (which have the caesium chloride structure*) crystallize with the sodium chloride structure and the radius ratios for many of these compounds do, in fact, lie between the limits 0·414 and 0·732 (*Table 4.7*). According to the radius ratio rule, LiCl, LiBr and LiI should have tetrahedrally co-ordinated structures and the simple theory is not able to account for their sodium chloride structure. It is worth

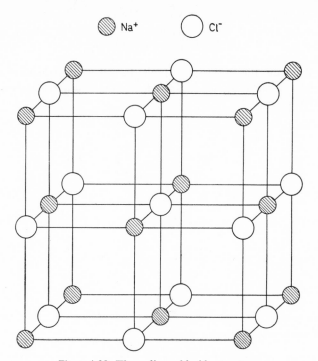

Figure 4.23. The sodium chloride structure

Table 4.7. Radius ratio values for the alkali halides

	Li⁺	Na⁺	K⁺	Rb⁺	Cs⁺
F⁻	0·44	0·70	0·98	1·09	1·24
Cl⁻	0·33	0·52	0·73	0·82	0·93
Br⁻	0·31	0·49	0·68	0·76	0·87
I⁻	0·28	0·44	0·62	0·69	0·78

noting, however, that of all the alkali halides, the lithium halides are those for which, according to Fajans' Rules, one would expect the greatest deviation from purely ionic bonding. Also, it is apparent that the ionic radii assigned to lithium and the halogens used in the calculation of the radius ratios of *Table 4.7* are not appropriate to the lithium halide crystals. For instance, if

* CsCl, CsBr and CsI have the sodium chloride arrangement when deposited from the vapour on to cleavage surfaces of mica and certain other crystals.

the radii of Li^+ (0·60 Å) and F^- (1·36 Å) are added together, a 'predicted' value of 1·96 Å is obtained for the interionic distance. This must be compared with the experimental value of 2·01 Å for LiF. Similar but larger differences are observed for the other lithium halides: LiCl, 2·41 (2·57); LiBr, 2·55 (2·75); LiI, 2·76 (3·02). In each case the predicted value in Ångstrom units is given first, followed by the experimental value in brackets.

PAULING interprets these differences in terms of anion–anion repulsion which becomes more significant near to the radius ratio limit, thus leading to an observed cation–anion distance larger than the sum of the radii.

A number of other ionic crystals having the sodium chloride structure are listed in *Table 4.8* together with the appropriate radius ratios. The caesium

Table 4.8. Some compounds with the sodium chloride structure

Compound	Radius ratio	Compound	Radius ratio
AgF	0·93	BaO	0·96
AgCl	0·70	MnO	0·57
AgBr	0·65	FeO	0·54
MgO	0·46	CoO	0·53
CaO	0·71	NiO	0·51
SrO	0·81	MnS	0·43

chloride structure is much less common than that of sodium chloride. Apart from the three caesium halides mentioned earlier, other compounds which show this structure are CsCN, TlCN, CsSH (the anions here attain spherical symmetry by rotation), TlCl and TlBr. NH_4Cl, NH_4Br and NH_4I crystallize with the sodium chloride structure at temperatures above 184·3°, 137·8° and −17·6°C respectively. Transitions occur at these temperatures to the caesium chloride structure.

Zinc Blende and Wurtzite

The structures of these two forms of ZnS are very closely related; in each case the co-ordination number is four with a tetrahedral arrangement of the four nearest neighbours of any particular ion (*Figure 4.24*). In wurtzite and zinc blende the sulphur atoms may be regarded as arranged in hexagonal and in cubic close-packing respectively. One structure is thus related to the other by movements of part of the structure in a direction parallel to the layers of close-packed atoms. The two arrangements must be very nearly equivalent energetically because many compounds are known which are dimorphous and crystallize with either one or the other structure. *Table 4.9* includes some of these compounds. The radius ratios are, however, frequently outside the limits for 4 co-ordination.

The structure of diamond is also tetrahedral and the disposition of atoms in space (*Figure 4.18*) is the same as in zinc blende. The bonding in diamond is purely covalent of course, while that in many of the compounds which show the zinc blende structure must have appreciable ionic character otherwise the formation of four covalent bonds by, for example, a Group II metal would result in the accumulation of negative charge on the metal atom, a situation wholly out of accord with its chemical properties. An examination of the compounds listed in *Table 4.9* indicates that considerable polarization, according to Fajans' Rules, is to be expected. It is therefore not surprising that the simple ionic model, which leads on to the concept of limiting radius ratios, cannot account satisfactorily for the structures observed.

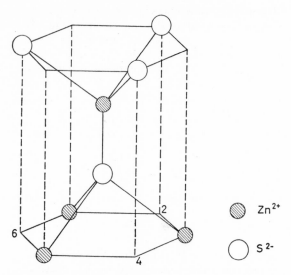

Figure 4.24. The zinc blende structure. (Wurtzite has the three atoms in the lower hexagon in positions 2, 4 and 6)

Table 4.9. Compounds showing either the zinc blende or wurtzite structure

Compound	Structure	Radius ratio
BeO	W	0·22
BeS	Z-B	0·17
ZnO	W	0·53
ZnS	Z-B, W	0·40
CdS	Z-B, W	0·53
HgS	Z-B	0·60
MnS	Z-B, W	0·43
CuF	Z-B	0·71
CuCl	Z-B	0·53
CuBr	Z-B	0·49
CuI	Z-B	0·44
AgI	Z-B	0·58

Z-B = zinc blende structure ; W = wurtzite structure

Fluorite and Rutile

These are ionic structures found for many oxides and fluorides of general formula AX_2. In fluorite, CaF_2, each calcium ion is surrounded by eight fluoride ions arranged at the corners of a cube (*Figure 4.25*) and each fluoride ion is surrounded tetrahedrally by four calcium ions. In rutile, TiO_2, each titanium ion is surrounded octahedrally by six oxide ions and each oxide ion by three titanium ions arranged at the corners of a triangle (*Figure 4.26*). In this type of structure, the octahedron is not necessarily regular and the triangle is not necessarily equilateral. X-ray measurements have shown that the departure from these conditions is usually small.

Geometrical considerations suggest that the fluorite structure should be

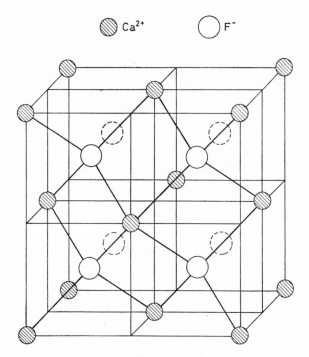

Figure 4.25. The fluorite structure

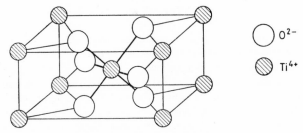

Figure 4.26. The rutile structure

found for radius ratios greater than 0·732 and the rutile structure for values below this. Some compounds which have these structures are listed in *Table 4.10*. PAULING has shown that for this type of compound the interionic distances are closely approximated by the sum of the crystal radii and the radius ratios quoted in *Table 4.10* have been calculated using the radii given in *Tables 4.4* and *4.5*.

The compounds A_2X, formed between the alkali metals (except Cs) and the elements of Group VI (oxygen, sulphur, *etc.*), crystallize with the antifluorite structure. In this, the positions of anions and cations are reversed relative to those in the fluorite structure.

Table 4.10. Compounds showing either the rutile or fluorite structure

Fluorite		Rutile	
Compound	*Radius ratio*	*Compound*	*Radius ratio*
CaF_2	0·73	MgF_2	0·48
CdF_2	0·71	ZnF_2	0·54
HgF_2	0·81	MnF_2	0·59
SrF_2	0·83	FeF_2	0·56
PbF_2	0·89	CoF_2	0·54
BaF_2	0·99	NiF_2	0·53
HfO_2	0·58		
CeO_2	0·72		

The Layer Lattices of Cadmium Chloride and Cadmium Iodide

These AX_2 structures can be regarded as formed by the superposition of a number of layers each of which is composed of a sheet of cations enclosed between two sheets of strongly polarized anions. Each cation is symmetrically

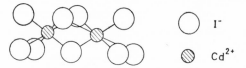

Figure 4.27. The cadmium iodide structure

surrounded by six anions at the corners of an octahedron while the three cation neighbours of an anion all lie on one side of it. The anion is at the apex and the three cations are at the base of triangular pyramid. The forces between these composite layers cannot be electrostatic in nature because atoms (or ions) of similar kind are next to one another.

These two structures differ only in the way in which the halogen atoms are packed together. In cadmium iodide (*Figure 4.27*), the arrangement is that of hexagonal close-packing: in cadmium chloride, the halogens are cubic close-packed. They may be regarded as intermediate between two limiting types— the ionic fluorite or rutile crystal and a molecular crystal (in which the small finite molecules are held together by weak residual forces). Such layer structures are observed only when there is considerable polarization of the anion by the cation. This is shown in *Table 4.11* where the transition from a symmetrical ionic structure to a layer lattice is related to the substitution of a more readily polarized ion such as chloride, bromide or iodide for one, like fluoride, which is less easily polarized. It is interesting to note the complementary example of caesium oxide, Cs_2O, which unlike the other alkali metal oxides

Table 4.11. Transition of structural type with increasing polarization

Symmetrical ionic structures		Layer lattices	
Fluorite	Rutile	Cadmium chloride	Cadmium iodide
CaF_2	$CaCl_2$, $CaBr_2$		CaI_2
	MgF_2	$MgCl_2$	$MgBr_2$, MgI_2
CdF_2		$CdCl_2$, $CdBr_2$	CdI_2
	FeF_2	$FeCl_2$	$FeBr_2$, FeI_2
	CoF_2	$CoCl_2$	$CoBr_2$, CoI_2
	SnO_2		SnS_2
	TiO_2		TiS_2

Increasing polarization→

does not crystallize in the anti-fluorite arrangement but forms instead the anti-cadmium chloride lattice. Here the formation of a layer lattice is attributed to the polarization of the large caesium cation by the oxide anion.

NON-STOICHIOMETRIC COMPOUNDS

One of the basic tenets of chemistry which emerged from the quantitative study of the formation of compounds was that a chemical compound, however prepared, had a constant composition and so contained its various elements in fixed proportions by weight. In the nineteenth century much research was directed towards devising new and improving existing methods for the measurement of combining, or equivalent, weights of the elements. An equivalent weight was assigned to each element that represented its combining weight in grammes relative to a fixed weight of another element chosen as a standard (1 g of hydrogen or 8 g of oxygen were commonly used). The atomic weight of an element (again a relative quantity) could also be determined by taking the valency into account. This resulted in the fundamental law that when atoms combine they do so in simple numerical ratios. This law is implicit in the formulation of a chemical compound and in the use of its formula in writing a chemical equation. It is also basic to the whole of quantitative analysis.

As analytical methods became further refined it became evident that although the vast majority of compounds obeyed the fundamental laws of chemical composition there were some substances which quite definitely did not. These cannot be represented by a simple chemical formula because their composition is not constant and varies over a definite range. Such compounds are examples of non-stoichiometry.

Some oxides and sulphides of the transition metals provide good examples of non-stoichiometric compounds. Thus iron (II) sulphide never has the exact composition FeS and sulphur is always present in slight excess. This is due to the fact that a proportion of the positions which would be occupied by iron atoms in an ideal crystal remain vacant. Iron (II) oxide does not have the ideal formula FeO but shows a range of composition from $Fe_{0.91}O$ to $Fe_{0.95}O$. Other transition metal oxides such as VO, NiO, and sulphides such as CrS, show similar non-stoichiometry. Titanium (II) oxide, with the sodium chloride structure, shows a particularly wide range of composition from $TiO_{0.69}$ to $TiO_{1.33}$. Praseodymium (IV) and terbium (IV) oxides are very difficult to prepare in the pure state. If the carbonate or hydroxide of the tripositive state of the metal is heated then the coloured oxides Pr_6O_{11} and Tb_4O_7 respectively are produced. These can be regarded as defect structures in which some of the oxygen positions are empty.

The compounds between hydrogen and transition metals show characteristic non-stoichiometry. For instance, the compounds represented by the formulae $PdH_{0.6}$, $ZrH_{1.92}$, $TiH_{1.73}$, $LaH_{2.76}$ and $CeH_{2.7}$.

Another type of variable composition is shown in the compounds known as the tungsten bronzes which are formed when alkali metal tungstates are reduced by heating with tungsten. They are deep-coloured unreactive substances with semi-metallic properties. The formula varies between $Na_{0.3}WO_3$ and $NaWO_3$. In $NaWO_3$, the tungsten is present entirely in the 5-valent state but when the compound is deficient in sodium ion, the tungsten is partly in the 6-valent state.

Non-stoichiometry is most commonly found in compounds of the transition metals where the metal can exist in more than one oxidation state and is in combination with polarizable anions. It is a property which is, however, not confined to these metals. For example, the colour change of zinc oxide from white to yellow on heating is associated with a non-stoichiometric composition with excess metal incorporated as interstitial cations. Even a compound like sodium chloride can show non-stoichiometry. Thus, on heating in sodium vapour, metal is taken up by the lattice to form a non-stoichiometric compound.

The number of such compounds known will undoubtedly increase as more searching studies are made of crystalline solids but the exact and simple stoichiometry of most substances is likely to remain a cornerstone of inorganic chemistry.

INTERSTITIAL COMPOUNDS

These are compounds in which small atoms of non-metals (particularly hydrogen, boron, carbon and nitrogen) occupy positions in the interstices of the lattice of transition metals. They are formed when the ratio of the atomic radius of the non-metal to that of the metal is below 0.59.

In their properties they strongly resemble the metals themselves. They show variable composition and the exact nature of the bonding in such compounds is not clearly understood at the present time. From a structural viewpoint, it is found that the arrangement of the metal atoms is usually not the same as in the pure element. In some cases, for instance when the metal has a face-centred cubic close-packed structure, this may be preserved in the interstitial compound and the non-metal atoms may occupy the six-fold co-ordinated interstices ('octahedral holes') at the centres of the sides of the unit cell. These are marked 'a' in *Figure 4.28*. When all these holes are occupied, the formula becomes AX and the arrangement is the same as in sodium chloride (p. 96) although the type of bonding is not, of course, the same. Examples of interstitial compounds which have the sodium chloride structure are TiC, TiN, ZrC, ZrN, NbC and TaC. If insufficient numbers of non-metal atoms are available, the formula is generally intermediate between AX and A_2X.

When the non-metal atoms are too small to achieve 6 co-ordination, they occupy the smaller 4 co-ordination sites ('tetrahedral holes') at the centres of the eight smaller cubes into which the unit cell can be divided. When all these sites are occupied, the structure is that of fluorite (p. 99); when only half are filled, the zinc blende structure results.

Interstitial compounds are of great technical importance, particularly in the carbon/iron system. The C—Fe atomic radius ratio is very close to the critical limit of 0·59 and, depending on the carbon content and heat treatment (the latter will determine which polymorphic form of iron is present), the carbon may be present in the free state, in interstitial solution or as a stoichiometric compound Fe_3C, known as cementite, and the physical properties of the iron will vary accordingly. The interstitial hydrides formed by metals such as

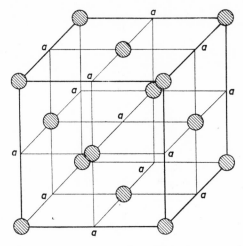

Figure 4.28. Octahedral holes in a face-centred close-packed structure

platinum, palladium and nickel are believed to account for the efficacy of these metals as catalysts in hydrogenation reactions. The strongly reducing properties of these hydrides suggests that the hydrogen may well be present in the atomic state, the molecules having dissociated on entering the metal lattice.

THE MINERAL SILICATES

The earth's crust consists almost entirely of silicates and silica. The glass, ceramic and cement industries are based on silicate chemistry and many metallurgical processes are concerned with the removal of silicates as a necessary stage in the extraction of pure metals. The elucidation of the structures has been difficult because of the chemical complexity of silicates but the basic principles are now well understood. Some of the more important aspects of silicate structures are dealt with below: for a more detailed survey, reference should be made elsewhere.

Silica itself is known in three different crystalline modifications, each of which has a high and low temperature form. In one of these, *cristobalite*, the silicon atoms are arranged in a diamond-type lattice with an oxygen atom between each pair of silicons. The co-ordination number of silicon is thus 4

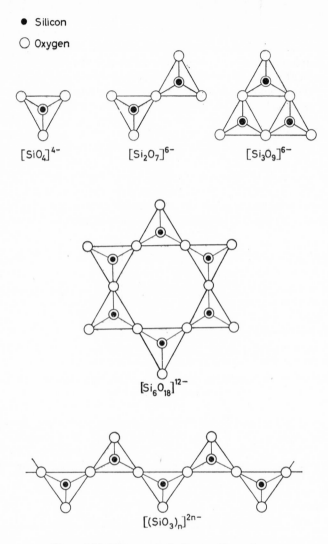

Figure 4.29. The structure of some silicate ions

and that of oxygen is 2. Alternatively, the three-dimensional lattice may be described as composed of SiO_4 tetrahedra, in which each oxygen is shared between two adjacent tetrahedra. *Quartz* and *tridymite*, the other two modifications of silica, have the same tetrahedral unit but there is a helical arrangement of atoms which gives rise to optical activity.

According to PAULING, the silicon–oxygen bond is 50 per cent ionic. The appreciable difference in electronegativity of the two elements leads to this conclusion. The fundamental unit for all silicate structures is the SiO_4 tetrahedron and various arrangements are possible because of the different ways in which the tetrahedra are joined together by the sharing of oxygens:

(a) *Discrete anions*—these include the orthosilicates which contain SiO_4^{4-} (for example, *zircon*, $ZrSiO_4$, and *phenacite*, Be_2SiO_4); the pyrosilicates which contain $[Si_2O_7]^{6-}$, wherein one oxygen is shared between two tetrahedra (*thortveitite*, $Sc_2Si_2O_7$); and closed rings such as $[Si_3O_9]^{6-}$ and $[Si_6O_{18}]^{12-}$, wherein each tetrahedron shares two oxygens (*benitoite*, $BaTiSi_3O_9$ and *beryl*, $Be_3Al_2Si_6O_{18}$).

(b) *Extended anions*—these may either be infinite chains, such as $[(SiO_3)_n]^{2n-}$ and $[(Si_4O_{11})_n]^{6n-}$, in which each tetrahedron again shares two oxygens; or sheets of composition $[(Si_2O_5)_n]^{2n-}$, in which each tetrahedron shares three oxygens. Examples of the first type are the *pyroxenes* like *diopside*, $CaMg(SiO_3)_2$, and *spodumene*, $LiAl(SiO_3)_2$ and the *amphiboles* like *tremolite*, $(OH)_2Ca_2Mg_5(Si_4O_{11})_2$. Ions of the second type are found in micas and clays.

(c) *Three-dimensional networks*—the tetrahedra are completely linked by all four oxygens. These are the various forms of *silica*, SiO_2.

The anions described in the preceding section are illustrated in *Figure 4.29*.

Another factor responsible for the complexity of mineral silicates is the freedom with which isomorphous replacement of one ion by another of similar charge or size has occurred during their formation. For instance, the mineral *olivine* has a variable composition depending on its source because of the replacement of magnesium by iron to differing extents. Although this mineral is essentially magnesium orthosilicate, Mg_2SiO_4, at least some of the magnesium ions have been replaced by iron (II). Calcium is another element whose ions can undergo isomorphous replacement with magnesium.

The replacement which has the greatest structural significance is the substitution of some of the silicon ions, $Si^{4+}(=0.41 \text{ Å})$, by aluminium, Al^{3+} $(=0.50 \text{ Å})$. Thus many alumino-silicates are based on a three-dimensional network of linked tetrahedra derived from silica itself by the replacement of tetrapositive silicon with tripositive aluminium. This substitution requires that a monovalent cation like Na^+ or K^+ be incorporated into the structure for every aluminium ion introduced or, in silicates where cations are already present, the replacement of one cation by another of higher charge. A third possibility is the addition of an anion such as fluoride or chloride.

The formulae of the *feldspar* and *zeolite* alumino-silicates illustrate the substitutions which have taken place:

Feldspars:	*orthoclase*	$KAlSi_3O_8$
	celsian	$BaAl_2Si_2O_8$
	albite	$NaAlSi_3O_8$
	anorthite	$CaAl_2Si_2O_8$
Zeolites:	*analcite*	$NaAlSi_2O_6 . H_2O$
	heulandite	$CaAl_2Si_7O_{18} . 6H_2O$
	natrolite	$Na_2Al_2Si_3O_{10} . 2H_2O$
	thomsonite	$NaCa_2Al_5Si_5O_{20} . 6H_2O$

In these crystals, the aluminium, like silicon, is tetrahedrally co-ordinated and the ratio of the number of oxygens to the combined total of aluminium and silicon is $2:1$. Sufficient alkali and alkaline-earth metal ions are also present to maintain electrical neutrality. Zeolites are characterized by a particularly open structure and this imparts the property of ion-exchange to these minerals. The cations are replaced by other positive ions when the zeolite is brought into contact with an aqueous solution containing these other ions. These naturally occurring materials and their synthetic analogues have found extensive use in water-softening.

Another factor which further complicates the structures is that aluminium can be 6- as well as 4-co-ordinate with respect to oxygen. For example, in *hydrargillite*, $Al(OH)_3$, the structure is built up from sheets of $Al(OH)_6$ octahedra, each octahedron sharing three of its edges with three adjacent octahedra. When such a sheet is combined with a silicon/oxygen sheet like $(H_2Si_2O_5)_n$, elimination of water occurs and composite layers are built up. *Kaolin*, $Al_2Si_2O_5(OH)_4$, is an example of this (*Figure 4.30*). When silicon/oxygen

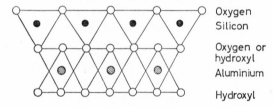

Oxygen
Silicon

Oxygen or
hydroxyl

Aluminium

Hydroxyl

Figure 4.30. Diagrammatic representation of the composite layers of kaolin

layers are condensed on both sides of a hydrargillite layer, the clay mineral *pyrophyllite*, $Al_2Si_4O_{10}(OH)_2$, is obtained.

Similarly, *brucite*, $Mg(OH)_2$, contains 6 co-ordinated metal ions and the mineral *talc*, $Mg_3Si_4O_{11}.H_2O$, is composed of a layer of brucite between two silicon/oxygen layers. These composite layers, in this case, are electrically neutral and they are loosely packed in the crystal. Hence the softness and pronounced cleavage of talc.

When one quarter of the silicon ions in a pyrophyllite layer are replaced by aluminium ions, a layer of composition $Al_2AlSi_3O_{10}(OH)_2$ is obtained. In the crystal, layers of this type alternate with layers of positive ions. This structure is typical of that found in micas such as *muscovite*, $KAl_3Si_3O_{10}(OH)_2$. A similar replacement in talc produces a mica having the composition $KMg_3AlSi_3O_{10}(OH)_2$, as in *phlogopite*. Mica crystals are held together by electrostatic bonds and so are not as soft as talc and pyrophyllite where the composite layers are held together by residual bonds alone. Cleavage in one plane, however, is still a very characteristic property.

SUGGESTED REFERENCES FOR FURTHER READING

ADDISON, W. E. *Structural Principles in Inorganic Compounds*, 1st edn, Longmans Green, London, 1961.

SUGGESTED REFERENCES FOR FURTHER READING

CROFT, R. C.   'Lamellar compounds of graphite', *Quart. Rev. chem. Soc., Lond.*, 14 (1961) 1.

EVANS, R. C.   *An Introduction to Crystal Chemistry*, Cambridge University Press, London, 1946.

MORDIKE, B. L.   'The electron theory of metals', *Research*, 13 (1960) 179.

WYCKOFF, R. W. G.   *Crystal Structures*, Interscience, New York, 1948 onward. (Several volumes of this comprehensive reference work have been published.)

5

REACTIONS IN WATER AND IN NON-AQUEOUS
SOLVENTS

OXIDATION AND REDUCTION

A VERY large number of inorganic reactions take place in aqueous solution and, of these, many may be classified under the heading of *oxidation–reduction* or *redox* reactions. The process of oxidation may be considered as the loss of electrons by an atom, ion or molecule and reduction as the reverse of this. It is, however, confusing to many students that some substances behave as reducing agents when reacted with certain compounds but as oxidizing agents with others. Thus, the nitrite ion, NO_2^-, reacts as an oxidizing agent with iodide ion in acid solution, converting it to iodine, yet reduces permanganate in acid solution to Mn^{2+}. Such behaviour can only be understood by the quantitative consideration of the electronic changes involved in oxidation and reduction.

The two processes of oxidation and reduction are inseparable and take place simultaneously. Thus, in the case of the reduction of the mercury (II) ion by the tin (II) ion, the overall reaction is

$$2Hg^{2+} + Sn^{2+} = Hg_2^{2+} + Sn^{4+}$$

and this may be split up into two ion half-reactions:

$$2Hg^{2+} + 2e^- = Hg_2^{2+}$$
$$Sn^{2+} - 2e^- = Sn^{4+}$$

the first of which is a reduction and the second an oxidation reaction. Similarly, the deposition of metallic copper from an aqueous solution of copper (II) sulphate by zinc may be written as

$$Zn + Cu^{2+} = Zn^{2+} + Cu$$

for which the two ion half-reactions are

$$Cu^{2+} + 2e^- = Cu \quad \text{(reduction)}$$
$$Zn \quad - 2e^- = Zn^{2+} \quad \text{(oxidation)}$$

Reactions such as those above will only take place if there is a decrease in *free energy* of the system. This means that the total free energy of the products must be less than that of the reactants. Absolute free energies for ions *etc.*, are not known, but relative values, or *standard free energies*, measured at 25°C have been determined and these may be used instead to predict the direction of chemical change.

If as an example we choose the system of copper (II) ions and zinc metal, the standard free energies of the elements are, by convention, zero and those of the two ions Zn^{2+} and Cu^{2+} are $-35,100$ and $+15,900$ cal/g atom respectively. Hence the free energy change ($\Delta G°$) for the reaction

$$Zn + Cu^{2+} = Zn^{2+} + Cu$$

108

is −51,000 cal and the reaction therefore proceeds spontaneously from left to right. Had the free energy change been positive, the reaction would have taken place from right to left.

Besides using free energy change, as such, for an estimate of the driving force behind a particular reaction it is possible to approach the subject from an electrochemical standpoint. The tendency for an element to lose electrons to a solution is measured by its *electrode* or *oxidation potential*. When a metal such as zinc is placed in a solution of one of its salts in water, a potential difference is set up between the metal and the solution that is dependent upon the metal, the *activity* of the metal ion in the aqueous solution and the temperature. When the ions are at unit activity and the temperature is 25°C, the

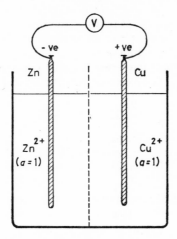

$$\text{Zn} \mid \text{Zn}^{2+} \ (a=1) \ \parallel \ \text{Cu}^{2+} \ (a=1) \mid \text{Cu} \qquad E^\circ = +1{\cdot}10 \text{ V}$$
$$-\text{ve} \hspace{7.5cm} +\text{ve}$$

Figure 5.1. Cell composed of the system Zn^{2+}/Zn and Cu^{2+}/Cu (unit activity)

potential difference is termed the *standard electrode potential* (E°). Standard electrode potentials are measured by comparison with the standard hydrogen electrode (S.H.E.) or any standard electrode such as the calomel electrode; the units used are volts (V).

The sign attributed to an electrode potential differs according to the particular sign convention being used; that used here will be the one recommended by the International Union of Pure and Applied Chemistry (I.U.P.A.C.). If we take the system $Cu^{2+}(aq)/Zn$ and consider the two half-reactions, we may set up a cell where the two systems undergoing oxidation and reduction are separated by a porous diaphragm (*Figure 5.1*) which acts as a salt-bridge in permitting the passage of ions but preventing the mixing of the two aqueous solutions. On the I.U.P.A.C. convention, the sign and magnitude of the e.m.f. of this cell are defined by the cell diagram and are identical with the

109

sign and magnitude of the potential of a lead to the electrode on the right-hand side with respect to a similar lead to the electrode on the left-hand side whose potential is zero, the cell being in open circuit. The e.m.f. of the cell is thus positive if the negative electrode is on the left-hand side and on discharging the cell, oxidation takes place at this electrode and reduction occurs at the right-hand electrode. The corresponding redox reaction must be written down in a similar manner with the metal atoms on the same sides of the redox equation as they are in the cell. Hence we write zinc metal on the left-hand side and copper on the right-hand side of the equation as above.

The relation between $\Delta G°$ and $E°$ is

$$\Delta G° = -nFE°$$

where n is the number of electrons transferred in the reduction process and F is the Faraday. Hence, if $E°$ is positive, the reaction proceeds as written.

The potential of the electrode is measured with reference to the S.H.E. in which hydrogen gas at 1 atmosphere pressure is bubbled over an inert metal electrode (*e.g.* platinum) immersed in a solution of HCl that is of unit activity with respect to H^+. The electrode potential at 25°C, under these conditions, for the system

$$H_2 = 2H^+ + 2e^-$$

is defined as zero volts. The potential of an ion half-reaction refers to the cell in which the S.H.E. is on the left-hand side and the electrode in question is on the right-hand side. The half-reaction thereby examined is always formulated as a reduction:

$$\text{Oxidized state} + ne^- = \text{Reduced state}$$
$$(Ox) \qquad\qquad (Red)$$

The electrode potential of the ion half-reaction is given by the Nernst equation

$$E = E°_{Ox/Red} + \frac{RT}{nF} \log_e \frac{\{Ox\}}{\{Red\}}$$

where R is the gas constant (8·314 joule/deg mole), T is the absolute temperature (°K), n is the number of electrons transferred, F is the Faraday (96,484 coulombs) and $\{\ \}$ denotes the activity of the species. When $\{Ox\}$ and $\{Red\}$ are both unity, the logarithmic term is zero and the electrode potential is the standard potential. The activities of elements under standard conditions are defined as unity.

If the system M^{n+}/M is a better reducing agent than hydrogen, under standard conditions, the electrode potential is negative and if it is a poorer reducing agent, the potential is positive. The standard electrode potentials for the systems Zn^{2+}/Zn and Cu^{2+}/Cu are $-0·763$ V and $+0·337$ V respectively, giving for the overall cell e.m.f., which is defined as

$$E°_{total} = (E°_{R.H.S.} - E°_{L.H.S.}) = (E°_{reduced} - E°_{oxidized})$$

a value of $+1·10$ V.

The standard electrode potentials of the elements arranged in order of the most negative to the most positive constitute the electrochemical series of the elements. This series may be used to interpret and also predict the reactivity

110

of the elements. A cation-forming element will displace from aqueous solution another element which lies below it in this series and an anion-forming element will displace from aqueous solution another element which is above it in the series.

The order in the series is, in a shortened form:

$Li^+/Li < K^+/K < Ca^{2+}/Ca < Na^+/Na < Mg^{2+}/Mg < Al^{3+}/Al < Zn^{2+}/Zn < Fe^{2+}/Fe < Sn^{2+}/Sn < H^+/\frac{1}{2}H_2 < Cu^{2+}/Cu < \frac{1}{2}I_2/I^- < Ag^+/Ag < \frac{1}{2}Br_2/Br^- < \frac{1}{2}Cl_2/Cl^- < \frac{1}{2}F_2/F^-$

VARIATION OF THE MAGNITUDE OF STANDARD ELECTRODE POTENTIALS

The factors affecting the magnitude of standard electrode potentials, both for metals and non-metals, may be discussed in terms of a Born–Haber cycle (*Figure 5.2*). Approximate comparisons may be made by using *enthalpy* changes ($\Delta H°$) instead of *free energy* changes ($\Delta G°$).

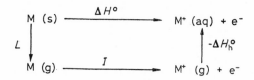

Figure 5.2. Born–Haber cycles for the formation of M^+(aq) and X^- (aq)

For metals, three steps may be considered in the formation of the metal ion M^+ in aqueous solution from the metal M. These are:

(*a*) sublimation of the metal (heat absorbed $= L$);
(*b*) ionization of the gaseous metal atom (heat absorbed $= I$);
(*c*) hydration of the gaseous ion (heat liberated $= -\Delta H_h°$).

The enthalpy change ($\Delta H°$) in going from M(s) to M^+(aq) is therefore given by

$$\Delta H° = L + I - \Delta H_h°.$$

If the sign of $\Delta H°$ be reversed the enthalpy change refers to the process

$$M^+(aq) + e^- = M$$

and may therefore be used as a measure of the electrode potential for this system.

A similar cycle could be drawn for hydrogen, where L is replaced by $\frac{1}{2}D$, D being the dissociation energy of the H_2 molecule.

111

For the alkali metals the following enthalpy changes apply

	Li	Na	K	Rb	Cs
$M(s) = M(g)$	$+38.0$	$+26.0$	$+21.5$	$+20.5$	$+18.8$ kcal
$M(g) = M^+(g)+e^-$	$+124.3$	$+118.4$	$+100.0$	$+96.3$	$+89.3$ kcal
$M^+(g) = M^+(aq)$	-121.2	-94.6	-75.8	-69.2	-62.0 kcal
$M(s) = M^+(aq)+e^-$	$+41.1$	$+49.8$	$+45.7$	$+47.6$	$+46.1$ kcal

For hydrogen the enthalpy changes are

$$\tfrac{1}{2}H_2(g) = H(g) \qquad\qquad +52.1 \text{ kcal}$$
$$H(g) = H^+(g)+e^- \qquad +313.6 \text{ kcal}$$
$$H^+(g) = H^+(aq) \qquad\qquad -256.0 \text{ kcal}$$
$$\tfrac{1}{2}H_2(g) = H^+(aq)+e^- \qquad +109.7 \text{ kcal}$$

Referring the values for the alkali metals to hydrogen equal to zero, gives values for the system $M^+(aq)+e^-(g)=M(s)$ of

	Li	Na	K	Rb	Cs
$-\Delta H°$	$+68.6$	$+59.9$	$+64.0$	$+62.1$	$+63.6$ kcal

Hence $E°$ becomes less negative from the Li^+/Li system to the Na^+/Na system in the order above.

For the halogens, the values of $(\tfrac{1}{2}D-E)$, where E is the electron affinity of the halogen atom, lie between -54 and -62 kcal; here, therefore, the heat of hydration is the determining factor in making the electrode potential less positive as the atomic number of the halogen increases.

	F	Cl	Br	I
$\tfrac{1}{2}X_2(g) = X(g)$	$+18.5$	$+29.0$	$+23.0$	$+18.0$ kcal
$X(g)+e^- = X^-(g)$	-80.2	-85.1	-79.5	-72.6 kcal
$X^-(g) = X^-(aq)$	-122.6	-88.7	-81.4	-72.1 kcal
$\tfrac{1}{2}X_2(g)+e^- = X^-(aq)$	-184.3	-145.4	-137.9	-126.7 kcal
$\Delta H° \ (H=0)$	-294.0	-255.1	-247.6	-236.4 kcal

Summarizing, we may say that a reducing metal is characterized by (i) a low ionization potential, (ii) a low sublimation energy and (iii) a high energy of hydration. Oxidizing potentials of high magnitude are favoured by (i) a large electron affinity, (ii) a small dissociation energy and (iii) a high energy of hydration.

So far, the discussion of electrode reactions has been limited to the system $M^{n+}(aq)/M(s)$. It is possible, however, that the oxidized and reduced forms are both ionic and soluble, for example Fe^{3+}/Fe^{2+} and MnO_4^-/Mn^{2+}. These systems also have standard electrode potentials which may be determined by constructing an electrode in which a platinum wire is immersed in a solution of unit activity with respect to both the oxidized and reduced forms and comparing its potential against a standard hydrogen electrode.

$$Pt|H_2(1 \text{ atm})|H^+(a=1)\left\|\begin{matrix}Fe^{3+}(a=1)\\Fe^{2+}(a=1)\end{matrix}\right\|Pt$$

112

The couple Fe^{3+}/Fe^{2+} under these conditions has an electrode potential of $+0.771$ V.

A reaction such as that of the reduction of permanganate to Mn^{2+}, besides involving a transfer of electrons in the reduction process, also leads to the transfer of atoms. Oxidation of compounds by MnO_4^- are pH dependent, the overall reaction being

$$MnO_4^- + 8H^+ + 5e^- = Mn^{2+} + 4H_2O$$

It is necessary that the activity of the hydrogen ion shall also be unity for the determination of $E°$ for this system, since

$$E = E° + \frac{RT}{nF} \log_e \frac{\{MnO_4^-\}\{H^+\}^8}{\{Mn^{2+}\}}$$

The value of $E°$ is $+1.51$ V.

Values of other standard electrode potentials similarly obtained are given in *Table 5.1.*

Standard electrode potentials may be used to indicate if a particular reaction is likely to take place. They can, however, give no information on the rapidity of the reaction nor will they indicate if the reaction is likely to take place in the absence of suitable catalysts. Thus, the reaction between arsenite and dichromate may be written as

$$Cr_2O_7^{2-} + 3HAsO_2 + 8H^+ = 2Cr^{3+} + 3H_3AsO_4 + H_2O$$

for which the half-reactions are

$$Cr_2O_7^{2-} + 6e^- + 14H^+ = 2Cr^{3+} + 7H_2O \quad E° = +1.33 \text{ V}$$
$$\text{and} \quad H_3AsO_4 + 2e^- + 2H^+ = HAsO_2 + 2H_2O \quad E° = +0.559 \text{ V}$$

The overall potential of a redox cell composed of these two systems would be $(+1.33 - 0.559)$ V and since $E°$ is positive, dichromate should oxidize arsenite. Unless the reaction is catalysed by the addition of a trace of KI or by OsO_4 it proceeds extremely slowly.

Similarly the halogens Cl_2, Br_2 and I_2 are all capable of oxidizing $S_2O_3^{2-}$ to SO_4^{2-} yet iodine only oxidizes as far as the intermediate tetrathionate $S_4O_6^{2-}$.

THE EFFECT OF NON-STANDARD CONDITIONS UPON ELECTRODE POTENTIALS

The Nernst equation

$$E = E° + \frac{RT}{nF} \log_e \frac{\{Ox\}}{\{Red\}}$$

indicates that the potential of a particular solution containing both the oxidized and reduced forms will vary with the concentrations of the various forms. Assuming for dilute solutions that concentrations are approximately equal to activities, then at 25°C the Nernst equation becomes

$$E = E° + \frac{0.059}{n} \log_{10} \frac{[Ox]}{[Red]}$$

Table 5.1. Standard oxidation potentials

Couple	$E°$ volts	Couple	$E°$ volts
$Li^+ + e^- = Li$	-3.045	$Fe(CN)_6^{3-} + e^- = Fe(CN)_6^{4-}$	$+0.36$
$K^+ + e^- = K$	-2.925	$2H_2SO_3 + 2H^+ + 2e^-$	
$Rb^+ + e^- = Rb$	-2.925	$\quad = S_2O_3^{2-} + 3H_2O$	$+0.40$
$Cs^+ + e^- = Cs$	-2.923	$4H_2SO_3 + 4H^+ + 6e^-$	
$Ba^{2+} + 2e^- = Ba$	-2.90	$\quad = S_4O_6^{2-} + 6H_2O$	$+0.51$
$Sr^{2+} + 2e^- = Sr$	-2.89	$Cu^+ + e^- = Cu$	$+0.521$
$Ca^{2+} + 2e^- = Ca$	-2.87	$I_2 + 2e^- = 2I^-$	$+0.5355$
$Na^+ + e^- = Na$	-2.714	$Cu^{2+} + Cl^- + e^- = CuCl$	$+0.538$
$Mg^{2+} + 2e^- = Mg$	-2.37	$H_3AsO_4 + 2H^+ + 2e^-$	
$Lu^{3+} + 3e^- = Lu$	-2.25	$\quad = HAsO_2 + 2H_2O$	$+0.559$
$\frac{1}{2}H_2 + e^- = H^-$	-2.25	$MnO_4^- + e^- = MnO_4^{2-}$	$+0.564$
$Sc^{3+} + 3e^- = Sc$	-2.08	$Cu^{2+} + Br^- + e^- = CuBr$	$+0.64$
$Be^{2+} + 2e^- = Be$	-1.85	$O_2 + 2H^+ + 2e^- = H_2O_2$	$+0.682$
$Al^{3+} + 3e^- = Al$	-1.66	$Fe^{3+} + e^- = Fe^{2+}$	$+0.771$
$Ti^{2+} + 2e^- = Ti$	-1.63	$Hg_2^{2+} + 2e^- = 2Hg$	$+0.789$
$Mn^{2+} + 2e^- = Mn$	-1.18	$Ag^+ + e^- = Ag$	$+0.7991$
$V^{2+} + 2e^- = V$	~ -1.18	$Cu^{2+} + I^- + e^- = CuI$	$+0.86$
$Zn^{2+} + 2e^- = Zn$	-0.763	$2Hg^{2+} + 2e^- = Hg_2^{2+}$	$+0.920$
$Cr^{3+} + 3e^- = Cr$	-0.74	$NO_3^- + 3H^+ + 2e^-$	
$Ga^{3+} + 3e^- = Ga$	-0.53	$\quad = HNO_2 + H_2O$	$+0.94$
$H_3PO_3 + 2H^+ + 2e^-$		$NO_3^- + 4H^+ + 4e^-$	
$\quad = H_3PO_2 + H_2O$	-0.50	$\quad = NO + 2H_2O$	$+0.96$
$Fe^{2+} + 2e^- = Fe$	-0.440	$Br_2(liq) + 2e^- = 2Br^-$	$+1.0652$
$Cr^{3+} + e^- = Cr^{2+}$	-0.41	$SeO_4^{2-} + 4H^+ + 2e^-$	
$Ti^{3+} + e^- = Ti^{2+}$	~ -0.37	$\quad = H_2SeO_3 + H_2O$	$+1.15$
$In^{3+} + 3e^- = In$	-0.342	$IO_3^- + 6H^+ + 5e^-$	
$Tl^+ + e^- = Tl$	-0.3363	$\quad = \frac{1}{2}I_2 + 3H_2O$	$+1.195$
$Co^{2+} + 2e^- = Co$	-0.277	$O_2 + 4H^+ + 4e^- = 2H_2O$	$+1.229$
$H_3PO_4 + 2H^+ + 2e^-$		$Tl^{3+} + 2e^- = Tl^+$	$+1.25$
$\quad = H_3PO_3 + H_2O$	-0.276	$Cr_2O_7^{2-} + 14H^+ + 6e^-$	
$V^{3+} + e^- = V^{2+}$	-0.255	$\quad = 2Cr^{3+} + 7H_2O$	$+1.33$
$Ni^{2+} + 2e^- = Ni$	-0.250	$Cl_2 + 2e^- = 2Cl^-$	$+1.3595$
$CuI + e^- = Cu + I^-$	-0.185	$Au^{3+} + 3e^- = Au$	$+1.50$
$AgI + e^- = Ag + I^-$	-0.151	$Mn^{3+} + e^- = Mn^{2+}$	$+1.51$
$Sn^{2+} + 2e^- = Sn$	-0.136	$MnO_4^- + 8H^+ + 5e^-$	
$Pb^{2+} + 2e^- = Pb$	-0.126	$\quad = Mn^{2+} + 4H_2O$	$+1.51$
$2H^+ + 2e^- = H_2$	0.00	$BrO_3^- + 6H^+ + 5e^-$	
$Ag(S_2O_3)_2^{3-} + e^-$		$\quad = \frac{1}{2}Br_2 + 3H_2O$	$+1.52$
$\quad = Ag + 2S_2O_3^{2-}$	$+0.01$	$Ce^{4+} + e^- = Ce^{3+}$	$+1.61$
$CuBr + e^- = Cu + Br^-$	$+0.033$	$Au^+ + e^- = Au$	$\sim +1.68$
$S_4O_6^{2-} + 2e^- = 2S_2O_3^{2-}$	$+0.08$	$MnO_4^- + 4H^+ + 3e^-$	
$CuCl + e^- = Cu + Cl^-$	$+0.137$	$\quad = MnO_2 + 2H_2O$	$+1.695$
$Sn^{4+} + 2e^- = Sn^{2+}$	$+0.15$	$H_2O_2 + 2H^+ + 2e^- = 2H_2O$	$+1.77$
$Cu^{2+} + e^- = Cu^+$	$+0.153$	$Co^{3+} + e^- = Co^{2+}$	$+1.82$
$SO_4^{2-} + 4H^+ + 2e^-$		$Ag^{2+} + e^- = Ag^+$	$+1.98$
$\quad = H_2SO_3 + H_2O$	$+0.17$	$S_2O_8^{2-} + 2e^- = 2SO_4^{2-}$	$+2.01$
$Cu^{2+} + 2e^- = Cu$	$+0.337$	$F_2 + 2e^- = 2F^-$	$+2.87$

Data from LATIMER, W. M. *The Oxidation States of the Elements and their Potentials in Aqueous Solutions*, 2nd edn, Prentice-Hall, New York, 1952.

Thus, in the case of the system Fe^{3+}/Fe^{2+}, with a ratio of $[Fe^{3+}]/[Fe^{2+}]$ of 10^2, the potential is given by

$$E = E° + \frac{0.059}{1} \log_{10} 10^2$$

$$= 0.771 + 0.118$$

$$= 0.889 \text{ V}$$

From this value it can be seen that in the titration of Fe^{2+} by $Cr_2O_7^{2-}$, an indicator such as diphenylamine sulphonate, for which the oxidation potential is $+0.83$ V, is suitable provided the concentration of Fe^{3+} is low. Otherwise the end point will be inaccurate since, for large concentrations of Fe^{3+}, the Fe^{3+}/Fe^{2+} system will have a potential greater than that required for oxidizing the indicator. This will occur before the equivalent amount of dichromate has been added and give a premature end point. This is the reason for the addition of phosphoric acid which suppresses the concentration of Fe^{3+} ions in the titration solution by the formation of complex ions.

A cell may be constructed from two electrodes of the same metal dipping into two solutions of the same compound but of different ionic strengths. This is termed a concentration cell and may be represented as

$$M|M^{n+}(c_1)\|M^{n+}(c_2)|M$$

hence

$$E_1 - E_2 = \frac{0.059}{n} \log_{10} \frac{c_1}{c_2} \quad (c_1 > c_2)$$

This type of cell has been used to determine the nature of the mercurous, Hg^I, ion (see p. 270).

CALCULATION OF EQUILIBRIUM CONSTANTS

Because redox reactions are of the reversible type, they are governed by the laws of chemical equilibrium. If a cell is set up and allowed to discharge until its e.m.f. is zero, the products and reactants are then at equilibrium since ΔG° is zero. Hence, the difference in potentials for the two component half-reactions must be zero. A general form of a redox reaction may be written as

$$a\ Ox_A + b\ Red_B \rightleftharpoons a\ Red_A + b\ Ox_B$$

$$E_A = E_A^\circ + \frac{RT}{nF} \log_e \frac{[Ox_A]^a}{[Red_A]^a}$$

$$E_B = E_B^\circ + \frac{RT}{nF} \log_e \frac{[Ox_B]^b}{[Red_B]^b}$$

at equilibrium and at 25°C

$$E_A - E_B = 0$$

or

$$E_A^\circ - E_B^\circ = \frac{0.059}{n} \log_{10} \frac{[Ox_B]^b [Red_A]^a}{[Ox_A]^a [Red_B]^b}$$

$$= \frac{0.059}{n} \log_{10} K$$

where K is the equilibrium constant.
Hence

$$\log_{10} K = \frac{(E_A^\circ - E_B^\circ)n}{0.059}$$

The value of K so derived is a measure of the completeness of the reaction under the conditions of the experiment. If K is large, then the reaction proceeds from left to right. Very small values of K mean the reaction takes place from right to left. If K is nearly unity the reaction will not be complete in either direction.

The following systems, under standard conditions, are examples:

(i) $\qquad MnO_4^- + 8H^+ + 5Fe^{2+} \rightleftharpoons Mn^{2+} + 5Fe^{3+} + 4H_2O$

(ii) $\qquad Sn^{4+} + 2Ce^{3+} \rightleftharpoons Sn^{2+} + 2Ce^{4+}$

(iii) $\qquad Ag + \tfrac{1}{2}Hg_2^{2+} \rightleftharpoons Hg + Ag^+$

The values of the equilibrium constants are

(i) $\log_{10}K_A = \log_{10} \dfrac{\{Mn^{2+}\}\{Fe^{3+}\}^5}{\{MnO_4^-\}\{H^+\}^8\{Fe^{2+}\}^5} = \dfrac{(1\cdot51 - 0\cdot77) \times 5}{0\cdot059}$

$$\sim +62 \quad (K_A \sim 10^{+62})$$

(ii) $\log_{10}K_B = \log_{10} \dfrac{\{Ce^{4+}\}^2\{Sn^{2+}\}}{\{Ce^{3+}\}^2\{Sn^{4+}\}} = \dfrac{(-0\cdot15 - 1\cdot61) \times 2}{0\cdot059}$

$$\sim -57 \quad (K_B \sim 10^{-57})$$

(iii) $\log_{10}K_C = \log_{10} \dfrac{\{Ag^+\}\{Hg\}}{\{Ag\}\{Hg_2^{2+}\}^{1/2}} = \dfrac{(+0\cdot789 - 0\cdot799) \times 1}{0\cdot059}$

$$\sim -0\cdot17 \quad (K_C \sim 0\cdot68)$$

DISPROPORTIONATION AND STABILIZATION OF VALENCY STATES

Many elements exhibit more than one oxidation state and for a particular element certain states are more stable than others. Oxidation potential data can be used to illustrate the relative stabilities of oxidation states.

If we take the case of the Fe^{II}/Fe^{III} system, the standard electrode potentials for Fe^{3+}/Fe^{2+} and Fe^{2+}/Fe are $+0\cdot771$ V and $-0\cdot44$ V respectively. The possibility of the following disproportionation occurring may now be considered:

$$3Fe^{2+} = 2Fe^{3+} + Fe$$
$$E^{\circ}_{system} = -0\cdot44 - 0\cdot771$$
$$= -1\cdot211 \text{ V}$$

Under these conditions ΔG° is positive and hence disproportionation does not occur.

With copper, the two main oxidation states are Cu^{2+} and Cu^+. The possibility of the disproportionation

$$2Cu^+ = Cu^{2+} + Cu$$

may be considered from a knowledge of the two standard electrode potentials for Cu^{2+}/Cu^+ and Cu^+/Cu which are $+0\cdot153$ V and $+0\cdot521$ V respectively.

$$E^{\circ}_{system} = +0\cdot521 - 0\cdot153$$
$$= +0\cdot368 \text{ V}$$

116

Since $\Delta G°$ is therefore negative, the disproportionation takes place as shown.

The disproportionation of MnO_4^{2-} and MnO_4^{3-} in solution are well-known characteristics of the higher oxidation states of manganese. The reactions occurring are

$$3MnO_4^{2-} + 2H_2O = 2MnO_4^- + MnO_2 + 4OH^-$$

and

$$2MnO_4^{3-} + 2H_2O = MnO_4^{2-} + MnO_2 + 2OH^-$$

Only if the hydroxyl ion is present in aqueous solutions of these ions do they remain stable. The manganate (V) ion, MnO_4^{3-}, needs a hydroxyl ion concentration of about 14–15 M for stability and the manganate (VI) ion requires a hydroxyl ion concentration of about 1–2 M for stability.

The standard oxidation potential for a system such as Fe^{3+}/Fe^{2+} is $+0.771$ V. If the standard oxidation potential of the system $[Fe(CN)_6]^{3-}/[Fe(CN)_6]^{4-}$ is measured the value is $+0.36$ V. The ferrocyanide ion is thus a better reducing agent than Fe^{2+}(aq) and the change in electrode potential has been brought about by complexing. This is an important factor in stabilizing oxidation states that in the normal ionic state would either react with the solvent or else disproportionate like Cu^+.

Thus, Co^{3+}/Co^{2+} has a standard oxidation potential of $+1.82$ V and simple cobalt (III) salts are easily reduced to the cobalt (II) state. In the presence of cyanide ion, however, the standard potential changes and for $[Co(CN_6]^{3-}/[Co(CN)_5]^{3-}$ has the value of -0.83 V. Similarly, the ammine complex has the standard electrode potential $[Co(NH_3)_6]^{3+}/[Co(NH_3)_6]^{2+}$ of $+0.1$ V.

Again, stabilization of Cu^+ may be effected by the presence of cyanide or iodide ions. The disproportionation

$$2CuI = Cu^{2+} + Cu + 2I^-$$

may be split into the two half-reactions

$$CuI + e^- = Cu + I^- \quad E° = -0.185 \text{ V}$$
$$Cu^{2+} + I^- + e^- = CuI \quad E° = +0.86 \text{ V}$$

Hence,
$$E°_{system} = -0.185 - 0.86$$
$$= -1.045 \text{ V}$$

This negative value of $E°$ means that the free energy change of the reaction is positive and hence CuI is stable.

ACIDS AND BASES

Many substances were formerly classified as acids or alkalis according to their chemical nature. Typical properties associated with acids were sour taste, high solvent power and ability to change the colour of vegetable dyes like litmus. Alkalis also had a number of positive properties such as detergency, the ability to dissolve sulphur and the distinctive soapiness of their solutions, but their chief characteristic was reaction with an acid to form a salt, a substance which had none of the properties of an acid or an alkali. This reaction of an alkali with an acid represented a neutralization of the characteristics of both.

Many other substances, including the oxides and hydroxides of most metals, neutralized acids but they did not have the characteristic properties associated with alkalis. Therefore the more general term *base* was introduced to denote any substance which would react with an acid to form a salt.

The historical development of ideas on the nature of acids and bases has been discussed elsewhere and we shall be concerned with the more modern concepts, particularly those which are useful in the interpretation of inorganic reactions in water and other solvents.

Water is the most familiar solvent in which chemical reactions have been studied. It is, however, quite exceptional in many of its properties. The water molecule is strongly polar, intermolecular hydrogen bonding occurs and therefore water behaves as an associated liquid. Moreover, the high dielectric constant (*Table 5.4*) promotes the ionization of solutes and so reactions in aqueous solutions generally take place between ions. Towards the end of the nineteenth century investigations were carried out on the properties of other ionizing solvents with the use of these as media for chemical reactions as a major objective. Acid–base concepts primarily defined for aqueous systems were not comprehensive enough to include all the non-aqueous solvents studied so more general definitions were made. Non-aqueous solvents are now increasingly used in synthetic inorganic chemistry. A more fundamental understanding of the chemical properties of the elements and their compounds is likely to emerge from these studies. Hitherto, the special nature of water as a solvent has tended to obscure this by over-emphasis on those chemical substances which exist in the presence of water.

THE BRONSTED–LOWRY CONCEPT OF PROTONIC ACIDS

Arising from the theory of electrolytic dissociation proposed in 1884 by ARRHENIUS and developed later by OSTWALD, a general definition of acids and bases was proposed in 1923 independently and almost simultaneously by J. N. BRONSTED and T. M. LOWRY. According to this, an acid is regarded as a donor of protons and a base as a proton-acceptor. Every acid A has its *conjugate base* B^- to which it is related by

$$A \rightleftharpoons B^- + H^+$$

The acid A can only release its proton when brought into contact with a substance of higher proton affinity than B^-.

In water, self-ionization occurs to a very limited extent:

$$H_2O + H_2O \rightleftharpoons H_3O^+ + OH^-$$

H_3O^+ is the solvated proton or oxonium ion. The bare proton has an enormous affinity for electrons and is invariably solvated in water. In the self-ionization of water some molecules behave as Bronsted–Lowry acids and an equal number as bases.

When an acid dissolves in water it releases protons which become solvated to produce a higher concentration of oxonium ions. For example, hydrogen chloride ionizes in water almost completely according to

$$H_2O + HCl \rightleftharpoons H_3O^+ + Cl^-$$

By definition, the ions HSO_4^- and NH_4^+ are also acids in aqueous media because of the dissociations

$$HSO_4^- + H_2O \rightleftharpoons SO_4^{2-} + H_3O^+$$

and

$$NH_4^+ + H_2O \rightleftharpoons NH_3 + H_3O^+$$

The sulphate ion and ammonia molecule are the conjugate bases of the acids HSO_4^- and NH_4^+ respectively. Other Bronsted–Lowry acids are listed in *Table 5.2*.

Table 5.2. *Bronsted–Lowry acids and bases in aqueous solution*

Species	Acids	Bases
Molecules	HI, HBr, HCl, HF, HNO$_3$, H$_2$SO$_4$, HClO$_4$, H$_3$PO$_4$, H$_2$S, H$_2$O	NH$_3$, N$_2$H$_4$, NH$_4$OH, amines, H$_2$O
Anions	HSO$_4^-$, H$_2$PO$_4^-$, HPO$_4^{2-}$, HS$^-$	I$^-$, Br$^-$, Cl$^-$, F$^-$, HSO$_4^-$, SO$_4^{2-}$, O^{2-}
Cations	NH$_4^+$, Al(H$_2$O)$_6^{3+}$, Fe(H$_2$O)$_6^{3+}$	HPO$_4^{2-}$, CO$_3^{2-}$, OH$^-$, Al(H$_2$O)$_5$(OH)$^{2+}$, Fe(H$_2$O)$_5$(OH)$^{2+}$

A base, B′, accepts a proton from the water molecule:

$$B' + H_2O \rightleftharpoons B'H^+ + OH^-$$

Many anions are bases and take up a proton to form a neutral molecule. Basic behaviour in an aqueous medium results in an increase in hydroxyl ion concentration and therefore a decrease in the concentration of H_3O^+. The oxides of electropositive metals are well-known bases. They contain the oxide ion which has an enormous affinity for protons:

$$O^{2-} + H_3O^+ \rightleftharpoons OH^- + H_2O$$

Metal hydroxides which ionize in water to produce hydroxyl ions directly are also classified as bases. Other typical bases are listed in *Table 5.2*.

An acid which has a great tendency to donate its proton is described as strong, one with only a slight tendency as weak. A base may be similarly described in terms of its proton affinity. A strong acid, *e.g.* HCl, has a weak conjugate base (Cl$^-$): a strong base, *e.g.* the carbonate ion, has a weak conjugate acid (H$_2$CO$_3$).

Hydrolysis

Neutralization of an acid by a base takes place in aqueous solution to form a salt and water. The process may go to completion as in the reaction between sodium hydroxide and hydrochloric acid which may be represented as follows in terms of the participating ions:

$$H_3O^+ + Cl^- + Na^+ + OH^- = 2H_2O + Na^+ + Cl^-$$

or it may be reversible as in the reaction between aluminium hydroxide and hydrochloric acid:

$$3HCl + Al(OH)_3 \rightleftharpoons AlCl_3 + 3H_2O$$

The reaction of aluminium chloride with water represents the hydrolysis of this compound. (Hydrolysis is used as a more general term to describe the reaction between a compound and water and includes, for instance, the decomposition of the halides of non-metals to produce two acids, e.g. the hydrolysis of phosphorus trichloride according to the equation

$$PCl_3 + 3H_2O = 3HCl + H_3PO_3)$$

Concerning the hydrolysis of salts, three types of reaction may be distinguished.

(a) When the salt of a strong acid and a strong base dissolves in water, the constituent ions become solvated. This is the only change which occurs and the pH remains constant. Sodium chloride is one of many examples.

(b) When a salt of a strong base and a weak acid dissolves, the cations become solvated as in (a). The anions are strongly basic, however, having a high proton affinity, and they remove protons from the solvent causing the pH to rise. Sodium carbonate is a case in point, the pH increase being due to the reaction

$$CO_3^{2-} + H_2O \rightleftharpoons HCO_3^- + OH^-$$

(c) When the salt of a weak base and a strong acid dissolves, the pH falls. The hydrolysis of aluminium chloride is an example of this.

It is interesting to consider the hydrolytic reactions (b) and (c) from the viewpoint of the Bronsted–Lowry concept. In (b) the carbonate ion may be regarded as having markedly basic properties compared with the extremely weak acidic properties of the hydrated sodium ion. This has very little tendency to donate a proton. The net removal of protons from solvent molecules results in a pH increase. In (c), the hydrated metal ion is $[Al(H_2O)_6]^{3+}$ and this is a Bronsted–Lowry acid. Its tendency to lose a proton is stronger than that of the chloride ion gain one and hence there is a decrease in pH.

THE RELATIVE STRENGTHS OF ACIDS AND BASES

It is very useful to have a quantitative measure of the tendency of an acid to lose a proton and of a base to gain one, i.e. of the acid and base strengths.

For a protonic acid HX, the following equilibrium is established in aqueous solution:

$$HX + H_2O \rightleftharpoons X^- + H_3O^+$$

The equilibrium constant of this system, K, expresses the relative tendencies of HX and H_3O^+ to donate a proton:

$$K = \frac{[X^-][H_3O^+]}{[HX][H_2O]} \qquad . \quad . \quad . \quad . \quad (1)$$

the square brackets denoting concentrations.

A true thermodynamic constant is defined in terms of the activities of the individual species. However, concentrations are more readily measured than activities and it is usually more convenient to deal with 'concentration' rather than 'activity' equilibrium constants.

120

[H$_2$O], the concentration of water molecules, is virtually constant for dilute solutions and it is usual to define a second constant, K_a, as

$$K_a = \frac{[X^-][H_3O^+]}{[HX]} = K[H_2O] \quad \ldots \quad (2)$$

K_a denotes the acid strength, that is, the extent to which HX is ionized. The reciprocal, $1/K_a$, represents the base strength of the anion X^-.

In the special case of the self-ionization of water,

$$K_a = \frac{[OH^-][H_3O^+]}{[H_2O][H_2O]}$$

As before, [H$_2$O] is taken as constant and the dissociation of water may be adequately described in terms of its ionic product

$$K_w = [H_3O^+][OH^-] = 1{\cdot}0 \times 10^{-14} \text{ at } 25°C$$

A number of experimental methods are available for the measurement of acid and base strengths; reference should be made to a text-book of physical chemistry for details of these. The values of K vary through many powers of ten for different acids and bases. It is generally more convenient to express acid strengths as dissociation exponents, $pK_a (= \log_{10} K_a)$. A large value of pK_a means that the acid is little dissociated and therefore weak: a small value is found for pK_a when the acid is strong.

THE ACIDIC AND BASIC PROPERTIES OF HYDRIDES

Any binary compound containing hydrogen which is chemically bound to a more electronegative element than itself can, in principle, behave as an acid. In aqueous solution, acid properties are associated chiefly with the hydrides of the non-metallic elements of Groups VI and VII. Values of pK_a are listed in *Table 5.3*. The values for HCl, HBr and HI are known only approximately

Table 5.3. Experimental pK$_a$ values for binary hydrides

Compound	pK$_a$	Compound	pK$_a$
H$_2$O	15·89	HF	3·17
H$_2$S	7·06	HCl	−7
H$_2$Se	3·72	HBr	< −7
H$_2$Te	2·64	HI	< −7

because of virtually complete ionization in dilute solutions. These compounds are all polar molecules with the positive end of the dipole located on the hydrogen atom. No simple relationship exists between polarity and acid strength, for the compounds of greatest polarity are the weakest acids (H$_2$O and HF). In the two series H$_2$O to H$_2$Te and HF to HI, the dipole moment decreases but the acid strength increases as the molecular weight increases. The observed trends in acid strength are contrary to expectation if the tendency to dissociate were simply related to the electronegativity of the non-metal present: the trend for the hydrogen halides is more profitably considered from the point of view of the energy changes when dissociation in aqueous solution takes place (p. 242).

It is interesting to note that ammonia is the only simple hydride which has basic properties in aqueous solution. Both the NH_3 and H_2O molecules have, as we have seen, a tendency to accept protons from donor molecules. Evidently, this tendency is the greater with ammonia.

THE PROPERTIES OF HYDROXIDES AND OXY-ACIDS

In an ionizing solvent like water, the group M—O—H, where M represents one atom of a particular element which may or may not be bound to other atoms or groups beside the hydroxyl group, can dissociate in one of two ways:

(i) $\qquad\qquad$ M—O—H $= (M—O)^- + H^+$

(ii) $\qquad\qquad$ M—O—H $= M^+ + (O—H)^-$

If M is an electronegative element, it exerts a strong attraction on the electrons associated with the oxygen. This withdrawal of electrons weakens the O—H bond and ionization according to (i) is favoured. MOH is then an oxy-acid. On the other hand, if M is an electropositive metal, dissociation (ii) occurs and MOH is a basic hydroxide. Certain MOH groups are amphoteric: that is, dissociation (i) is promoted by the presence of a base to remove hydrogen ions, (ii) is favoured when an acid is present. Amphoteric properties arise when M is a weakly electropositive metal.

Two empirical rules, enunciated by PAULING, are useful approximate relationships between the strengths of oxy-acids.

Rule 1: The successive dissociation constants, K_1, K_2, K_3, *etc.*, for a polybasic acid are in the ratios

$$1 : 10^{-5} : 10^{-10} : \ldots$$

For example, for phosphoric acid, H_3PO_4,

$$K_1 = 0\cdot75 \times 10^{-2}$$
$$K_2 = 0\cdot62 \times 10^{-7}$$
$$K_3 = 1\cdot0 \ \times 10^{-12}$$

Rule 2: The first dissociation constant of the oxy-acid $XO_m(OH)_n$ is determined by the value of m.

When $m=0$, the acid is very weak and $K \leqslant 10^{-7}$.
Examples:

$\qquad$ boric acid, $B(OH)_3$; $K_1 = 5\cdot8 \times 10^{-10}$
$\qquad$ hypobromous acid, $Br(OH)$; $K_1 = 2\cdot0 \times 10^{-9}$.

When $m=1$, the acid is moderately weak and $K_1 = \sim 10^{-2}$.
Examples:

$\qquad$ sulphurous acid, $SO(OH)_2$; $K_1 = 1\cdot2 \times 10^{-2}$
$\qquad$ arsenic acid, $AsO(OH)_3$; $\quad K_1 = 0\cdot5 \times 10^{-2}$
$\qquad$ nitrous acid, $NO(OH)$; $\quad K_1 = 4\cdot5 \times 10^{-4}$.

When $m=2$, the acid is strong and K_1 is large.

Examples:

$$\text{nitric acid, } NO_2(OH); \qquad K_1 = \sim 10^1$$
$$\text{chloric acid, } ClO_2(OH); \quad K_1 = \sim 10^1$$
$$\text{sulphuric acid, } SO_2(OH)_2; K_1 = \sim 10^3$$

When $m=3$, the acid is very strong and K_1 is very large.

Example: perchloric acid, $ClO_3(OH); K_1 = \sim 10^8$

The first rule reflects the increase in electrostatic attraction of the negative ion for a proton as the extent of ionization increases. The second rule expresses the well-known fact that the acid strength increases with the proportion of oxygen in the molecule. For example, the four oxy-acids of chlorine ionize to give the anions ClO^- (hypochlorite), ClO_2^- (chlorite), ClO_3^- (chlorate) and ClO_4^- (perchlorate). The single negative charge may be regarded as located on one oxygen in ClO^-, 'shared' between two oxygens in ClO_2^-, and so on. The attraction of the anion for a proton therefore decreases as the number of oxygen atoms present increases and the acid strength increases in the order

$$HClO < HClO_2 < HClO_3 < HClO_4$$

It is interesting to note that phosphorous acid, H_3PO_3, and hypophosphorous acid, H_3PO_2, are both moderately weak with K_1 values of 1.6×10^{-2} and 1×10^{-2} respectively. At first sight it does not appear possible to classify them according to *Rule 2*. However, their chemical properties and structures show that P—H bonds are present and that their formulae are more accurately written as $HPO(OH)_2$ and $H_2PO(OH)$. Their K_1 values are then typical of the oxy-acids for which $m=1$.

EXTENSION OF THE PROTONIC CONCEPT TO NON-AQUEOUS SOLVENTS

Non-aqueous solvents which have been most extensively studied include NH_3, HF, HCN; anhydrous acids such as H_2SO_4, HNO_3 and CH_3COOH; SO_2, N_2O_4; and covalent halides like BrF_3, ICl and $AsCl_3$. The relevant physical properties are summarized in *Table 5.4*.

With the necessary exception of those solvents which do not contain hydrogen, the protonic concept can be applied to reactions in non-aqueous solvents. Four types of solvent can be recognized:

Acidic. These have a marked tendency to release protons.

Examples: HF, H_2SO_4, CH_3COOH, HCN.

Basic. These accept protons strongly.

Examples: NH_3, N_2H_4.

Amphiprotic. These can either accept or release protons.

Examples: Water and the alcohols.

Aprotic. No tendency to release or accept protons.

Examples: Benzene, chloroform.

A typical acidic solvent such as glacial acetic acid undergoes a limited amount of self-ionization:

$$2CH_3COOH \rightleftharpoons CH_3COO^- + CH_3COOH_2^+$$

This accounts for the electrical conductivity shown by the pure solvent.

Table 5.4. Some physical constants of water and other solvents

Solvent	Melting point °C	Boiling point °C	Dielectric constant	Specific conductivity (mho/cm³)
H_2O	0	100	81·8 (18°C)	6×10^{-8} (25°C)
NH_3	−77·7	−33·35	22 (−33°C)	4×10^{-11} (−77·7°C)
HF	−85	19·5	83·6 (0°C)	1×10^{-5} (−37°C)
HCN	−13·4	25·6	123·0 (16°C)	5×10^{-7} (0°C)
H_2SO_4	10·4	274	~85 (20°C)	2×10^{-2} (18°C)
HNO_3	−41·4	86		9×10^{-3} (0°C)
CH_3COOH	16·6	118	9·7 (18°C)	4×10^{-9} (25°C)
SO_2	−75·7	−10	13·8 (15°C)	1×10^{-7} (0°C)
N_2O_4	−11·3	21·1	2·4 (18°C)	1×10^{-12} (17°C)
BrF_3	−9	127		8×10^{-3} (25°C)
ICl	27·2	97·4		5×10^{-3} (35°C)
$AsCl_3$	−18	130·2	12·8 (20°C)	1×10^{-7} (20°C)
$POCl_3$	1·2	105·8	13·9 (22°C)	2×10^{-8} (20°C)
$SOCl_2$	−104·5	75·7	9·1 (20°C)	3×10^{-9} (20°C)

The molecule is a poor proton acceptor but a somewhat better proton donor. Only those compounds which behave as strong acids in water exhibit markedly acid character in acetic acid solution. This solvent therefore acts as a *differentiating* solvent towards acidic solutes, and many acids which are completely dissociated in water, that is, appear equally strong in water, are only partially ionized in acetic acid. Conductivity measurements on their solutions in glacial acetic acid have shown that the strengths of a number of common mineral acids decrease in the order

$$HClO_4 > HBr > H_2SO_4 > HCl > HNO_3$$

The proton-donor property of acetic acid means that a solute which acts as a weak base in aqueous solution usually becomes a strong base in acetic acid. The solvent thus exerts a *levelling effect* on bases because in it they tend to become equally strong. By analogy with the behaviour of metal hydroxides in water, metal acetates in glacial acetic acid act as bases. They can, for instance, be neutralized by a strong acid such as perchloric.

Liquid ammonia typifies a solvent with predominant basic properties. Self-ionization occurs thus:

$$2NH_3 \rightleftharpoons NH_4^+ + NH_2^-$$

Ammonia co-ordinates the proton strongly and enhances the acidic character of hydrogen-containing solutes. A solute which is a weak acid in water becomes much stronger when dissolved in ammonia. All acids tend to become equally strong, that is, a basic solvent exerts a levelling effect towards them. The ammonium ion, NH_4^+, in liquid ammonia corresponds to the oxonium ion, H_3O^+, in water. An ammonium salt dissolved in liquid ammonia acts as an acid. Conversely, a solute such as a metal amide which increases the concentration of amide ions, NH_2^-, is a base.

Many reactions in non-aqueous solvents have important analytical applications. For instance, it is often feasible to carry out rapid and reliable volumetric analyses for weak bases or acids in a suitable non-aqueous solvent in

124

cases where the use of aqueous solutions is precluded because of the limited ionization therein. For details, reference should be made to appropriate text-books on analytical chemistry.

Lewis Acids and Bases

According to the electronic theory of G. N. LEWIS, proposed in 1923, an acid is a substance which accepts an electron pair, whereas a base is a substance which can donate an electron pair. The process of neutralization involves the formation of a co-ordinate bond. The compound formed may subsequently ionize.

For example, ammonia is a Lewis base because the nitrogen atom carries a lone pair of electrons which it can donate to a proton:

$$H^+ + {}^x_x NH_3 \rightleftharpoons (H \leftarrow NH_3)^+$$

Hydrogen chloride is a Lewis acid because it can co-ordinate with a base and then ionization takes place. The reaction with water can be represented as

$$H_2O + HCl = H_2O \rightarrow HCl = H_3O^+ + Cl^-$$

and that with a tertiary amine as

$$R_3N + HCl = R_3N \rightarrow HCl = R_3NH^+ + Cl^-$$

This is a more general approach than the protonic concept in so far as acid–base behaviour is not dependent on the presence of one particular element or on the presence or absence of a solvent. However, it does mean that many substances must be regarded as Lewis acids which are not acids at all in the Bronsted–Lowry sense. For example, the Lewis definition requires that the reaction between a metal ion and a ligand shall be regarded as the neutral-ization of an acid (the metal ion) by a base (the ligand), *i.e.* a case such as

$$Ag^+ + {}^x_x NH_3 \rightleftharpoons (Ag \leftarrow NH_3)^+$$

is exactly comparable with the formation of the ammonium ion. The analogy here is of great utility in the correlation of the behaviour of an electron-pair donor (*i*) as a base which reacts with a proton-donating acid and (*ii*) as a ligand which forms complexes with metals (p. 133).

One disadvantage of the Lewis approach is the lack of a uniform scale of acid or base strength. Instead, acid and base strengths are variable and depen-dent on the reaction chosen. It is, however, of great value in circumstances where the protonic concept is inapplicable, as in reactions between acidic and basic oxides in the fused state (p. 131).

A convenient general definition which can be used for non-aqueous solvents is that due to CADY and ELSEY who defined acids as solutes which increase the concentration of cations characteristic of the pure solvent and bases as solutes which increase the concentration of anions characteristic of the pure solvent. This applies equally well to protonic systems, such as

$$2NH_3 \rightleftharpoons NH_4^+ + NH_2^-$$

and to non-protonic systems like

$$2BrF_3 \rightleftharpoons BrF_2^+ + BrF_4^-$$

5*   125

In bromine trifluoride, potassium fluoride behaves as a base because it increases the concentration of BrF_4^- ions:

$$KF + BrF_3 \rightleftharpoons K^+ + BrF_4^-$$

Antimony pentafluoride acts as an acid in this solvent because of the reaction

$$SbF_5 + BrF_3 = BrF_2^+ + SbF_6^-$$

A neutralization reaction in this solvent proceeds according to

$$KBrF_4 + BrF_2SbF_6 = KSbF_6 + 2BrF_3$$

REACTIONS IN NON-AQUEOUS SOLVENTS

Many inorganic substances dissolve in a solvent with chemical change, that is, they undergo solvolysis. A particular example is the hydrolysis of salts in aqueous solution (p. 120). Alternatively, the solvent itself may not be involved but is merely used as a medium in which to carry out the reaction. Four non-aqueous solvents which are of special interest are now discussed in more detail.

Liquid Ammonia

Ammonia has been extensively used as a solvent. Although it shows certain resemblances to water in its solvent properties, it is less strongly associated through hydrogen bonding and its melting point and boiling point are correspondingly lower than those of water. Its dielectric constant is also comparatively low (*Table 5.4*) and this means that the solubility of many salts is less in liquid ammonia than in water. Ammonia does dissolve a large variety of solutes, especially nitrogen compounds like the ammonium halides, NH_4X, substituted ammonium halides, NR_4X, amines, nitriles, nitrates and nitrites. Also soluble are iodides, alcohols, ketones, esters and ethers.

Neutralization reactions take place between an acid and a base. Representative of these are the reactions between an ammonium halide (acid) and a metal amide, imide or nitride (base):

$$NH_4Cl + KNH_2 = KCl + 2NH_3$$
$$2NH_4I + PbNH = PbI_2 + 3NH_3$$
$$3NH_4I + BiN = BiI_3 + 4NH_3$$

The course of such reactions may be followed by conductometric titration methods and sometimes by the use of indicators. For example, phenolphthalein is colourless in liquid ammonia but becomes intensely red in the presence of amides. As a result, the alkali amides can be titrated with ammonium salts in liquid ammonia with phenolphthalein as indicator in exactly the same way as acids can be titrated with alkalis in aqueous solution.

In some cases it is preferable to carry out a reaction in liquid ammonia rather than in water. For instance, ammonium bromide in ammonia gives a better yield than aqueous hydrochloric acid in the preparation of silanes from magnesium silicide:

$$Mg_2Si + HCl \text{ (in } H_2O) = \text{Silanes (} Si_2H_6, \textit{etc.}) \text{ 25\% yield}$$

$$Mg_2Si + NH_4Br \text{ (in } NH_3) = \text{Silanes (chiefly } SiH_4, Si_2H_6) \text{ 70–80\% yield}$$

Extensive hydrolysis of the products reduces the yield in aqueous solution.

126

The solubility relationships are often different in this solvent from those in water and hence metathetical reactions may be carried out, such as the reaction between silver chloride and barium nitrate, to precipitate sparingly soluble barium chloride:

$$2AgCl + Ba(NO_3)_2 = BaCl_2 \downarrow + 2AgNO_3$$

Solvolysis is well-known. Thus silicon tetrachloride, $SiCl_4$, is completely decomposed:

$$SiCl_4 + 8NH_3 = Si(NH_2)_4 + 4NH_4Cl$$

The comparable reaction with water is complete hydrolysis to hydrated silica. On the other hand, some compounds, like the bismuth trihalides, do not react significantly with ammonia but undergo extensive hydrolysis.

Metal–Ammonia Solutions

One characteristic property of liquid ammonia is its ability to dissolve the alkali and alkaline-earth metals. The alkali metals can be recovered unchanged by evaporation of their ammonia solutions; an alkaline-earth metal is obtained as its hexammoniate, $M.6NH_3$. In this respect, ammonia and water differ sharply in their behaviour.

Dilute solutions of alkali metals in ammonia have a deep-blue colour, they are less dense than the parent solvent, excellent electrical conductors and strongly paramagnetic. At high concentrations, the conductivity approaches that of the metals themselves; at low concentrations it is similar to that of electrolytic solutions in water. Metal–ammonia solutions are noted for their powerful reducing properties. To account for their behaviour it has been suggested that the metal dissolves in liquid ammonia to produce solvated cations and free electrons,

$$e.g. \quad Na(solvent)^+ + e^-$$

Many compounds which cannot be made in the presence of water have been prepared using metal–ammonia solutions to effect reduction. A powerful reducing agent in aqueous solution may reduce water to hydrogen instead of reducing the compound under examination. Solutions of sodium in ammonia, for instance, can reduce many compounds to the free elements and sometimes to intermetallic compounds. Silver salts are reduced to the metal; bismuth tri-iodide, on the other hand, is reduced to the metal and various intermetallic substances which have been assigned the formulae Na_3Bi, Na_3Bi_3 and Na_3Bi_5. These formulae were deduced from potentiometric and conductometric titrations on ammoniacal solutions of BiI_3 with sodium in ammonia. The species indicated by the formulae do not necessarily correspond with compounds which can be isolated as distinct entities. Again, lead iodide is first converted to the metal, then the normal plumbide, Na_4Pb, and finally a polyplumbide, Na_4Pb_9, is formed. Sulphur reacts with alkali metal solutions in ammonia to give a variety of sulphides of general formulae M_2S_4, M_2S_2 and M_2S.

Reactions of special interest are those which lead to the preparation of compounds of metals showing an unusual oxidation state. One of the best known

127

examples is the reduction of the complex cyanide $K_2M(CN)_4$ (where M is Ni, Co or Pd) using potassium in liquid ammonia. In the case of nickel, reduction of $[Ni^{II}(CN)_4]^{2-}$ proceeds via the complex $[Ni^I(CN)_3]_2^{4-}$ to $[Ni(CN)_4]^{4-}$, in which the nickel is zerovalent:

$$2[Ni(CN)_4]^{2-} + 2e^- \quad\quad = \quad [Ni(CN)_3]_2^{4-} + 2CN^-$$

$$[Ni(CN)_3]_2^{4-} + 2CN^- + 2e^- = 2[Ni(CN)_4]^{4-}$$

The corresponding tetracyano-complexes of Co^0 and Pd^0, $[Co(CN)_4]^{4-}$ and $[Pd(CN)_4]^{4-}$ respectively, are also known.

Another example of the use of alkali metal solutions in ammonia is in the preparation of the metal carbonyl hydrides (p. 164).

Hydrogen Fluoride

This solvent has a high dielectric constant; it is an excellent ionizing solvent and dissolves many inorganic and organic compounds to give highly conducting solutions. HF is a strongly acid solvent and its proton-donor tendency is so powerful that even a molecule like nitric acid becomes a proton-acceptor or base when dissolved in this solvent:

$$HF + HNO_3 \rightleftharpoons H_2NO_3^+ + F^-$$

The self-ionization of hydrogen fluoride may be written as:

$$2HF \rightleftharpoons H_2F^+ + F^-$$

Ionic fluorides like potassium fluoride dissolve readily and are bases because they increase the concentration of fluoride ion in solution. Usually the existence of basic solutes only need be considered because, with the possible exception of very strong acids like perchloric, no substances capable of increasing the H_2F^+ concentration in liquid hydrogen fluoride have been reported. Certain fluorides, notably SbF_5, AsF_5 and BF_3 dissolve in HF to give solutions which are capable of dissolving an electropositive metal like magnesium. This has been suggested as evidence in support of the acid nature of these solutes.

Many metallic salts of other acids (chlorides, bromides, iodides, cyanides, *etc.*) react with HF and are converted to fluorides with the liberation of the appropriate hydrogen halide:

$$e.g. \quad\quad MCl + HF = M^+ + F^- + HCl$$

The reaction proceeds further with salts of oxy-acids such as nitrates:

$$KNO_3 + 2HF = K^+ + H_2NO_3^+ + 2F^-$$

Solvolysis occurs with sulphuric acid with the formation of fluorosulphonic acid, $HO.SO_2F$.

One of the many preparations which have been carried out in anhydrous hydrogen fluoride as solvent is that of anhydrous silver tetrafluoroborate, $AgBF_4$. This is strongly hygroscopic and so can only be made anhydrous in the complete absence of water. $AgBF_4$ is precipitated when silver nitrate and boron trifluoride solutions in HF are mixed. On the assumption that BF_3 acts as an acid, the reactions may be written:

$$AgNO_3 + 2HF = Ag^+ + H_2NO_3^+ + 2F^-$$
$$BF_3 \quad + 2HF = H_2F^+ + BF_4^-$$
$$Ag^+ \quad + BF_4^- = AgBF_4 \downarrow$$

Dinitrogen Tetroxide

This is the diamagnetic compound formed by the dimerization of two molecules of paramagnetic nitrogen dioxide, NO_2.

$$2NO_2 \rightleftharpoons N_2O_4$$

The extent of dimerization is temperature-dependent and is greater the lower the temperature. At high temperatures in the gas phase, NO_2 is the more important but in the liquid state N_2O_4 predominates. Dissociation to NO_2 is only 0·13 per cent at the boiling point.

N_2O_4 is not an ionizing solvent and no simple salts are soluble in it. As a solvent it has been compared with diethyl ether. Many organic compounds are soluble in dinitrogen tetroxide and it has been widely used as a medium for carrying out organic reactions.

The pure liquid is a poor electrical conductor (*Table 5.4*) but ionization to NO^+ and NO_3^- is promoted by the presence of a second solvent of higher dielectric constant. Thus in nitromethane, dielectric constant $= 37$, the specific conductivity rises to $\sim 10^{-5}$ and in pure sulphuric acid the ionization to NO^+ is complete.

The salt nitrosonium bisulphate, $NO.HSO_4$, can be crystallized from solutions of N_2O_4 in excess sulphuric acid. Other nitrosonium salts have been made by solution of the tetroxide in the appropriate acid. For example, nitrosonium perchlorate, $NOClO_4$, is prepared by the reaction

$$N_2O_4 + HClO_4 = NOClO_4 + HNO_3$$

Dinitrogen tetroxide is of current interest because of its use in the preparation of anhydrous metal nitrates, the properties of which are strikingly different from those of the more familiar hydrated salts. A number of nitrates have been prepared by C. C. ADDISON and co-workers using mixed solvents consisting of N_2O_4 diluted with an organic solvent of higher dielectric constant to promote ionization. This type of mixed solvent attacks metals which are unattacked by pure N_2O_4. For example, copper dissolves in an ethyl acetate/N_2O_4 mixture (1:1 by volume): from this solution the solvated compound $Cu(NO_3)_2.N_2O_4$ can be precipitated by the addition of excess N_2O_4. This loses N_2O_4 at 85°C to give pale blue anhydrous copper nitrate, a solid which is appreciably soluble in many organic solvents containing oxygen or nitrogen. It sublimes readily when heated *in vacuo* above 200°C. Electron diffraction measurements on the compound in the vapour phase have shown that it has the structure

The copper atom has a square-planar co-ordination by four oxygen atoms each at a distance of 2·00 Å.

Other anhydrous nitrates such as those of lithium and sodium have been made by the action of liquid N_2O_4 on the metal carbonates. One of the most recently prepared nitrates is basic beryllium nitrate, $Be_4O(NO_3)_6$. Beryllium chloride undergoes solvolysis in ethyl acetate/dinitrogen tetroxide mixtures to give the crystalline addition compound, $Be(NO_3)_2.2N_2O_4$. On heating this, anhydrous beryllium nitrate is first formed, but this decomposes at 125°C to N_2O_4 and the volatile basic beryllium nitrate of the above formula. The composition is analogous to that of basic beryllium acetate (p. 205) and it is probable that the two structures are similar with the nitrate group acting as a bridging group in exactly the same way as the acetate group. The properties of the nitrate group are becoming more fully understood as the result of these investigations.

Sulphur Dioxide

This solvent is used industrially as a refrigerant and as an extractive solvent in petroleum refining. It is thus readily available and extensive chemical investigations have been carried out using it. The relatively low value of its dielectric constant (*Table 5.4*) accords with its property of dissolving covalent rather than ionic compounds. For instance, the halogen compounds Br_2, $AsCl_3$, BCl_3, CCl_4, ICl, PCl_3, $POCl_3$ and SO_2Cl_2 are all miscible with SO_2. Iodides and thiocyanates are the most soluble inorganic salts.

Solvolysis of solutes can occur, for example:

$$4KBr + 4SO_2 = 2K_2SO_4 \downarrow + S_2Br_2 + Br_2$$

Preparations carried out in this solvent include thionyl bromide:

$$2KBr + SOCl_2 = SOBr_2 + 2KCl$$

and potassium hexachloroantimonate (III)

$$6KI + 3SbCl_5 = 2K_3SbCl_6 \downarrow + 3I_2 + SbCl_3$$

Boron trifluoride, BF_3, reacts with acetyl fluoride, CH_3COF, to form acetyl fluoroborate:

$$CH_3COF + BF_3 = CH_3COBF_4$$

The solvent has been used experimentally to demonstrate the existence of the oxonium ion. H_2O and HBr dissolve in sulphur dioxide in equimolar proportions; the addition of more water merely causes the excess to separate as a second phase. This suggests some kind of compound formation. On electrolysis of the sulphur dioxide phase, the cathode products are water and hydrogen, the anode product is bromine. These observations can be explained only on the assumption of the formation of the oxonium compound H_3OBr, ionized to H_3O^+ and Br^-.

The reaction between thionyl compounds and sulphites takes place according to

$$SOCl_2 + Cs_2SO_3 = 2CsCl + 2SO_2$$

130

It was believed that this reaction supported the idea of self-ionization according to:

$$2SO_2 \rightleftharpoons SO^{2+} + SO_3^{2-}$$

and therefore that a thionyl compound would be defined as an acid and a sulphite as a base in the sulphur dioxide solvent system. However, the nature of the products of the above reaction does not establish the mechanism of the reaction by which they are formed and there appears at present to be no undisputed evidence that sulphur dioxide can ionize as shown.

HIGH-TEMPERATURE REACTIONS IN LIQUID MEDIA

Many important metallurgical reactions are carried out at high temperatures where at least some of the reactants or products are liquid. Reactions are possible under these conditions which cannot be effected in the presence of water. For example, the reactive metals sodium, magnesium, calcium and aluminium are prepared industrially from their fused compounds by electrolytic reduction, and fusion electrolysis is also used in the preparation of tantalum metal on a small scale and in the refining of titanium (p. 180).

Most pyrometallurgical processes involve the chemical reduction of a metallic oxide to the metal (p. 179). Only in a few cases are the compounds to be reduced available in the pure state and usually the metal produced must be separated from the impurities present. This separation is more easily effected when the metal is formed as a vapour (*e.g.* Zn, Mg) or as a liquid (Fe, Cu) than when it is produced as a solid (Ti, Zr, Mo). However, it is common practice to remove impurities by slag formation during the final reduction process.

Where the impurities are refractory, that is they are of high melting point, it is necessary to add materials (known as fluxes) which will combine with them to form a mixture, or slag, of compounds. Maximum removal of impurity is achieved when the slag is a liquid immiscible with the molten metal at the operating temperature. For example, lime is added as a flux to the blast furnace charge used in the reduction of iron oxide; the flux forms a slag with SiO_2 and P_2O_5 consisting of calcium silicate and phosphate.

Most industrial slags are formed by the mutual solution or combination of oxides which are classified according to their chemical behaviour as acidic, amphoteric or basic. SiO_2, P_2O_5, B_2O_3, Sb_2O_3 and TeO_2 are among the acidic oxides. Al_2O_3, Fe_2O_3, SnO_2 and ZnO are amphoteric because they behave as acids in the presence of a basic oxide and as bases in the presence of an acidic oxide. The oxides of Mg, the alkaline earths and the alkali metals are basic.

Slag formation can be regarded as the neutralization of a Lewis base by a Lewis acid. For example, a basic oxide (or a carbonate which thermally decomposes to the oxide) supplies oxide ions. These co-ordinate with acidic oxides such as SiO_2,

$$O^{2-} + SiO_2 = SiO_3^{2-}$$

and P_2O_5,

$$3O^{2-} + P_2O_5 = 2PO_4^{3-}$$

Similar types of neutralization are known in qualitative analysis in the borax

131

bead and metaphosphate bead tests. For example, the reaction of a meta-phosphate, $(PO_3)_x^{x-}$, a Lewis acid, with the oxide ion, a Lewis base, produces an orthophosphate:

$$(PO_3)_x^{x-} + xO^{2-} = xPO_4^{3-}$$

One further example is the conversion of refractory, insoluble oxides such as titanium dioxide to a soluble derivative by acid fusion with pyrosulphate or bisulphate:

$$O^{2-} + S_2O_7^{2-} = 2SO_4^{2-}$$

SUGGESTED REFERENCES FOR FURTHER READING

BELL, R. P. *Acids and Bases*, Methuen, London, 1952.
GUTMANN, V. 'Ionizing non-aqueous solvents' *Quart. Rev. chem. Soc., Lond.*, 10 (1956) 451.
JONES, A. G. *Analytical Chemistry—Some New Techniques*, Butterworths, London, 1959.
SISLER, H. H. *Chemistry in Non-aqueous Solvents*, Reinhold, New York, 1961.

CO-ORDINATION CHEMISTRY

INTRODUCTION

THE term *co-ordination compound* is used to describe a great range of chemical substances. Some of these exist only in the solid state; others dissolve to give molecules or ions and can be recovered from solution unchanged; others again can be studied in solution only.

A co-ordination compound contains a central metal atom or ion surrounded by a number of oppositely charged ions or neutral molecules known as *ligands*. The number of ligands attached to the metal is its *co-ordination number*. When the group comprising the metal and its ligands carries a positive or negative charge it constitutes a *complex ion*.

Each ligand molecule or ion has at least one pair of unshared electrons which is donated to the metal to form a co-ordinate bond. The metal must have vacant orbitals of appropriate energy which can accept these electrons. Complexes are most commonly formed by transition metals and then the *d* orbitals of the penultimate quantum shell of the metal are generally involved in the bonding. Hexamminecobalt (III) chloride, $Co(NH_3)_6Cl_3$, is a well-known co-ordination compound readily prepared by the oxidation of an ammoniacal solution of cobalt (II) chloride. The complex ion $[Co(NH_3)_6]^{3+}$ is made up of a tripositive cobalt ion and six ammonia ligands, each nitrogen atom donating its lone pair of electrons to the metal. Water acts as a ligand in exactly the same way as ammonia because the oxygen atom can donate one of its lone pairs to a metal. Many salts in aqueous solution and in the crystalline state contain metal ions complexed (hydrated) with water molecules. There is a useful analogy here with acid–base reactions for the metal ion can be regarded as a Lewis acid with the ligand as base. The basic behaviour of ammonia

$$H^+ + NH_3 \rightleftharpoons (H{\leftarrow}NH_3)^+$$

is then directly comparable with co-ordination to a metal:

$$M^{n+} + NH_3 \rightleftharpoons (M{\leftarrow}NH_3)^{n+}$$

When the ligand molecule or ion contains two atoms which each have a lone pair of electrons, it may be stereochemically possible for the molecule to form two co-ordinate bonds with the same metal ion. For instance, tris-(ethylenediamine) cobalt (III), formula (I), contains 6 co-ordinate cobalt with each ethylenediamine molecule occupying two co-ordinate positions. In this complex, three rings which each contain five atoms have been established. The process of ring formation is called *chelation*. In the above example, ethylenediamine is acting as a *bidentate* chelating agent because it occupies two co-ordinate positions. Many other bidentate and *multidentate* ligands (the latter contain more than two co-ordinating atoms per molecule) are known and examples are given in the succeeding pages.

(I) $[Co(en)_3]^{3+}$

STEREOCHEMISTRY

Present ideas on the shapes of co-ordination compounds owe their origin to the work of A. WERNER who in 1893 suggested what proved to be the correct explanation for the structures of the co-ordination compounds of tripositive cobalt and dipositive platinum. Using the ammines of these metals as examples, the evidence on which Werner's theory was based will now be reviewed.

The Cobaltammines and other 6 Co-ordinated Complexes

In addition to hexamminecobalt (III) chloride, a number of other complex salts have been prepared in which ammonia is strongly bound to tripositive cobalt. The distinctive properties of these are summarized in *Table 6.1*,

Table 6.1. The ammines of cobalt

Compound	Salt	Colour	No. of ions	Werner's formulation
$CoCl_3.6NH_3$	Luteo	Orange	4	$[Co(NH_3)_6]Cl_3$
$CoCl_3.5NH_3.H_2O$	Roseo	Pink	4	$[Co(NH_3)_5H_2O]Cl_3$
$CoCl_3.5NH_3$	Purpureo	Purple	3	$[Co(NH_3)_5Cl]Cl_2$
$CoCl_3.4NH_3$	Praseo	Green	2	$[Co(NH_3)_4Cl_2]Cl$
$CoCl_3.4NH_3$	Violeo	Violet	2	$[Co(NH_3)_4Cl_2]Cl$
$CoCl_3.3NH_3$		Blue-green	0	$[Co(NH_3)_3Cl_3]$

together with Werner's formulations. Chemical evidence to support Werner's formulations came, for example, from conductance measurements on aqueous solutions which indicated what ions were present; also from the proportion of chlorine present as the chloride ion, that is, the fraction which was precipitated by silver nitrate.

WERNER proposed that each metal had both a primary and a secondary valency. In the ammines of cobalt, the primary valency (or electrovalency) is 3 and the secondary valency is 6. He also suggested that the secondary valencies were directed in space about the central ion and that for 6 co-ordinate cobalt the ligands were arranged octahedrally about the metal ion. Then the two compounds of empirical formula $CoCl_3.4NH_3$ were regarded as geometrical isomers (formulae (II) and (III)). Two isomers only are possible for an octahedral arrangement and in practice no more than two are known. If the arrangement were either of the other possibilities—namely trigonal prismatic or planar hexagonal—then three isomers would be expected.

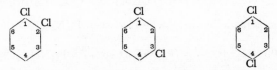

(II)

cis-[Co(NH$_3$)$_4$Cl$_2$]$^+$

(III)

$trans$-[Co(NH$_3$)$_4$Cl$_2$]$^+$

For example, in a plane hexagon the chlorine atoms could be in the 1,2 or 1,3 or 1,4 positions:

The isolation of the predicted number of isomers is indicative but not conclusive support for Werner's hypothesis. However, another consequence of an octahedral, but not of a planar or trigonal prismatic, configuration is that

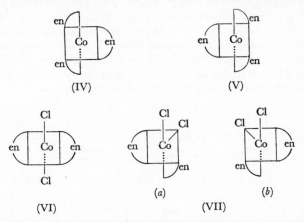

(IV)

(V)

(VI)

(VII)

(a)

(b)

optical activity is to be expected for an ion such as tris(ethylenediamine) cobalt (III) (abbreviated to [Co(en)$_3$]$^{3+}$ where en=ethylenediamine). Two configurations, related as object and mirror image, formulae (IV) and (V), are possible. Again the dichlorobis(ethylenediamine) cobalt (III) ion, [Co(en)$_2$Cl$_2$]$^+$ exists in $trans$- and cis-forms (formulae (VI) and (VII) respectively) for an octahedral configuration. Moreover, whilst the *trans* isomer has a plane of symmetry, the *cis* does not and should therefore show two optically-active forms, (formulae (VII) *a* and *b*). WERNER achieved resolution of $[Co(en)_3]^{3+}$ into optically active isomers by using the techniques of organic chemistry, for example, treatment of the racemic mixture with an optically active resolving agent and then separating the diastereoisomers formed by fractional crystallization.

X-ray crystal analysis has confirmed the octahedral arrangement around tripositive cobalt and the same orientation of groups has been shown for many other 6 co-ordinated metal ions.

The Platinum Ammines and other 4 Co-ordinated Complexes

The shape of a 4 co-ordinated complex may be either square planar or tetra-hedral. Platinum (II) complexes are some of the best-known examples of the first of these.

Two isomeric dichlorodiammines of Pt^{II} can be made. The α-form is prepared by the treatment of K_2PtCl_4 with aqueous ammonia

$$[PtCl_4]^{2-} \xrightarrow{NH_3} [Pt(NH_3)Cl_3]^- \xrightarrow{NH_3} Pt(NH_3)_2Cl_2$$

and the β-form is made by the reaction between $Pt(NH_3)_4Cl_2$ and HCl

$$[Pt(NH_3)_4]^{2+} \xrightarrow{Cl^-} [Pt(NH_3)_3Cl]^+ \xrightarrow{Cl^-} Pt(NH_3)_2Cl_2$$

WERNER proposed that these compounds were geometrical isomers, formulae (VIII) and (IX) below, and these are only possible for four bonds coplanar with the metal.

Chemical support for these configurations came from the preparation of the corresponding isomeric dinitratodiammines. When these were treated with oxalic acid, the nitrato-groups were replaced and two complexes were formed. The one from the α-isomer had the composition $Pt(NH_3)_2C_2O_4$; the one from the β-isomer had the formula $Pt(NH_3)_2(C_2O_4H)_2$. Assuming that the oxalato-group acts as a bidentate ligand only if it replaces two nitrato-groups in the *cis*-position, then the reactions may be represented as follows:

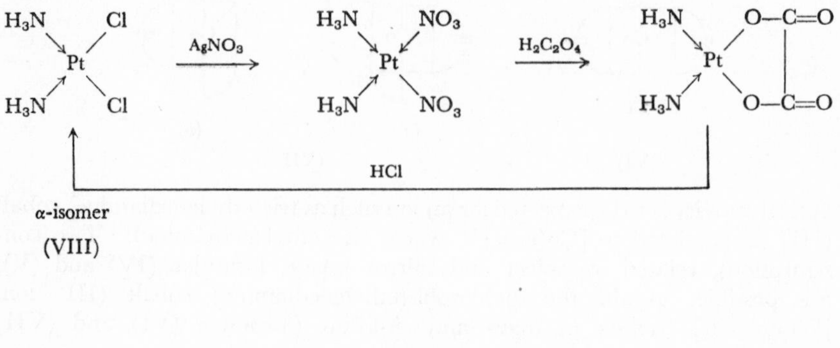

α-isomer

(VIII)

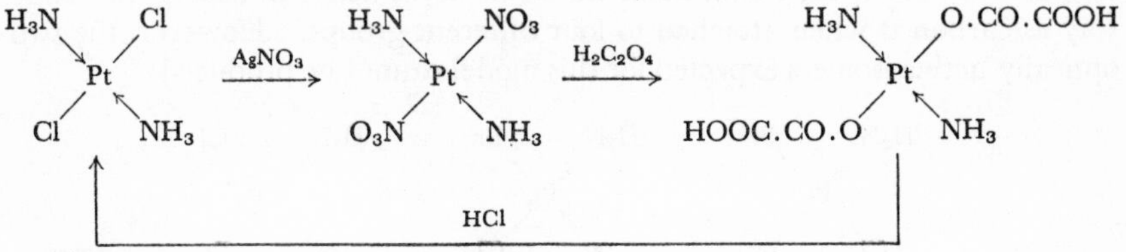

$$\underset{Cl}{\overset{H_3N}{\diagdown}}\underset{}{\overset{Cl}{\diagup}}Pt\underset{NH_3}{\overset{}{\diagup\diagdown}} \xrightarrow{AgNO_3} \underset{O_3N}{\overset{H_3N}{\diagdown}}\underset{}{\overset{NO_3}{\diagup}}Pt\underset{NH_3}{\overset{}{\diagup\diagdown}} \xrightarrow{H_2C_2O_4} \underset{HOOC.CO.O}{\overset{H_3N}{\diagdown}}\underset{}{\overset{O.CO.COOH}{\diagup}}Pt\underset{NH_3}{\overset{}{\diagup\diagdown}}$$

HCl

β-isomer

(IX)

They are consistent with Werner's formulation provided that no change in configuration occurred during the sequence of reactions.

When two unsymmetrical chelate groups such as isobutylenediamine (formula (X)) are tetrahedrally co-ordinated to a central atom, the resulting complex exists in mirror-image but not *cis–trans* forms. When the chelate

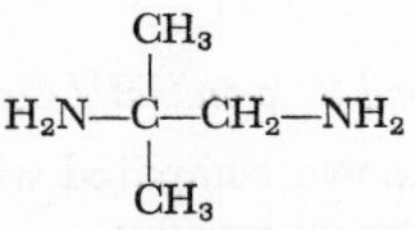

$$\overset{\overset{\displaystyle CH_3}{|}}{\underset{\underset{\displaystyle CH_3}{|}}{H_2N-C-CH_2-NH_2}}$$

(X)

groups are coplanar, *cis–trans* isomerism is possible but not optical activity. Although various claims of optical isomerism in Pt[II] complexes have been made, in every case the activity appears to have been associated with the presence of the resolving acid or base as impurity and there is consequently no evidence for tetrahedral co-ordination.

However, one Pt[II] complex has been synthesized which possesses asymmetry if the 4 co-ordinating groups are arranged at the corners of a square plane but not if the grouping is tetrahedral. This is the complex salt, isobutylenedi-amine-*meso*stilbenediamine platinum (II) chloride (formula (XI)). The

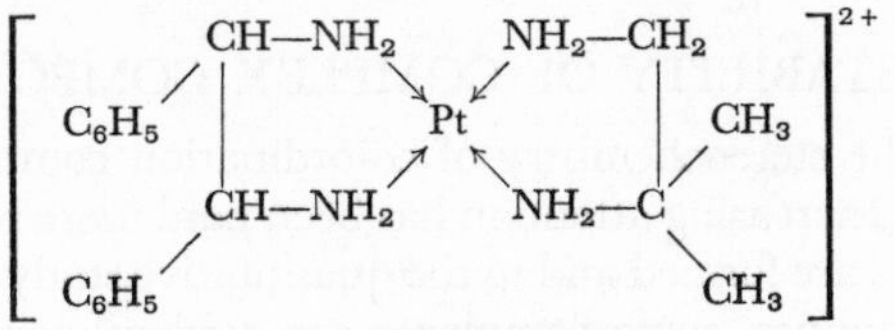

$$\left[\underset{\substack{C_6H_5 \\ \diagup \\ CH-NH_2 \\ \diagup \\ C_6H_5}}{\overset{CH-NH_2}{}} Pt \underset{\substack{NH_2-C \\ \diagdown \\ CH_3}}{\overset{NH_2-CH_2 \diagdown CH_3}{}} \right]^{2+}$$

(XI)

asymmetry and hence planarity of the ligand atoms around the metal was demonstrated by the resolution of this compound in 1935 by MILLS and QUIBELL.

Finally, it has proved possible to prepare three geometrical isomers of compounds such as $[Pt(NH_3)(py)]ClBr$ (where py = pyridine). These, on a

137

planar configuration, are represented by formulae (XII) *a*, *b* and *c*. In a tetrahedral model, the metal atom would be asymmetric in exactly the same way as carbon is when attached to four different groups. However, the two optically active isomers expected for this model cannot be produced.

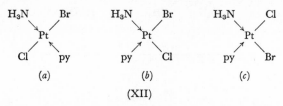

(XII)

X-ray crystal analyses and dipole moment measurements (see Appendix, p. 275) of several Pt^{II} complexes have confirmed the square-planarity of the bonds around the metal atom. This arrangement has also been established for 4 co-ordinated Pd^{II}, Ag^{II}, Cu^{II} and Au^{III}. Tetrahedral configurations have been assigned to Cu^{I}, Ag^{I}, Au^{I}, Be^{II}, Al^{III}, Zn^{II}, Cd^{II}, Hg^{II} and Co^{II} in their co-ordination compounds. Some metals, for example, Ni^{II}, appear to show either configuration for 4 co-ordination (p. 155).

5, 7 and 8 Co-ordinated Complexes

Relatively few of these are known compared with the numerous 4 and 6 co-ordinated complexes. Some examples are:

Co-ordination number 5—Iron pentacarbonyl, $Fe(CO)_5$, with the five carbonyl groups located at the corners of a trigonal bipyramid (p. 162).

Co-ordination number 7—Various heptafluoro complex ions. $[ZrF_7]^{3-}$ has the shape of a pentagonal bipyramid. $[TaF_7]^{2-}$ and $[NbF_7]^{2-}$ have six fluorines situated at the corners of a trigonal prism with the seventh situated at a face-centre.

Co-ordination number 8—Octafluorotantalate (V), $[TaF_8]^{3-}$, has the eight fluorines situated around the metal atom at the corners of a square antiprism. The alternative dodecahedral shape for an isolated group in which one atom shows this co-ordination number is shown by octacyanomolybdate (V), $[Mo(CN)_8]^{3-}$.

THE STABILITY OF COMPLEX COMPOUNDS

For many years the stereochemistry of co-ordination compounds was of the greatest interest. Increasing attention has been paid more recently to the way in which complexes are formed and to the quantitative study of their stabilities. Like the cobaltammines, some complexes are evidently very stable because they can be kept indefinitely without decomposition and in solution they do not give the usual analytical reactions of their constituent groups. Other complexes, such as the metal carbonyls are unstable, being destroyed by the action of heat or water.

Apart from the work of a few chemists, notably ABEGG, BODLANDER and N. BJERRUM in the early part of this century, the chief impetus behind the current intensive study of the stability of metal complexes was the work, first published in 1941, of J. Bjerrum on the formation of metal ammines in aqueous solution. According to Bjerrum, the formation of a complex in solution proceeds by the step-wise addition of ligands to the metal. Thus, when a neutral ligand A complexes with the metal ion M^{n+}, a number of successive equilibria can be formulated. These are represented by equations (1), (2),...(X) and for each of these an equilibrium constant $k_1, k_2,...k_X$ can be defined. X is the maximum number of ligands attached to one metal ion for a particular set of experimental conditions and therefore represents its co-ordination number.

$$M + A \rightleftharpoons MA \qquad k_1 = \frac{[MA]}{[M][A]} \qquad \cdots \cdots \quad (1)$$

$$MA + A \rightleftharpoons MA_2 \qquad k_2 = \frac{[MA_2]}{[MA][A]} \qquad \cdots \cdots \quad (2)$$

$$MA_2 + A \rightleftharpoons MA_3 \qquad k_3 = \frac{[MA_3]}{[MA_2][A]} \qquad \cdots \cdots \quad (3)$$

$$\cdots \qquad \cdots \qquad \cdots \cdots$$

$$MA_{(X-1)} + A \rightleftharpoons MA_X \qquad k_X = \frac{[MA_X]}{[MA_{(X-1)}][A]} \qquad \cdots \cdot \quad (X)$$

$k_1, k_2,...k_X$ are the step-wise formation or stability constants and are related to the total formation constant, K_t, by the equation:

$$k_1.k_2.k_3...k_X = K_t = \frac{[MA_X]}{[M][A]^X}$$

It should be noted that, for the sake of clarity, charges have been omitted. Also it must be remembered that when the reaction between a ligand and a metal ion takes place in an aqueous medium, the metal ion is hydrated and complex formation therefore involves the replacement of water by ligand molecules. It is again customary to omit the co-ordinated water molecules from the equilibrium equations.

As defined above, the k values are constant only at a specific ionic strength because they are related to the concentrations of the participating species. True thermodynamic stability constants, defined in terms of the activities of the reacting species, do not vary with the ionic strength and these can be calculated from the experimentally measured k values provided that the activity coefficients of the various ionic species are known at the ionic strength concerned. Alternatively, it may prove more accurate to measure the concentration constants, $k_1, k_2,...k_X$ at different ionic strengths and then to extrapolate the data to zero ionic strength to obtain values for the thermodynamic constants.

The calculation of a series of stability constants is usually a difficult procedure and involves considerable mathematical manipulation. This is because of the inherent complexity of the equilibrium systems being studied. When a metal salt and a ligand are present together in aqueous solution, equilibrium is established between the metal ion M^{n+} and its various complexes MA_1^{n+},

$MA_2^{n+}, \ldots MA_x^{n+}$. ('A' represents an uncharged ligand.) Experimentally, it may be possible to measure one of the following:

 (a) the concentration of free uncomplexed metal ion [M] ;
or (b) the concentration of one or more of the complexes [MA_1], etc.;
or (c) the concentration of free ligand [A].

The choice between these is largely determined by the nature of the system under investigation.

The experimental side of the determination of stability constants is essentially a matter of the measurement of (a), (b) or (c) in a range of equilibrium mixtures which contain the metal ion and ligand in different proportions. The ionic strength is generally maintained constant by the addition of some electrolyte (sodium perchlorate is frequently used) which does not form competitive complexes with the metal to any significant extent in the conditions of the experiment. Details of the calculation of stability constants from experimental data cannot be given here.

A wide variety of methods has been used in the measurement of the required concentrations. The more important of these methods are now considered very briefly.

(a) *The concentration of metal ion*—Several electrochemical procedures are used, particularly polarography and potentiometry with suitable electrodes. Ion-exchange resins have also been utilized. Thus a cation-exchange resin, when brought to equilibrium with an aqueous solution containing metal ion, will sorb a certain proportion of this ion from solution. If a complexing anion is now added to the aqueous solution, complexes of lower positive and even of zero or negative charge may be formed. The amount of metal taken up by the resin at equilibrium will therefore decrease. The magnitude of the decrease for a given concentration of complexing anion will be related to the concentration of free metal ion remaining in solution. For example, Zn^{2+} carries a double positive charge and is therefore appreciably sorbed from aqueous solutions of zinc salts by a cation-exchange resin. In the presence of chloride ion, the complexes $[ZnCl]^+$, $ZnCl_2$, $[ZnCl_3]^-$ and $[ZnCl_4]^{2-}$ will be formed and there will be a decrease in the amount of metal taken up by the resin.

Solubility measurements have also been used. These are of value where salts which are sparingly soluble in water are rendered more soluble by the presence of complex-forming ions. For example, silver chloride is more soluble in sodium chloride solutions than in pure water because of the formation of complex chloro-ions:

$$AgCl + Cl^- \rightleftharpoons [AgCl_2]^- \quad etc.$$

For the same reason sodium thiosulphate solution will dissolve AgCl and AgBr:

$$AgBr + S_2O_3^{2-} \rightleftharpoons [Ag(S_2O_3)]^- + Br^- \quad etc.$$

(b) *The concentration of metal complex*—Spectrophotometric methods are used where a colour change is associated with complex formation. The metal ion, ligand or one of the complexes may be the coloured species. The measurement of the absorption of light by this species at a particular wavelength, suitably chosen so that the absorption of other coloured species is minimal, serves as a measure of its concentration. For example, when aqueous copper

(II) sulphate is treated with HCl, the initial blue colour of the hydrated Cu^{2+} ion changes to green because of the formation of chloro-complexes:

$$[Cu(H_2O)_4]^{2+} + Cl^- \rightleftharpoons [Cu(H_2O)_3Cl]^+ + H_2O$$

and so on up to $[CuCl_4]^{2-}$.

Spectrophotometry may be combined with solvent extraction in the special case of the formation of an uncharged coloured metal complex. This can be formed in aqueous solution and then extracted into an immiscible organic solvent. Important applications are in the study of inner complexes (p. 142) formed between metals and various organic reagents.

In many systems, for example, those in which the reacting species are colourless, a radioisotope of the metal can be used for measuring the total concentration of metal in aqueous or organic phases or the quantity of metal sorbed by an ion-exchange resin. Stability constants can be calculated from such measurements.

(c) *The concentration of free ligand*—When A is a weak base, its concentration may be determined by a pH measurement on the solution containing the metal and ligand. A and its conjugate acid (p. 119) HA^+, are related as follows:

$$A + H^+ \rightleftharpoons HA^+$$

From a knowledge of the pH value and of the dissociation constant of HA^+, it is possible to calculate the concentration of A.

In the subsequent pages, the stability constants quoted will, unless otherwise stated, be concentration constants and are therefore only valid for a particular ionic strength.

CHELATION

Many compounds and ions, most of them organic in nature, form chelate rings on reaction with metal ions. Ring closure may take place with the establishment of covalent or co-ordinate bonds or both. The ability to form a covalent bond requires the presence of an acidic group in the ligand such as —COOH (carboxyl), —SO₃H (sulphonyl), —OH (enol), —SH (thioenol) or $\geqslant$N—OH (oxime). The most common functional groups containing donor atoms and therefore able to co-ordinate with a metal are:

—NH₂, $\geqslant$NH and $\Rightarrow$N (amines); $\geqslant$N—OH (oxime),

—OH (alcohol), $\geqslant$CO (carbonyl), —O— (ether) and —S— (thioether).

Chelation is favoured when any two of these groups occur in the 1,4 or 1,5 positions of an organic molecule, with the formation of 5- and 6-membered rings respectively.

Multidentate ligands can thus be attached to a metal atom by two kinds of functional group and chelate compounds are classified according to the number and kind of attachments involved. For example, the bidentate chelating agents, which have been the most extensively studied, have been divided into three classes, each of which will be dealt with in turn.

1. *Two Acidic Groups*

In this class are included inorganic acids like carbonic and sulphuric; organic dicarboxylic acids like malonic, oxalic and phthalic; α-hydroxycarboxylic acids like glycollic and salicylic; and dihydroxy-compounds like the glycols and pyrocatechol. Formulae (XIII), (XIV) and (XV) are examples of metal complexes formed by this type.

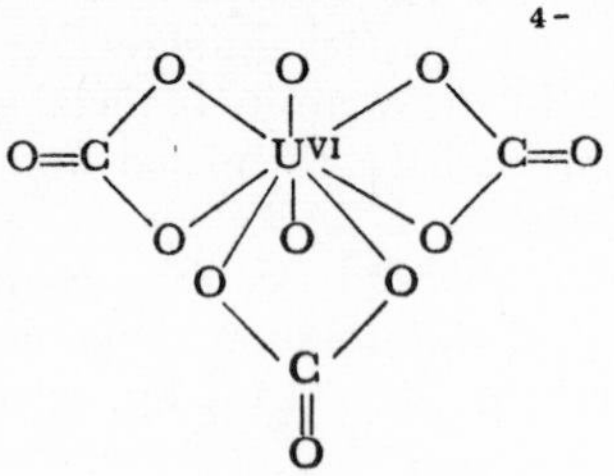

tris(carbonato)uranyl ion

(XIII)

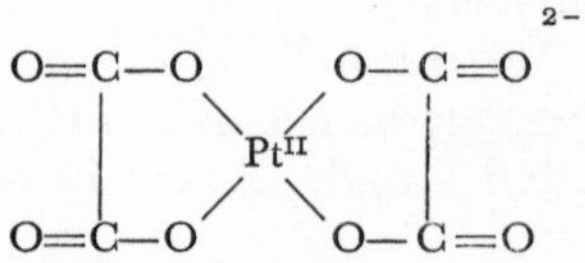

bis(oxalato)platinate (II) ion

(XIV)

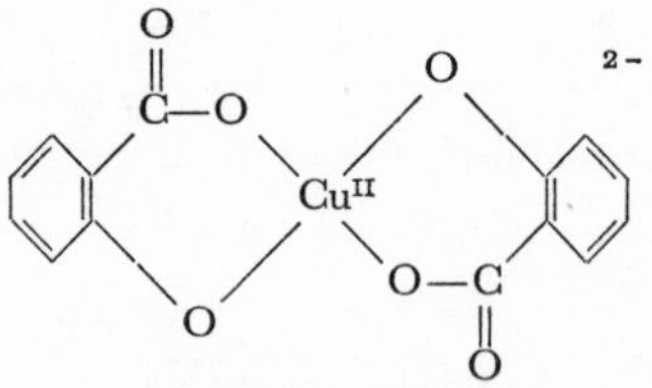

bis(salicylato)cuprate (II) ion

(XV)

2. *One Acidic and One Co-ordinating Group*

This is an especially useful class of organic reagents which can, through chelation, often satisfy simultaneously the oxidation number and the co-ordination number of a metal ion. When this occurs, an uncharged species or *inner complex* is produced. 8-Hydroxyquinoline (formula (XVI)) is one of many examples. In its complex with Fe^{III} (formula (XVII)) the tripositive iron has a co-ordination number of 6. The reaction between the reagent HOx and Fe^{3+} can be represented as a series of steps:

$$Fe^{3+} + HOx \rightleftharpoons [FeOx]^{2+} + H^+$$
$$[FeOx]^{2+} + HOx \rightleftharpoons [Fe(Ox)_2]^+ + H^+$$
$$[Fe(Ox)_2]^+ + HOx \rightleftharpoons FeOx_3 + H^+$$

When the reaction is carried out in aqueous solution the uncharged complex, $FeOx_3$, is precipitated because of its low solubility. When excess reagent is present, complex formation proceeds with the virtually complete

142

precipitation of the metal from solution. Since the reactions are reversible, metal complexes of this type can often be redissolved by the addition of acid. The extent to which the dissociation of a metal complex proceeds at a given pH depends on its stability and the more stable a complex the lower the pH at which it can be precipitated from aqueous solution. When the stabilities of the complexes formed between 8-hydroxyquinoline and two different metals are very different, it may be possible to select a pH at which one is precipitated and the other is not and so to effect an analytically useful separation. However, this reagent like many others is not very selective and it usually complexes with several different metals under a given set of conditions. Its practical value will depend on whether it can be rendered more specific in its reactions. There are a number of ways in which this can be done, such as pH control by buffering, competitive complexing with a second reagent to remove interfering metal ions or extraction with a variety of immiscible organic solvents.

(XVI)

(XVII)

(XVIII)   (XIX)

(XX)

β-Diketones, such as acetylacetone (formula (XVIII)), are also valuable chelating agents. Here, inner complex formation involves the participation of the enol form (formula (XIX)) of the ketone. The complex formed with a dipositive 4 co-ordinate metal is illustrated in formula (XX). Another diketone, trifluoroacetylacetone (which differs from formula (XIX) only in the replacement of one —CH_3 by —CF_3) has been used to realize the difficult separation of zirconium and hafnium by selective extraction of the neutral zirconium complex from aqueous hydrochloric acid into benzene. The hafnium complex is not so readily extracted and the zirconium is thereby freed from some of its hafnium content. The extraction process must be repeated many times to effect an appreciable increase in the purity of the zirconium (see also p. 189).

Many other inner-complexing reagents have been developed and are widely used in analysis. These include dimethylglyoxime (formula (XXI)), dithizone (formula (XXII)) and salicylaldehyde (formula (XXIII)). For instance, dimethylglyoxime forms a water-insoluble red complex with nickel ions (XXIV) which is used in the gravimetric determination of this metal. Dithizone, itself soluble in organic solvents to give deep-green solutions, reacts with

143

many metals to give highly coloured complexes which are variously pink, yellow, orange, *etc*. The striking colour change when the complex is formed is the basis of many colorimetric analytical methods. The hydrogen atom of the thioenol group in dithizone is replaced by a metal and ring closure takes place by co-ordination of one of the nitrogen atoms to the metal.

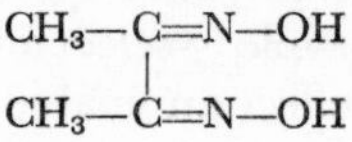

$$CH_3\!-\!C\!=\!N\!-\!OH$$
$$CH_3\!-\!C\!=\!N\!-\!OH$$

(XXI)

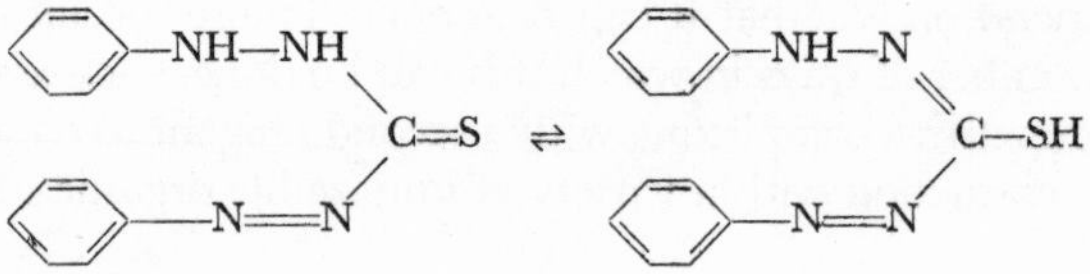

$$
\text{Ph}\!-\!NH\!-\!NH \\
\qquad\qquad C\!=\!S \\
\text{Ph}\!-\!N\!=\!N
\quad\rightleftharpoons\quad
\text{Ph}\!-\!NH\!-\!N \\
\qquad\qquad C\!-\!SH \\
\text{Ph}\!-\!N\!=\!N
$$

(XXII)

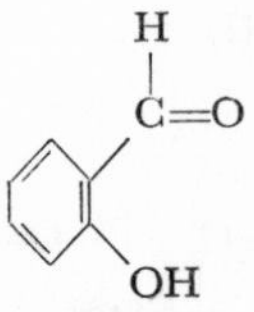

$$
\begin{array}{c}
\text{H} \\
\text{C}\!=\!\text{O} \\
\text{OH}
\end{array}
$$

(XXIII)

$$
CH_3\!-\!C\!=\!N \qquad N\!=\!C\!-\!CH_3 \\
\qquad\qquad\quad \text{Ni} \\
CH_3\!-\!C\!=\!N \qquad N\!=\!C\!-\!CH_3 \\
\text{with OH and O co-ordinating}
$$

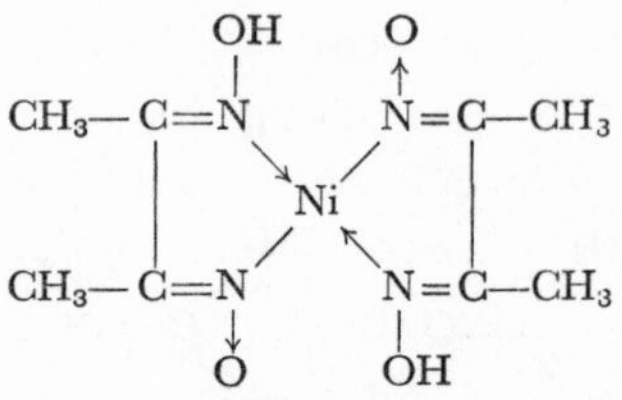

(XXIV)

3. *Two Co-ordinating Groups*

These include diamines like ethylenediamine, α,α′- dipyridyl (XXV), and *o*-phenanthroline (XXVI). *o*-Phenanthroline is a heterocyclic base which has

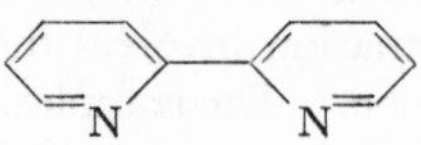

(XXV) 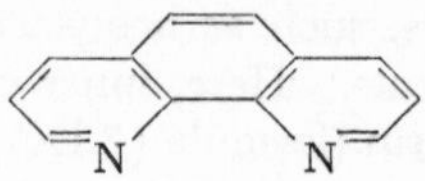   (XXVI)

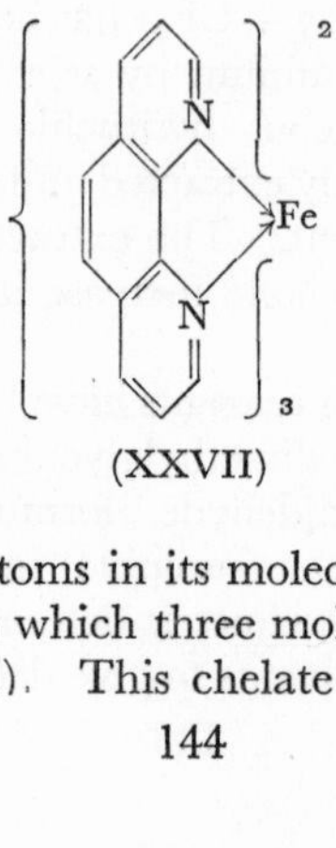

$$
\left[\; \text{phenanthroline} \;\right]_3\!Fe \qquad {}^{2+}
$$

(XXVII)

two co-ordinating nitrogen atoms in its molecule. It forms an intensely red complex with ferrous iron in which three molecules of the base are attached to one metal atom (XXVII). This chelate is a useful redox indicator for

144

titrations involving dichromate or ceric ions because of the sharp colour difference between the tris(o-phenanthroline) iron (II) complex, intense red, and that of tris(o-phenanthroline) iron (III), pale blue.

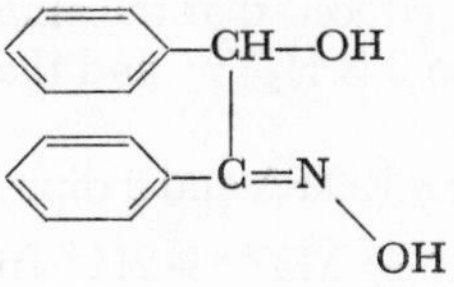

(XXVIII)

Other chelating agents in this class are dihydroxy-compounds like 1,2-glycols and glycerol and α-hydroxy oximes like α-benzoin oxime (XXVIII).

Bidentate chelating agents of the above three classes have been extensively investigated because of their particular utility in analytical chemistry.

COMPLEXONES

These are a class of aminopolycarboxylic acids which have been much studied during the past 15 years by SCHWARZENBACH and many other workers. They have proved to be especially valuable in the rapid volumetric analysis of many elements.

The best known is ethylenediaminetetracetic acid (XXIX), usually abbreviated to EDTA. The molecule contains four carboxyl groups and two

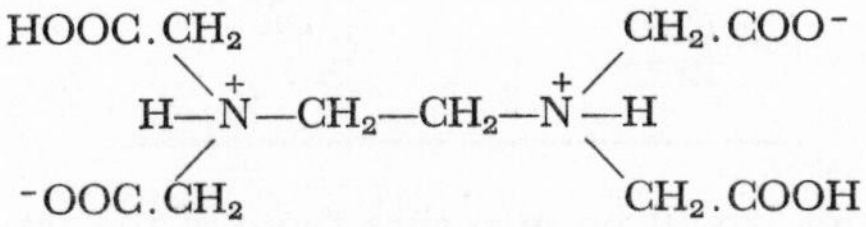

(XXIX)

basic nitrogen atoms and hence there are up to six points of attachment available for the co-ordination of a metal ion. Although a single carboxyl group, for example in the acetate ion, forms only weak complexes with metals, the incorporation of four such groups into one molecule means that chelation occurs with the formation of several rings when a metal–EDTA complex is formed. Thus, if EDTA acts as a hexadentate ligand, five 5-membered rings are established. This complexone appears to be hexadentate towards Co^{III} but is only quinquedentate towards Ni^{II} and many other metal ions. This suggests that the co-ordination of all six groups in EDTA by one metal ion is critically dependent on stereochemical requirements. In other words, the size of the metal ion must be within quite narrow limits for the EDTA molecule to 'wrap around' it completely.

EDTA is a tetrabasic acid (H_4Y). In aqueous solution dissociation takes place to an extent which is determined by the pH value:

$$H_4Y \rightleftharpoons H_3Y^- + H^+$$
$$H_3Y^- \rightleftharpoons H_2Y^{2-} + H^+ \quad etc.$$

145

The acid dissociation constants for the 4 protons, K_1, K_2, K_3 and K_4 respectively have been determined experimentally to be:

$$\log_{10} K_1 = -2 \cdot 0, \log_{10} K_2 = -2 \cdot 67, \log_{10} K_3 = -6 \cdot 16 \text{ and } \log_{10} K_4 = -10 \cdot 26$$

From these figures it can be deduced that the anion predominating in aqueous solutions of EDTA of pH 4 to 5 is H_2Y^{2-} and that in solutions of pH 7 to 9 is HY^{3-}.

Complex formation between EDTA and a dipositive metal occurs as follows:

$$M^{2+} + H_2Y^{2-} \rightleftharpoons MY^{2-} + 2H^+ \text{ (pH = 4 to 5)}$$
$$M^{2+} + HY^{3-} \rightleftharpoons MY^{2-} + H^+ \text{ (pH = 7 to 9)}$$

In most cases, 1:1 complexes are formed. Some tetravalent metal ions complex with two molecules of EDTA but these complexes will not be considered here. *Table 6.2* indicates the relative stabilities of a number of 1:1 EDTA

Table 6.2. Stability constants, $\log_{10} K_{MY}$, *for a number of metal–EDTA complexes*

Cation	$\mathrm{Log_{10}}\, K_{MY}$
Li^+	2·79
Na^+	1·66
Mg^{2+}	8·69
Ca^{2+}	10·70
Sr^{2+}	8·63
Ba^{2+}	7·76
Mn^{2+}	13·79
Fe^{2+}	14·33
Co^{2+}	16·31
Ni^{2+}	18·62
Cu^{2+}	18·80
Zn^{2+}	16·5

complexes. From this it will be seen that those of the transition metals are the most stable and that even in the case of the alkaline earth metals, complexes of appreciable stability are formed.

The chief practical application of EDTA is the use of its solutions in volumetric analysis and it has proved especially valuable for the rapid determination of magnesium and calcium. The disodium salt of EDTA, Na_2H_2Y, is commonly used in aqueous solution because the parent acid is not very soluble in water. This EDTA reagent is added to the solution of the metal salt to be determined and it converts the hydrated metal ion to its EDTA complex. At the equivalence point, usually when the ratio of metal ions to EDTA ions is 1:1, there is a sharp decrease in the concentration of free metal ion. This change can be detected potentiometrically, amperometrically or by a suitable metal indicator.

A metal indicator is an organic dyestuff which, like the complexones themselves, acts as a chelating agent. It possesses several ligand atoms suitably arranged for co-ordination and it can also take up or lose protons, depending on the pH of the solution in which it is dissolved. An essential property of a metal indicator is that its complex with a metal must be weaker than the metal–EDTA complex. It is also necessary that the colour of the indicator ion which predominates at the pH of the titration be different from that of the metal–

indicator complex. Then, as a solution containing metal ion and its indicator is titrated with the aqueous solution of Na_2H_2Y, the metal is progressively complexed by the EDTA and at the equivalence point the colour changes from that of the metal–indicator complex to that of the indicator ion.

Eriochrome Black T (XXX), a derivative of o,o'-dihydroxyazonaphthalene, is one of many metal indicators which have been developed for EDTA titrations. In this dyestuff, there are three acidic hydrogens, one sulphonic and two phenolic. The sulphonic group loses its proton at a low pH and the phenolic groups are those involved in colour changes above pH 7. The anion

H_2D^-

(XXX)

shown as (XXX) is, for these reasons, often abbreviated to H_2D^-. Below pH 6, Eriochrome Black T exists largely in the form of this ion, which is red in aqueous solution. Between pH 7 and 11, the indicator is blue due to the predominance of HD^{2-}. Over this range of pH, metal ions such as magnesium, calcium and the lanthanons give red-coloured complexes. Above pH 12, the solution becomes yellow-orange owing to the formation of D^{3-}, the fully ionized species. When the titration of a metal salt is carried out over the pH range 7 to 11 using EDTA in the presence of Eriochrome Black T, the solution is red until the equivalence point is reached, when it assumes the blue colour of the HD^{2-} ion. The pH of the titrated solution must be controlled by buffering for if it should fall below 6 there would be no significant colour change at the equivalence point because of the similar colours of the metal–indicator complex and the H_2D^- ions.

For details of other complexones and metal indicators and of their analytical uses, reference must be made to texts on analytical chemistry.

FACTORS INFLUENCING THE STABILITY OF COMPLEXES

Several factors determine the stability of a complex formed between a particular metal ion and ligand. The values of stability constants vary over an extremely wide range and it is not always easy to estimate the relative importance of the various factors which contribute towards stability. However, some trends are apparent in the experimental data and these may be discussed in relation to the properties of the metal ion and of the ligand.

Properties of the Metal

1. Metals which Form Ions with an Inert-gas Structure

These ions are formed by Li, Na and the metals of Group I A; Be, Mg and the metals of Group II A; Al and the metals of Group III A, including the

147

lanthanides and actinides. Complexes of these ions are not nearly as numerous nor as stable as those containing transition metal ions. The most stable appear to be those formed with small ionic ligands like fluoride, for example AlF_6^{3-}, and with ligands which contain oxygen as a donor atom, such as acetylacetone (XVIII), its various derivatives and aminopolycarboxylic acids like EDTA. Co-ordination by nitrogen also occurs in EDTA complexes, of course, and in some metal complexes of biological importance; for example, the magnesium complex with a porphyrin ring system in the chlorophyll pigments (XXXI).

Chlorophyll b
(XXXI)

The metals of this class are generally present as ions in their simple compounds and it is logical to suppose that in their complexes as well it is the characteristics of the ion which are of paramount importance. This is borne out by the observation that the stability of the complexes formed by one group of metals and a certain ligand usually increases as the size of the metal ion decreases. Thus the complexes of the alkali metals decrease in stability in the sequence

$$Li^+ > Na^+ > K^+ > Rb^+ > Cs^+$$

and those of Group II A similarly

$$Mg^{2+} > Ca^{2+} > Sr^{2+} > Ba^{2+}, \ etc.$$

Table 6.3. Stability constants of the lanthanide–EDTA complexes

Atomic number	Ion	Stability constant ($\log_{10} K$)	Atomic number	Ion	Stability constant ($\log_{10} K$)
57	La^{3+}	15·5	65	Tb^{3+}	17·93
58	Ce^{3+}	15·98	66	Dy^{3+}	18·3
59	Pr^{3+}	16·4	67	Ho^{3+}	18·74
60	Nd^{3+}	16·61	68	Er^{3+}	18·85
62	Sm^{3+}	17·14	69	Tm^{3+}	19·32
63	Eu^{3+}	17·35	70	Yb^{3+}	19·51
64	Gd^{3+}	17·37	71	Lu^{3+}	19·83

Data from SCHWARZENBACH, G. *et al.*, *Helv. chim. acta*, 37 (1954) 937.

There are exceptions to these general rules. For instance, the EDTA complex with Mg is less stable than that with Ca. The reason for this may well be the difficulty of co-ordinating a small ion like Mg^{2+} with such a large ligand. However, the lanthanide–EDTA complexes illustrate clearly (*Table 6.3*) the increase in stability with decrease in size of the trivalent metal ion.

2. Transition metal ions

The most extensively studied complexes are those of the cations of the first transition series. The complexes formed by the stable divalent ions (that is, from manganese onward) with upwards of 80 ligands, co-ordinating generally through either oxygen or nitrogen, follow the sequence of stabilities

$$Mn^{2+} < Fe^{2+} < Co^{2+} < Ni^{2+} < Cu^{2+} > Zn^{2+}$$

This, after the original proposers, is usually referred to as the Irving–Williams order. An approximately linear correlation has been established of stability with the sum of the first and second ionization potentials of the metal. The ionization potential is a measure of the electron affinity (or power of attraction for electrons) of the metal ion and hence of its tendency to accept electrons from a ligand.

When a transition metal shows different valencies with the same ligand, the complexes of higher valency are nearly always the more stable. This again is related to the charge on the metal ion; the greater the charge the stronger the power of attraction for electrons.

Most transition metals form their strongest complexes with ligands carrying oxygen or nitrogen as donor atoms. There is a small group of ions, however, including Pd^{2+}, Pt^{2+}, Au^+, Ag^+, Cu^+ and Hg^{2+}, which form their most stable complexes with elements of the second or succeeding periods (for example P, S and As). These are the same metals which form stable olefin complexes (p. 164) and are characterized by d^8 or d^{10} electronic configurations. It has been proposed that in the complexes formed by this group of ions there is transfer (back-donation) of electrons from the metal to the ligand as well as from the ligand to the metal. For this to be possible, the ligand must possess vacant orbitals capable of receiving electrons and so back-donation is usually found only with ligand atoms of the second and later periods.

Properties of the Ligand

1. Nature of the ligand atom

The atoms which are bound directly to metal ions in complexes are those of the more electronegative elements on the right-hand side of the Periodic Table, namely C; N, P, As, Sb; O, S, Se, Te; F, Cl, Br, I; H. Any of these atoms present in a ligand molecule or ion may co-ordinate with a metal ion. In the case of Group VII non-metals, the complexes formed by the monatomic anions have been widely studied. For most metals the sequence of stabilities follows the sequence

$$F^- > Cl^- > Br^- > I^-$$

but this order is reversed for a few metals including Pt^{II}, Cu^I, Ag^I, Hg^{II} and Tl^I.

2. Basicity

When the ligand shows basic properties with respect to water as a solvent, a correlation is often noted between the base strength (*i.e.* the proton affinity) of a ligand and the stability of its metal complexes (*i.e.* its cation affinity). BJERRUM first pointed out this relationship from the results of his studies on the amine complexes of Ag^+ and Hg^{2+}. In general, unless steric effects interfered, the ratio of the metal/amine stability constant to the base strength of the ligand was approximately constant when considering a series of ligands of the same type, for example, primary amines.

3. Chelation

The establishment of a chelate ring increases the stability of a complex over that of comparable complexes where chelation is not possible. For example, two ethylenediamine molecules, like four ammonias, occupy four co-ordinate positions around the Cu^{II} ion. In the case of ethylenediamine (en), the overall stability constant for $[Cu(en)_2]^{2+}$ was found to be: $\log_{10} K_t = 20\cdot07$ (measured in $1M$ KNO_3). For the complex $[Cu(NH_3)_4]^{2+}$, $\log_{10} K_t = 12\cdot63$ (in $1M$ NH_4NO_3). The enhanced stability of $Cu(en)_2^{2+}$ is associated with the presence of two 5-membered chelate rings (*cf.* $[Co(en)_3]^{3+}$, formula (I), p. 134).

Table 6.4. *The stability constants for the calcium complexes of the aminocarboxylic acids*
$$(HOOC.CH_2)_2.N.(CH_2)_n.N.(CH_2.COOH)_2$$

n	Ring size	Stability constant ($\log_{10} K$)
2	5	10·7
3	6	7·1
4	7	5·1
5	8	4·6

EDTA complexes are particularly stable because of the presence of several chelate rings. *Table 6.4* shows the variation with ring size of the stability constants of the calcium complexes of a series of acids of general formula

$$(HOOC.CH_2)_2.N.(CH_2)_n.N.(CH_2.COOH)_2$$

When $n=2$, a 5-membered ring is formed between the two nitrogens and the metal; when $n=3$, a 6-membered ring is set up, and so on. The greatest stability is found when $n=2$.

For conjugated ligands, a 6-membered ring is usually more stable than one containing only 5 atoms. The reason for this extra stability is the effect of the aromatic type of resonance which is possible with an even but not an odd number of atoms.

The chelate effect can be regarded thermodynamically as due to the entropy change of the reaction. When a solvated metal ion in solution reacts with a chelating ligand, solvent molecules in the co-ordination sphere of the metal ion are displaced. For example,

in $$Ni(H_2O)_6^{2+} + 3\ en = Ni(en)_3^{2+} + 6H_2O$$

150

the chelation process results in an increase of three in the number of molecules present. The replacement of monodentate by chelating ligands must always have this effect; hence chelation is associated with a positive entropy change and chelate complexes have a greater probability of formation than the corresponding complexes with monodentate ligands.

4. Steric effects

These are associated with the presence of a bulky group either attached to or near enough to a donor atom to cause mutual repulsion between the ligands and therefore a weakening of the metal–ligand bonds. This, for instance, accounts for the observation that the metal complexes of 2-methyl-8-hydroxyquinoline are less stable than those of either 8-hydroxyquinoline itself or its 4-methyl derivative. The values for $\log_{10} k_1 k_2$ for a number of metal complexes are given in *Table 6.5*. Here the pK_{HOx} values in the second column

Table 6.5. The stability constants of 8-hydroxyquinoline complexes

Substituent	pK_{HOx}	$\log_{10} k_1 k_2$				
		Mn	Co	Ni	Cu	Zn
None	11·5	15·5	19·7	21·4	26·2	18·9
2-CH$_3$	11·7	14·0	18·5	17·8	23·8	18·7
4-CH$_3$	11·6	15·5	20·0	22·3	—	20·2

represent the acid strengths of the ligands and are approximately constant. One would therefore expect similar stabilities of their metal complexes. The lower stability which is in fact shown by the complexes in which a methyl group is present in the 2-position is attributable to the greater difficulty of chelation caused by the steric hindrance of this group. 4-Methyl-8-hydroxyquinoline behaves like the unsubstituted reagent because the methyl group is too far away from the nitrogen to affect sterically the process of complex formation.

THEORETICAL ASPECTS OF CO-ORDINATION CHEMISTRY

Early theories of co-ordination regarded this as the donation of an electron pair from the ligand to the metal atom or ion. Based on this approach, SIDGWICK suggested that the maximum co-ordination number of a metal is reached when it accepts sufficient electrons to raise its total electronic content to that of the next highest inert gas. This total is called the *Effective Atomic Number* (E.A.N.) of the metal. *Table 6.6* gives some examples of complexes

Table 6.6. Some complexes which obey the E.A.N. rule

Complex	Atomic number of metal	Oxidation state	Number of donated electrons	E.A.N.
$[Fe(CN)_6]^{4-}$	26	2	12	$24+12=36$
$[Co(NH_3)_6]^{3+}$	27	3	12	$24+12=36$
$Fe(CO)_5$	26	0	10	$26+10=36$
$Ni(CO)_4$	28	0	8	$28+8=3$

which obey this rule. The rule has some usefulness in that it permits the correlation of a large number of co-ordination compounds. It has, however, only qualitative significance because there are numerous exceptions. For example, although hexacyanoferrate (II), $[Fe(CN)_6]^{4-}$, follows the rule, hexacyanoferrate (III), $[Fe(CN)_6]^{3-}$, does not, having an E.A.N. of 35.

THE ELECTRONEUTRALITY PRINCIPLE

The simple theory implies that when co-ordination occurs and the metal accepts several pairs of electrons there must be an accumulation of negative charge on the metal atom. For instance, Co^{III} in $[Co(NH_3)_6]^{3+}$ gains a half-share in 12 electrons on co-ordination and so the charge on the cobalt changes from $+3$ to -3. Such a build-up of negative charge on the metal is most unlikely and PAULING expressed this in his *Electroneutrality Principle*. This states that complexes are stable when each atom carries only a small electric charge in the range -1 to $+1$. The principle requires that the bonds in $[Co(NH_3)_6]^{3+}$ have some ionic character: in other words the electron pair is not shared equally between the cobalt and nitrogen atoms but is attracted more strongly by the non-metal. This prevents the accumulation of negative charge on the cobalt and is in keeping with the greater electronegativity of nitrogen compared with cobalt.

For some complexes, the ionic character of the bonding will predominate and we can regard, for instance, the forces between the halide and metal in many fluoro-complexes as essentially electrostatic. This ionic approach to co-ordination chemistry will be described later after a discussion of the valence-bond approach, also due to PAULING.

VALENCE-BOND APPROACH

The stereochemistry of complex compounds is here treated in terms of hybridized orbitals. In the transition metals, with which we are largely concerned here, the *d* orbitals of the penultimate quantum shell are near in energy to the *s* and *p* orbitals of the outermost shell and various hybridizations are possible. The same types of hybridization can occur in the non-transition metals but here the *d*, *s* and *p* orbitals are all of the same principal quantum number.

Octahedral Co-ordination (d²sp³ *hybrids*)

This approach may be illustrated with reference to the complexes of Fe^{II}.

In the free Fe^{2+} ion, the electronic arrangement in the $3d$ orbitals is:

$$3d$$

1↓	1	1	1	1

Fe^{2+}

and the presence of four unpaired electrons is shown by the strong paramagnetism (p. 279) of this ion. In the presence of excess CN^-, the complex hexacyanoferrate (II) is formed. This is octahedral and contains no unpaired electrons.

To account for these observations, PAULING proposed a redistribution of electrons in the metal orbitals. The six electrons, originally in the five $3d$ orbitals, are paired off so that they occupy only three. The remaining two d orbitals are now available for hybridization with the vacant $4s$ and $4p$ orbitals. Each hybrid orbital accepts a pair of electrons donated by a cyanide ligand and the distribution of electrons in the complex becomes accordingly:

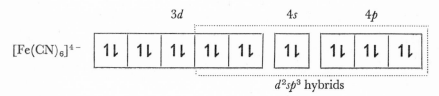

The hexacyanoferrate (III) ion has one electron less. It therefore has one unpaired electron in the $3d$ sub-shell and this agrees with its observed paramagnetism.

The situation is different for the hydrated ion $[Fe(H_2O)_6]^{2+}$. This has a paramagnetic moment corresponding to four unpaired electrons and evidently no rearrangement of electrons within the $3d$ sub-shell occurs when hydration of Fe^{2+} takes place. Here PAULING regards the d orbitals required for hybridization as of the same principal quantum number as the s and p orbitals involved. The arrangement of electrons is accordingly:

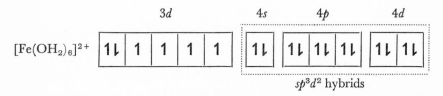

$[Fe(OH_2)_6]^{2+}$ is an example of a complex described variously as 'ionic', 'outer-orbital' or 'spin-free'. The number of unpaired electrons is the same as in the isolated ion. $[Fe(CN)_6]^{4-}$ is classed as a 'covalent', 'inner-orbital' or 'spin-paired' complex. In this example, the number of unpaired electrons is four less than in the isolated ion.

The differentiation into 'ionic' and 'covalent' complexes is misleading because covalent-bond formation is an essential feature of Pauling's approach to all co-ordination compounds. It is not generally used now for this reason and complexes are described in one of the other ways.

The knowledge of the magnetic moment (p. 280) of a complex can be of great value in deciding what type of complex is present and in his work PAULING made great use of this 'magnetic criterion of bond type'. The preceding examples of iron (II) complexes illustrate clearly how the distribution of electrons in the orbitals of the metal is deduced from the measured magnetic moment of the complex.

In some cases, Pauling's approach makes possible a logical explanation of the change in stability of the valency state of a metal which is associated with complex formation. For example, although simple Co^{III} salts have strong oxidizing properties, Co^{III} complexes have remarkable stability. In contrast, simple Co^{II} salts are quite stable but Co^{II} complexes are easily oxidized to Co^{III}. The arrangement of electrons in the $3d$ level for Co^{II} is:

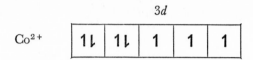

When complexing occurs with octahedral co-ordination of the metal, for instance with CN^-, the use of two of the $3d$ orbitals for d^2sp^3 hybridization requires that one $3d$ electron is promoted to the nearest vacant orbital of higher energy, namely the $5s$.

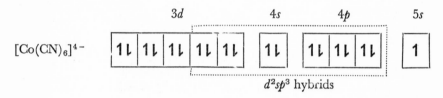

The electron is easily lost from this high level and so oxidation to $[Co(CN)_6]^{3-}$ readily occurs.

Tetrahedral and Square-Planar Co-ordination

Two shapes are found for 4 co-ordinated complexes of the transition metals; tetrahedral with sp^3 hybridization and square planar with dsp^2 hybridization. For example, the simple Pt^{II} ion has eight $5d$ electrons which are distributed in the available orbitals in the following manner:

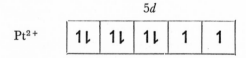

When complex formation occurs these electrons are rearranged to leave one d orbital vacant. When hybridized with the $6s$ and two of the $6p$ orbitals, this provides four equivalent orbitals, each of which contains a pair of electrons in the square-planar complexes of Pt^{II}.

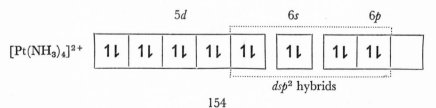

PAULING was able to predict correctly that certain diamagnetic nickel (II) complexes must be square planar, even before their structures were experimentally determined. The distribution of electrons in the outer orbitals of Ni^{II} before and after co-ordination can be represented as:

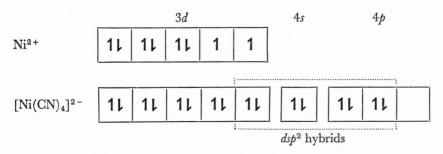

When the complete x-ray analysis of the compound $Na_2Ni(CN)_4.3H_2O$ was carried out later, the square planar arrangement of the four cyanides around the nickel was demonstrated. The complex of nickel with dimethylglyoxime (XXIV) is another example of the planar distribution around Ni^{II}. However, it has been observed that certain paramagnetic complexes of Ni^{II}, such as $[Ni(NH_3)_4]^{2+}$ and $[NiCl_4]^{2-}$, are tetrahedral and Pauling's theory cannot account for these.

When nickel is zerovalent, the tetrahedral shape of its complexes can be satisfactorily explained:

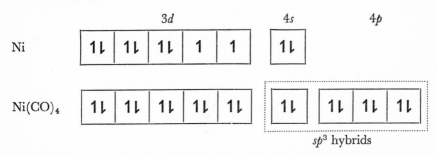

The formation of four single covalent bonds from the carbon atoms to the nickel would result in a large negative charge on the metal. PAULING suggested that, in such a situation, double bonding takes place with the back-donation of d electrons from the metal to the ligand to such an extent that the electroneutrality principle is obeyed. X-ray studies have shown that the nickel–carbon interatomic distance is distinctly shorter than the sum of the covalent radii of the two atoms. This is experimental support of Pauling's contention that the electronic structure of nickel tetracarbonyl is best described in terms of a resonance hybrid of various possible forms with important contributions from double-bonded structures.

Cu^{II}, with one more electron than Ni^{II}, also forms planar complexes with paramagnetic moments corresponding with the presence of one unpaired electron. Pauling's magnetic criterion is of no help here in deciding between

155

dsp^2 and sp^3 hybridization because each of these would leave the complex ion with one odd electron either in a $4p$ or a $3d$ orbital. The x-ray analysis of Cu^{II} complexes has provided unambiguous evidence for their planarity and the electronic arrangement in terms of hybrid orbitals is therefore:

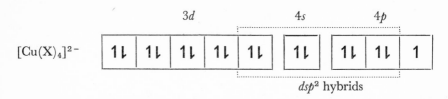

where X is an anionic ligand such as halide ion.

Cu^I forms tetrahedral 4 co-ordinated complexes. The electronic distribution therein is:

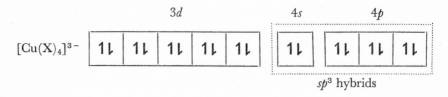

According to Pauling's theory, the stereochemistry of metal complexes is determined by the hybridized orbitals used in bond formation. In many cases, a comparison of the magnetic moment of the complex with that of the free metal ion indicates clearly the orbital distribution of the electrons which is consistent with the shape of the complex determined by x-ray analysis. The accumulation of negative charge on the metal is reduced by (i) the partial ionic character of the metal–ligand bonds and/or (ii) the formation of multiple bonds with back-donation of metal d electrons to the ligand.

Emphasis on the covalent nature of the bonds does impose certain limitations on the theory. Although it provides a satisfying pictorial representation of co-ordination compounds based on the concept of orbital hybridization, quantitative interpretations are not possible. For example, the striking colour changes frequently associated with complex formation are evidently due to the transitions of d electrons between different energy levels. Complex formation must alter the electronic energies significantly but the theory gives no information about this.

Another unsatisfactory feature is that the theory sometimes requires the promotion of one electron to a vacant orbital of higher energy by the intake of an amount of energy which is unrealistically large. For instance, in accounting for the square planarity of Cu^{II} complexes the promotion of a $3d$ electron to a $4p$ energy level is postulated to allow for the dsp^2 hybridization to occur. This process requires 340 kcal in the free Cu^{II} ion and probably a large fraction of this in the complex. It is not easy to see where this energy can come from and one would also expect, by analogy with the explanation for the stability of Cn^{III} complexes, that Cu^{II} complexes would lose this unpaired $4p$ electron and be readily oxidized to Cu^{III}. Although a number of Cu^{III} compounds are

156

known, for example K_3CuF_6, their stabilities are certainly not comparable with those of Cu^{II} compounds.

CRYSTAL FIELD THEORY

This is an alternative approach to the theoretical interpretation of the properties of complexes. It regards the metal ion as situated in an electrostatic field caused by surrounding molecules or ions. This theory, first developed by BETHE and by VAN VLECK, considers that the ligands, which are either negative ions or molecules containing at least one atom carrying a lone pair of electrons oriented towards the metal ion, produce a field approximately equivalent to that of a set of negative point charges. In the case of transition metal ions, this electrical field alters the energies of the d electrons and the energy changes have an important bearing on many of the properties of the complex formed.

The angular dependence of the wave functions for d electrons has been illustrated earlier (p. 32) and it is apparent that although these electrons are degenerate (that is, have the same energy), their wave functions are not of the same shape in an isolated atom or ion. Thus the d_{z^2} and $d_{x^2-y^2}$ orbitals have substantial amplitudes along the three co-ordinate axes whereas d_{xy}, d_{yz} and d_{xz} have maximum charge densities along another set of three axes, inclined at 45° to the first set.

In a complex, the energies of d electrons will be altered by the presence of the ligands. For example, consider the effect on the d electrons of ligands approaching along the x, y and z axes in octahedral co-ordination. When a ligand approaches along the x or y axis the negative charge repels electrons in all the metal d orbitals, but the effect is greater on one in the $d_{x^2-y^2}$ than one in the d_{xy} orbital. As a result the energy of both is increased, that of the $d_{x^2-y^2}$ orbital by a larger amount than the d_{xy} orbital. d_{xz} and d_{yz} have the same orientation relative to the ligands in the xz and yz planes as d_{xy} has to the ligands in the xy plane. These three orbitals are degenerate in the complex. The d_{z^2} orbital will be strongly affected by a ligand which approaches along the z axis and calculations show, in fact, that this orbital has the same energy as $d_{x^2-y^2}$.

Therefore, we find that for octahedral co-ordination the five d orbitals are split into two sets, d_{z^2} and $d_{x^2-y^2}$ (designated d_γ) and d_{xy}, d_{xz} and d_{yz} (designated d_ε). This is illustrated in *Figure 6.1(a)*. It is of interest to note here that if quite different directions had been chosen for the five d orbitals, that is, so that the ligands no longer approach along the main co-ordinate axes in octahedral co-ordination, the theory predicts the same splitting into two sets of orbitals.

In *Figure 6.1*, Δ is the energy difference between the two levels and the magnitude of Δ is determined by the field strength of the ligand. Δ can be found from measurements on the absorption spectra of the complexed ions because in many cases an absorption band can be definitely related to an electronic transition between two d orbitals of different energies. For example, the hydrated titanium (III) ion, $[Ti(H_2O)_6]^{3+}$, is coloured violet due to absorption in the visible region at 5000 Å (20,000 cm^{-1}). The metal has one d electron, located in a d_ε orbital, and the simplest explanation of the observed absorption band is that this is associated with a transition of this electron to the d_γ orbital of higher energy. This suggests that Δ for this ion is 20,000 cm^{-1}

6*

($\sim$60 kcal). From this type of empirical data, it has been concluded that Δ is in the range 7500 to 12,500 cm^{-1} for the divalent ions of the first transition series and between 14,000 and 21,000 cm^{-1} for the corresponding hydrated trivalent ions.

When more than one d electron is present in an octahedrally co-ordinated

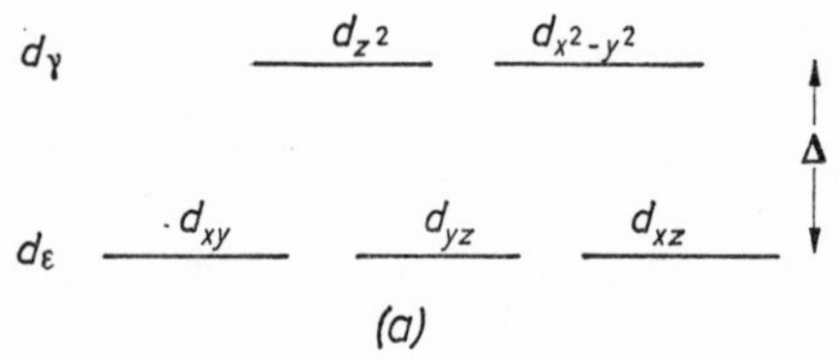

d_γ d_{z^2} $d_{x^2-y^2}$

d_ε $\cdot d_{xy}$ d_{yz} d_{xz} $\updownarrow \Delta$

(a)

Figure 6.1(a). Orbital splitting in octahedral ligand field

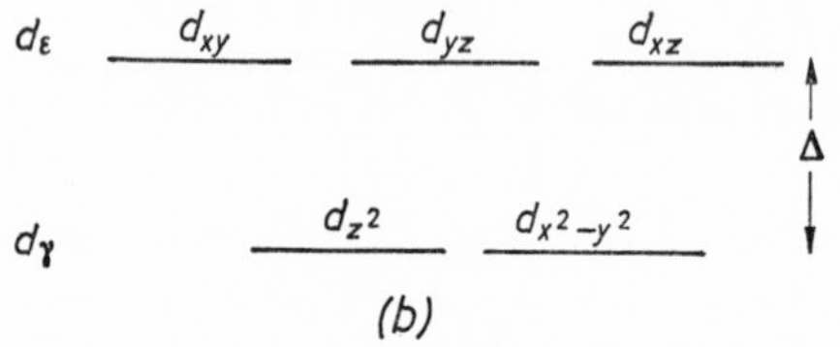

d_ε d_{xy} d_{yz} d_{xz}

d_γ d_{z^2} $d_{x^2-y^2}$ $\updownarrow \Delta$

(b)

Figure 6.1(b). Orbital splitting in tetrahedral ligand field

Increasing ligand field $\longrightarrow$

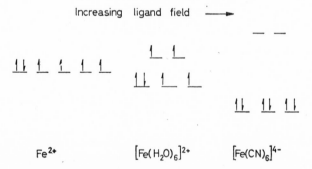

Fe^{2+} $[Fe(H_2O)_6]^{2+}$ $[Fe(CN)_6]^{4-}$

Figure 6.2. The distribution of d electrons in the Fe^{2+} ion in the free state and when subjected to an increasing ligand field

metal ion, the electronic distribution between the available orbitals is determined by the relative importance of two opposing tendencies. The electrons tend to enter the d_ε orbitals of lower energy but also, as expressed in Hund's rule of maximum multiplicity (p. 34), tend to enter different orbitals with their spins parallel.

With 2 or 3 d electrons, there is no conflict between these tendencies since the electrons can be placed in different d_ε orbitals with parallel spins. With 4 to 7 d electrons, two alternative arrangements are possible (*Table 6.7*);

either $\varDelta$ is large enough to force the electrons to pair up and fill the d_ε orbitals (strong ligand field), or $\varDelta$ is small and the maximum number of unpaired electrons is found (weak ligand field). With more than 7 electrons, there is again only one possible arrangement. As an illustration of the different configurations for a d^6 metal ion, we may cite the case of the complexes of iron (II). *Figure 6.2* shows the electronic distributions in the free ion, in $[Fe(H_2O)_6]^{2+}$ (weak ligand field), and in $[Fe(CN)_6]^{4-}$ (strong ligand field). This description may be compared with that of PAULING (p. 153), the first

Table 6.7. Electron distribution in octahedral complexes

Number of d electrons	Arrangement in weak ligand field		Number of unpaired electrons
	d_ε	d_γ	
1	1		1
2	1 1		2
3	1 1 1		3
4	1 1 1	1	4
5	1 1 1	1 1	5
6	1↓ 1 1	1 1	4
7	1↓ 1↓ 1	1 1	3
8	1↓ 1↓ 1↓	1 1	2
9	1↓ 1↓ 1↓	1↓ 1	1

Number of d electrons	Arrangement in strong ligand field		Number of unpaired electrons
	d_ε	d_γ	
1	1		1
2	1 1		2
3	1 1 1		3
4	1↓ 1 1		2
5	1↓ 1↓ 1		1
6	1↓ 1↓ 1↓		0
7	1↓ 1↓ 1↓	1	1
8	1↓ 1↓ 1↓	1 1	2
9	1↓ 1↓ 1↓	1↓ 1	1

being an electrostatic, the second a covalent view of the bonding. These two lines of approach are not mutually exclusive and both are of value when discussing the properties of complexes. In contrast to the valence-bond approach of PAULING, crystal-field theory has been of great value in quantitative interpretations, in particular of the absorption spectra of complexes of the first transition series.

The theory has been extended to include other situations beside octahedral co-ordination. *Figure 6.1(b)* shows the orbital splitting for tetrahedral co-ordination. Significant features here are that the d_{xy}, d_{xz} and d_{yz} set is the one of higher energy and the $d_{x^2-y^2}$ and d_{z^2} are of lower energy, and that the magnitude of the splitting is less than for octahedral co-ordination (the number of ligands is reduced from 6 to 4). *Table 6.8* shows how the d electrons are distributed among available orbitals for weak and strong ligand fields respectively.

One important consequence of the electrostatic approach is that in certain cases a regular octahedral environment does not appear to be the most stable for 6 co-ordination. This point may be illustrated by reference to Cu^{II} complexes. The Cu^{2+} ion contains 9 d electrons, 6 situated in the three d_ε orbitals and the remaining 3 in the two d_y orbitals. The electronic distribution around the nucleus is therefore not symmetrical because there is one orbital

Table 6.8. Electron distribution in tetrahedral complexes

Number of d electrons	Arrangement in weak ligand field		Number of unpaired electrons
	d_y	d_ε	
1	↑ ↑		1
2	↑ ↑		2
3	↑ ↑	↑	3
4	↑ ↑	↑ ↑	4
5	↑ ↑	↑ ↑ ↑	5
6	↑↓ ↑	↑ ↑ ↑	4
7	↑↓ ↑↓	↑ ↑ ↑	3
8	↑↓ ↑↓	↑↓ ↑ ↑	2
9	↑↓ ↑↓	↑↓ ↑↓ ↑	1

Number of d electrons	Arrangement in strong ligand field		Number of unpaired electrons
	d_y	d_ε	
1	↑		1
2	↑ ↑		2
3	↑↓ ↑		1
4	↑↓ ↑↓		0
5	↑↓ ↑↓	↑	1
6	↑↓ ↑↓	↑ ↑	2
7	↑↓ ↑↓	↑ ↑ ↑	3
8	↑↓ ↑↓	↑↓ ↑ ↑	2
9	↑↓ ↑↓	↑↓ ↑↓ ↑	1

which is only half-filled (either the $d_{x^2-y^2}$ or the d_{z^2}). If it is the $d_{x^2-y^2}$, then the nucleus of the metal ion is less screened along the x and y axes than along the z axis. As a result, if the ligands are considered to be situated at the corners of a perfectly regular octahedron, those in the xy plane are attracted by a larger nuclear charge than those along the z axis. This unsymmetrical attraction leads to a distortion of the octahedron with four short bonds, co-planar with the metal atom, and two longer ones, perpendicular to this plane. If it is the d_{z^2} orbital which contains one electron, then an exactly opposite distortion would be predicted, that is, the 6 ligands are bound by two short and four longer bonds to the metal. The simple theory does not indicate which of the two distortions is favoured energetically. The first appears to occur for Cu^{II}; thus the x-ray analysis of $CuBr_2$ shows four bromines located at 2·40 Å from the copper and a further two neighbours at 3·18 Å; in $CuCl_2$ there are four chlorines at a distance of 2·30 Å and two more at 2·95 Å. Hence, the 'square planarity' of Cu^{II} complexes emerges as a distortion of octahedral symmetry caused by an unsymmetrical electronic distribution on the metal. This may be contrasted with Pauling's description in terms of dsp^2 hybridized orbitals.

THE MOLECULAR-ORBITAL AND LIGAND-FIELD THEORIES

The electronic description of simple covalent molecules in terms of molecular orbitals has been referred to earlier (p. 57). Essentially, molecular-orbital theory assigns electrons to orbitals in order of increasing energy in a similar way to the distribution of electrons in isolated atoms. When this theory is applied to transition-metal complexes, the metal–ligand interaction is expressed in terms of σ- and π-bonds. For example, when the metal is in a low or zero valent state, then the formation of a number of σ-bonds, in which the participating electrons are those donated by the ligand, results in a build-up of negative charge on the central atom. This is reduced by π-bonding involving the electrons originally in the metal d orbitals. Both types of bonds are present in a compound such as $Ni(CO)_4$.

When the crystal-field splitting of d energy levels is considered in conjunction with σ- and π-bonding, this constitutes the more comprehensive ligand-field theory of complexes. This appears to be the best theory so far developed although the mathematical difficulties exclude any treatment of it here.

METAL CARBONYLS AND RELATED COMPOUNDS

The carbonyls are molecular co-ordination compounds formed between metals and carbon monoxide. Two types are known: mononuclear, containing one metal atom per molecule and polynuclear, containing more than one metal atom per molecule. In the first type of carbonyl the metal shows a zero oxidation state, that is, co-ordination occurs between the metal atom and the carbon monoxide ligand. In the second type, direct metal–metal bonds appear to be formed. This is a sufficiently rare phenomenon in chemistry as to be of special note.

Iron pentacarbonyl, $Fe(CO)_5$, and nickel tetracarbonyl, $Ni(CO)_4$, were originally prepared by MOND in 1890 by direct reaction between carbon monoxide gas and the finely divided metal. The formation of the nickel compound is the basis of the Mond process for nickel refining. Interaction between the impure metal and CO at 60°C produces $Ni(CO)_4$; other metals do not form carbonyls under these conditions (atmospheric pressure). Pure nickel is obtained by contacting $Ni(CO)_4$ vapour with nickel pellets at 180°C, the compound being thermally unstable at this temperature:

$$Ni + 4CO \rightleftharpoons Ni(CO)_4$$

Carbonyls of transition metals other than iron and nickel are obtained by the reduction of compounds of the metal in a suitable solvent under high CO pressure. Often a neutral complex in an organic solvent is used: for example, tris(acetylacetonato)chromium (III), dissolved in pyridine, is reduced by

161

Zn or Mg under a pressure of 100–300 atmospheres of CO to give an 82 per cent yield of chromium hexacarbonyl, $Cr(CO)_6$. An organometallic compound, such as a Grignard reagent, may be used in place of the metal as a reducing agent.

The carbonyls of the transition metals are listed in *Table 6.9*. $Ni(CO)_4$, $Fe(CO)_5$, $Ru(CO)_5$ and $Os(CO)_5$ are liquid at ordinary temperatures: the remaining carbonyls are low-melting, readily sublimed solids. All are typical covalent compounds and show solubility in non-polar solvents.

Table 6.9. The carbonyls of the transition metals

Group	V	VI	VII	VIII		
	$V(CO)_6$	$Cr(CO)_6$	$Mn_2(CO)_{10}$	$Fe(CO)_5$	$Co_2(CO)_8$	$Ni(CO)_4$
				$Fe_2(CO)_9$	$Co_4(CO)_{12}$	
				$Fe_3(CO)_{12}$		
		$Mo(CO)_6$		$Ru(CO)_5$	$[Rh(CO)_4]_n$	
				$Ru_2(CO)_9$	$[Rh(CO)_3]_n$	
				$Ru_3(CO)_{12}$	$[Rh_4(CO)_{11}]_n$	
		$W(CO)_6$	$[Re(CO)_5]_n$	$Os(CO)_5$	$[Ir(CO)_4]_n$	
				$Os_2(CO)_9$	$[Ir(CO)_3]_n$	

The carbonyls are decomposed eventually by heat to the metal and CO. Those of Group VI are more stable than those of the other groups. Polynuclear carbonyls are often formed as intermediates in the decomposition of the mononuclear compounds. For example:

$$6Fe(CO)_5 \xrightarrow[\text{light}]{\text{Exposure to}} 3Fe_2(CO)_9 + 3CO$$

$$\searrow 60°C$$

$$Fe_3(CO)_{12} + 3Fe(CO)_5$$

With the exception of vanadium hexacarbonyl, all carbonyls are diamagnetic. $V(CO)_6$ is monomeric in the solid state and is paramagnetic with one unpaired electron.

The mononuclear carbonyls of Cr, Fe and Ni obey the effective atomic number rule. The metal atom, in each compound, attains a krypton configuration of 36 electrons if it assumed that each CO molecule donates two electrons to the zerovalent metal. $V(CO)_6$ is easily reduced to the anion, $[V(CO)_6]^-$, which is isoelectronic with $Cr(CO)_6$. The stereochemistry of the molecules has been established: $V(CO)_6$ and $Cr(CO)_6$, octahedral; $Fe(CO)_5$, trigonal bipyramid; $Ni(CO)_4$, tetrahedral.

The diamagnetism of the polynuclear carbonyls is accounted for on the assumption that metal–metal bonds are formed. For instance, crystallographic studies of iron enneacarbonyl, $Fe_2(CO)_9$, have shown that the two iron atoms are joined by three ketonic ($>C=O$) bridges; the other six CO groups are joined three to each iron atom by co-ordinate bonds; the Fe—Fe distance of 2·46 Å is so small as to suggest chemical bonding between the two atoms. The structure is therefore as illustrated in formula (XXXII). Metal–metal bonding is also evident in $Mn_2(CO)_{10}$, formula (XXXIII), although

162

bridging ketonic groups are absent here. Intermetallic bonds also occur in the more complex carbonyls such as $Fe_3(CO)_{12}$ and $Co_4(CO)_{12}$.

One striking feature of carbonyl chemistry is the facility with which the CO groups can be replaced by other ligand groups. For example, $Fe_2(CO)_9$ and $Co_2(CO)_8$ react with nitric oxide to form mixed metal carbonyl nitrosyls, $Fe(CO)_2(NO)_2$ and $Co(CO)_3(NO)$ respectively. The manganese compound $Mn(CO)(NO)_3$ has recently been prepared. Chemically these compounds resemble the parent carbonyls, although the nitrosyl group is more firmly attached to the metal than is the carbonyl group. The formulae of these

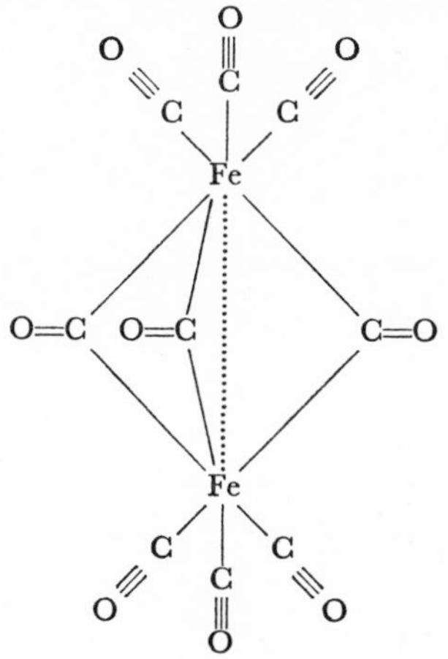

(XXXII)

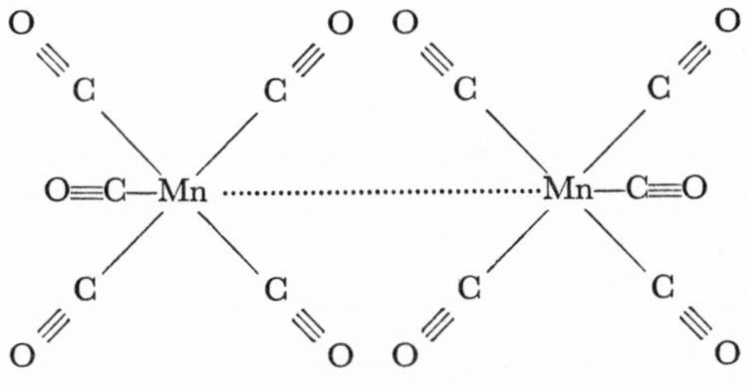

(XXXIII)

compounds may be rationalized by regarding NO as contributing 3 electrons to the bonding. It loses one to the metal in forming the nitrosyl ion, NO^+; this is isoelectronic with the CO molecule and co-ordinates with a metal by means of the lone pair on the nitrogen. It is interesting to note that a related series of compounds is known in which the E.A.N. of the metal is always 36: $Ni(CO)_4$, $Co(CO)_3(NO)$, $Fe(CO)_2(NO)_2$ and $Mn(CO)(NO)_3$. The last member of the series would be $Cr(NO)_4$ but this has not so far been prepared.

The cyanide ion, CN^-, is also isoelectronic with carbon monoxide and NO^+ and it is not surprising that in complex ions such as $[Fe(CN)_6]^{4-}$ the CN^- can be partly replaced by either of these groups. Thus the reaction between CO and a solution containing $[Fe(CN)_6]^{4-}$ produces a salt of carbonylferrocyanic acid, for example, $K_3[Fe(CN)_5(CO)]$. Replacement of one cyanide ion by a nitrosyl ion produces the 'nitroprusside' ion, $[Fe(CN)_5(NO)]^{2-}$. The sodium salt is a well-known analytical reagent for sulphides and active methylene groups in organic compounds. In the three anions $[Fe(CN)_6]^{4-}$, $[Fe(CN)_5(CO)]^{3-}$ and $[Fe(CN)_5(NO)]^{2-}$, the electronic configuration of the iron (II) is exactly the same. The charge on the complex decreases as the negative ion is replaced successively by a neutral molecule and then by a positive ion.

The metal carbonyl hydrides are obtained when the parent metal carbonyl reacts with either alcoholic alkali or sodium in liquid ammonia. In both cases, the alkali metal salt is first made and the hydride itself produced on hydrolysis:

$$Fe(CO)_5 + 4KOH \longrightarrow Fe(CO)_4K_2 + K_2CO_3 + 2H_2O$$

$$Fe(CO)_5 + 2Na \longrightarrow Na_2Fe(CO)_4 + CO$$

The three best-defined carbonyl hydrides are: $MnH(CO)_5$, $FeH_2(CO)_4$ and $CoH(CO)_4$. They are volatile, unstable liquids, and are notable for their strong reducing action and the acid character of the hydrogen atoms. Similar compounds are also known for the heavier transition metals. The most puzzling feature of the molecules is the position and mode of bonding of the hydrogen atom(s). Thus in the series $Ni(CO)_4$, $CoH(CO)_4$ and $FeH_2(CO)_4$, tetrahedral co-ordination of the metal by CO is preserved and the introduction of hydrogen appears to cause no distortion. The most recent experimental evidence suggests that the hydrogen atom is embedded in the molecule and is covalently bound directly to the metal.

COMPLEXES BETWEEN METALS AND UNSATURATED HYDROCARBONS

The first compound of an unsaturated hydrocarbon with a metal, $PtCl_2 . C_2H_4$, was prepared by the Danish chemist ZEISE and was reported in the chemical literature as early as 1827. This compound may be prepared by reaction between a tetrachloroplatinate (II), $[PtCl_4]^{2-}$, and ethylene in aqueous solution, followed by extraction with ether. The reaction proceeds with a step-wise replacement of chloride by olefin:

$$[PtCl_4]^{2-} \longrightarrow [PtCl_3(C_2H_4)]^- \longrightarrow [PtCl_2(C_2H_4)]_2^0$$
(the anion of Zeise's salt)

The neutral compound is a dimer as shown by freezing point depression measurements in benzene and has a bridged structure with *trans*-arrangement of the two ethylene molecules:

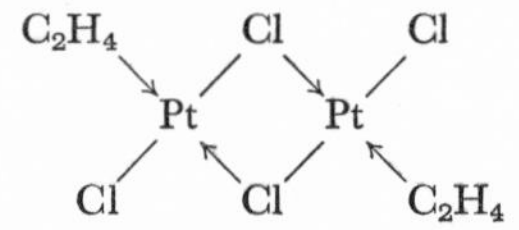

Other unsaturated hydrocarbons, for example acetylene, may be used instead of ethylene but the ability to form such complexes appears to be

164

restricted to a limited group of transition metal ions: Rh^I, Ir^{II}, Pd^{II}, Pt^{II}, Cu^I, Ag^I and Hg^{II}. The last three ions have their full complement of ten d electrons so evidently empty d orbitals on the metal are not essential for binding the olefin molecules.

X-ray analysis has shown that in the ion $PtCl_3(C_2H_4)^-$, the two carbon atoms are equidistant from and on one side of the metal (**XXXIV**). In 1953, CHATT and DUNCANSON suggested that the bonding involves co-ordination of

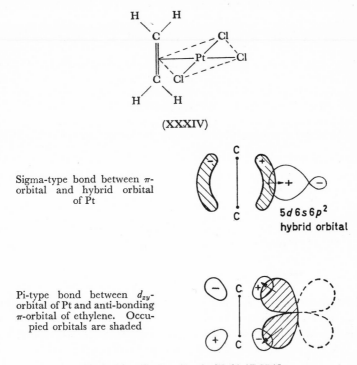

(**XXXIV**)

Sigma-type bond between π-orbital and hybrid orbital of Pt

$5d\,6s\,6p^2$
hybrid orbital

Pi-type bond between d_{xy}-orbital of Pt and anti-bonding π-orbital of ethylene. Occupied orbitals are shaded

Figure 6.3. The bonding in $[PtCl_3(C_2H_4)]^-$

the two π-electrons of the ethylene double bond. The π-orbital of ethylene has, in fact, the same symmetry, with respect to the metal–ligand bond, as a σ-orbital on a simple ligand. A co-ordinate bond of σ symmetry results. These workers also proposed that the strength of the bond is reinforced by back co-ordination of non-bonding d electrons of the platinum atom to the vacant (antibonding) π-orbitals of the ethylene molecule. The orbitals used in the bonding are illustrated in *Figure 6.3*.

In the last ten years, interest in this type of compound has greatly intensified, following the discovery of complexes between transition metals and cyclopentadiene.

The Metal Cyclopentadienyls and Related Compounds

The discovery that finely divided iron can react with cyclopentadiene to form an organometallic compound of unusual stability was made in 1951. This compound, dicyclopentadienyl iron, $Fe(C_5H_5)_2$, commonly known as ferrocene, can also be made by reaction between iron (II) chloride and cyclopentadienyl magnesium bromide, C_5H_5MgBr, in an organic solvent:

$$2C_5H_5MgBr + FeCl_2 = (C_5H_5)_2Fe + MgBr_2 + MgCl_2$$

Ferrocene is an orange crystalline solid, m.p. 173°C, which is insoluble in water but readily soluble in organic solvents. It is remarkably stable to heat and does not decompose below 470°C.

The cyclopentadienyl derivatives of many other transition metals are now known. For example, the dicyclopentadienyls of Co, Ni, Cr and V have all been synthesized and found to be isomorphous with ferrocene (crystallizing in the monoclinic system).

Structural investigations have shown that these compounds have a 'sandwich' structure in which the metal atom lies between two planar C_5H_5 rings and is equidistant from all ten carbon atoms. In ferrocene itself, the iron atom lies at the centre of an antiprismatic 'double-cone' structure (XXXV).

It was soon remarked that the hydrogen atoms of the C_5H_5 rings in ferrocene can be replaced by other groups in reactions similar to those used for effecting

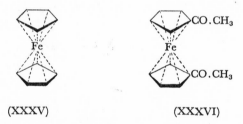

(XXXV)   (XXXVI)

aromatic substitutions. For example, ferrocene reacts with acetyl chloride in the presence of aluminium chloride to form diacetyl ferrocene (XXXVI). Condensation with aldehydes and reactions with diazonium compounds also support the view that the hydrocarbon rings in ferrocene have 'aromatic character'. This behaviour strongly suggests that each ring has a non-localized sextet of electrons. (The C_5H_5 group has 5 non-localized electrons and by gaining one electron from the iron atom is converted to $C_5H_5^-$.)

E. O. FISCHER has proposed that the bonding in ferrocene involves the donation of three pairs of electrons from each $C_5H_5^-$ ring to the iron (II) ion. Accordingly, the metal in ferrocene has the krypton configuration and so the electronic distribution is exactly the same as in the valence-bond description of $[Fe(CN)_6]^{4-}$ (p. 153). However, the aromatic substitution reactions of ferrocene imply a high electron availability in each ring and this is incompatible with the involvement of 6 electrons in the bonding to the metal. An alternative proposal by DUNITZ and ORGEL is that the iron is joined by essentially two single covalent bonds to the two cyclopentadienyl rings. The two possible electronic configurations are given in *Figure 6.4*.

The direct action of cyclopentadiene on the metal is effective only for the preparation of ferrocene. A more general method is that based on the reaction (in benzene or ether) of the Grignard reagent cyclopentadienyl magnesium bromide with an anhydrous halide of the metal or one of its co-ordination compounds, for example the acetylacetonato complex. This method gives a satisfactory preparation of $Ni(C_5H_5)_2$ and $V(C_5H_5)_2$, but in the case of cobalt, the cobalticinium ion, $[Co(C_5H_5)_2]^+$, is obtained. This is isoelectronic with ferrocene and salts containing this anion strongly resist oxidation. It can, however, be reduced to cobaltocene, $Co(C_5H_5)_2$, by the powerful reducing

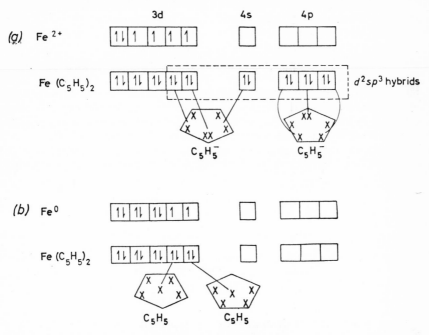

Figure 6.4. Alternative formulations of the bonding in ferrocene due to (*a*) FISCHER (*b*) DUNITZ and ORGEL

Table 6.10. Metal complexes of cyclopentadiene

Formula	Metals
$M(C_5H_5)$	Li, Na, K, Rb, Cs, Tl and In
$M(C_5H_5)_2$	Be, Mg, Ca, Zn, Hg, Ti, V, Cr, Mn, Fe, Co, Ni, Sn, Pb, Ru and Os
$M(C_5H_5)_3$	Sc, Ga, Y, In, Sb, Bi and the rare earths
Cations such as $Zr^{IV}(C_5H_5)_2^{2+}$, $Co^{III}(C_5H_5)_2^+$ and $Nb^V(C_5H_5)_2^{3+}$	Transition metals in high valency states

agent lithium aluminium hydride. Cobaltocene is a paramagnetic complex which is very sensitive to atmospheric oxidation to $Co(C_5H_5)_2^+$. In this sense, cobaltocene and the cobalticinium ion resemble Co^{II} and Co^{III} complexes respectively (p. 154).

The metal cyclopentadienyls are summarized in *Table 6.10*. For completeness, the compounds with non-transition metals are included. Those which

167

contain electropositive metals such as the alkalis and alkaline earths are typically salt-like. For instance, cyclopentadienyl potassium, KC_5H_5, first prepared by THIELE in 1901 by the action of the metal on a solution of cyclopentadiene in benzene, is a colourless salt which decomposes rapidly on exposure to air. It ionizes in polar solvents and complete hydrolysis occurs with water:

$$KC_5H_5 + H_2O = KOH + C_5H_6$$

Its general properties indicate that this compound is ionic, $K^+C_5H_5^-$. Compounds of weakly electropositive metals such as Hg, Sn, Pb and Bi are intermediate in properties between the salt-like cyclopentadienyls of the alkali metals and the covalent complexes of the transition metals. Thus, $Sn(C_5H_5)_2$ is a colourless compound which is unstable in air, moderately soluble in benzene and ether, unaffected by cold water but decomposed by acids to cyclopentadiene. It has been suggested that this type of compound contains a relatively weak σ-bond between the metal and one carbon atom of the C_5H_5 ring.

(XXXVII)

Many more complex derivatives of the transition metal cyclopentadienyls have been prepared in which the cyclopentadiene is partly replaced by other ligands such as CO, NO and CN^-, but details of these are outside the scope of the present treatment.

It is very interesting to note that some complexes have also been made which contain 6-membered rings. For example in 1955 dibenzene chromium, $Cr(C_6H_6)_2$, was synthesized by heating anhydrous chromic chloride, aluminium chloride, aluminium and benzene in an autoclave to 180°C. This produced the $[Cr(C_6H_6)_2]^+$ ion:

$$3CrCl_3 + 2Al + AlCl_3 + 6C_6H_6 = 3[Cr(C_6H_6)_2]^+AlCl_4^-$$

Reduction with sodium dithionite gave dibenzene chromium as a brown-black diamagnetic solid of m.p. 284°C. This compound has a sandwich structure (XXXVII), analogous to that of ferrocene. On the hypothesis that each benzene ring contributes 6 electrons to the electronic shells of the chromium atom (atomic number 24), the metal in this complex has an effective atomic number of 36 (krypton configuration).

In place of benzene itself, substituted benzenes such as mesitylene have been used and other complexes are known which contain the unsaturated hydrocarbon rings—cyclobutadiene, C_4H_4; cycloheptatrienyl, C_7H_7; and cycloöctatetraene, C_8H_8.

SUGGESTED REFERENCES FOR FURTHER READING

BELCHER, R., and NUTTEN, A. J. *Quantitative Inorganic Analysis—a Laboratory Manual*, 2nd edn, Butterworths, London, 1960.

FLASCHKA, H. *EDTA Titrations—an Introduction to Theory and Practice*, Pergamon Press, Oxford, 1959.

GRADDON, D. P. *Introduction to Co-ordination Chemistry*, Pergamon Press, Oxford, 1961.

MARTELL, A. E., and CALVIN, M. *The Chemistry of the Metal Chelates*, Prentice-Hall, New York, 1952.

ORGEL, L. *An Introduction to Transition Metal Chemistry—Ligand-Field Theory*, Methuen, London, 1960.

PAULSON, P. L. 'Ferrocene and related compounds' *Quart. Rev. chem. Soc., Lond.*, 3 (1949) 263.

7

THE DISTRIBUTION AND EXTRACTION OF THE CHEMICAL ELEMENTS

DISTRIBUTION

OUR present knowledge of the terrestrial distribution of the elements is due largely to the pioneering work of V. M. GOLDSCHMIDT. Using the techniques of emission and x-ray spectroscopy, he obtained data on the relative abundance of the elements in a wide range of rocks, minerals, *etc.* He also stated for the first time the theoretical principles which determine the segregation of the elements.

In the cooling of the earth, the initial gaseous matter condensed to a liquid, then solidification took place forming igneous rocks and finally the constituents of rocks were selectively extracted into aqueous solution by weathering processes with the formation of sedimentary rocks and sea-water. Major separations or partings of the elements occurred at each of these three changes.

The First Parting of the Elements

GOLDSCHMIDT suggested that in the process of liquefaction, separation occurred into a metallic core, an intermediate sulphidic zone, a siliceous crust and an atmosphere. A similar separation of three largely immiscible liquid phases occurs in many metallurgical operations. He classified the elements according to their preferential concentration in one of these phases:

Metallic Core (Siderophil)—contains mainly the transition metals Mn, Fe, Co, Ni, Mo, Ru, Rh, Pd, Re, Os, Ir, Pt, Au.

Sulphidic Zone (Chalcophil)—contains the B sub-group elements Cu, Ag, Zn, Cd, Hg, Ga, In, Tl, Ge, Sn, Pb, As, Sb, Bi, P, S, Se, Te.

Siliceous Crust (Lithophil)—comprises the A sub-group elements, many of which give ions of the inert-gas type—the alkali metals, the alkaline earths, Be, Al, the rare earths, Ti, V, Cr, Zr, Nb, Mo, Hf, Ta, W. Also found are the halogens, C, Si, and combined oxygen and nitrogen.

Atmosphere (Atmophil)—O, N, C, the inert gases.

Many elements will be present in more than one phase but an important consequence of Goldschmidt's classification is that the lithophil elements appear to be abundant simply because of their accessibility. The relative abundance of the elements in the earth's crust is summarized in *Table 7.1*.

A more recent view of the earth's evolution, put forward by two Swiss workers W. KUHN and A. RITTMANN, suggests that the core consists of undifferentiated solar material and contains up to 30 per cent hydrogen. This alternative theory does not invalidate Goldschmidt's work on the preferential concentration or elimination of elements in the earth's crust.

Geophysical evidence suggests that the outer crust of the earth is only a thin

170

skin of some 10 to 20 miles in thickness.   Below this skin lies the mantle which is believed to extend about half way to the centre of the earth.   It encloses the core, the fluid nature of which has been demonstrated by a study of earthquake waves.   The boundary between the mantle and the assorted surface rocks constitutes the Mohorovicic discontinuity or 'Moho'.   The depth of the Moho can be determined by using artificial earthquake waves generated by explosions, since there is a sudden change in the velocity of compressional seismic

Table 7.1. *The relative abundance of the elements*

Element	Abundance (%)	Element	Abundance (%)
O	49·6	K	2·4
Si	25·8	Mg	1·9
Al	7·4	H	0·9
Fe	4·6	Ti	0·6
Ca	3·4	Cl	0·2
Na	2·6	P	0·1

Together, these elements constitute 99·5% of the earth's crust and the remaining elements total 0·5%

waves at this point.   The Moho is about thirty miles deep under land but less than ten miles below the sea surface in deep parts of the ocean.   Attempts are now being made, such as 'Operation Mohole' of the U.S. Navy, to reach the Moho by drilling through the earth's crust at a carefully selected site on the sea-bed.   It is thereby hoped to determine the chemical composition of the mantle and so to gain further knowledge of the earth's interior.

The Second Parting of the Elements

In the solidification of the earth's crust, the igneous rocks were formed by fractional crystallization over a considerable length of time.   This involved the building up of regular space lattices of ions.   The most important factor governing the distribution of elements in minerals is a grading according to ionic size.

The second parting may be subdivided into three main stages:

(*a*) The first crystallization, above 1200°C, which produced the heavy refractory oxides such as magnetite, chromite, ilmenite, spinel and olivine. These are usually inaccessible because of their density.

(*b*) The main crystallization, 500° to 1200°C, which produced ortho- and meta-silicates and alumino-silicates.   The chief cations incorporated were Fe^{2+}, Mg^{2+}, Ca^{2+}, Na^+ and K^+.   These minerals, together with quartz constitute approximately four-fifths of the earth's crust.   Less common elements tended to enter the lattice most suited to their size and valency. Thus random replacement of one ion for another has occurred where the two ions concerned have the same charge and similar size, for example, nickel has displaced magnesium in some silicates.   Small ions, particularly if they also carry a large charge, are found concentrated in the early crystals; larger ions and those of small charge are found preferentially in the late crystals.   Thus scandium is found more in early silicates, whereas lithium and rubidium are found in the late crystals.

171

(*c*) The final crystallization, below 500°C, gave rise to the pegmatites. These contain cations and anions which were either too large or small to be accepted into the silicate lattices. Examples are W, Sn, Bi, Ag, Cu, Zn, Pb, Sb, Hg and U: borate, phosphate, sulphide, niobate and molybdate. Pegmatites are of great economic value since they are more accessible and more differentiated than the products of the first two crystallizations.

The Third Parting of the Elements

Ninety five per cent of the earth's crust consists of igneous rock. The remaining 5 per cent has undergone physical, mechanical and chemical weathering processes, thereby producing at least 90 per cent of our mineral sources. From the chemical point of view, weathering is the selective extraction on igneous rock by the action of water, carbon dioxide and humic acids, carrying away some constituents into solution (such as Na^+, Ca^{2+}, Fe^{2+} and Mg^{2+}) and leaving insoluble residues (including TiO_2, Fe_2O_3 and SiO_2).

In weathering, both the valency and size of the cation are important. If the ionic potential, defined as the ratio of the ionic charge to ionic radius, is low for an element (<4) the ion readily goes into solution and remains there (for example, sodium, magnesium and other constituents of sea-water). If this ratio is high (>12), then the element shares electrons more readily and is found in an oxy-anion such as SO_4^{2-} or PO_4^{3-}. Those elements with intermediate values of ionic potential go into solution in reducing media and are reprecipitated in oxidizing media. Thus iron and manganese pass into solution as divalent ions in the presence of decaying organic matter. In an oxidizing environment, ferric iron is formed and hydrolysed to ferric hydroxide, a positive colloid which absorbs anions such as phosphate. Manganese is converted to the hydrated dioxide, a negative colloid, which takes up the cations of metals such as copper and barium. These two colloids precipitate each other and form deposits on the sea-bed. Reduction can occur again and so a cycle of solution and precipitation is established.

Other elements are also in steady circulation in the earth's crust. Calcium and magnesium enter into biological processes, calcium to form bone and magnesium to form chlorophyll. Potassium participates in plant growth and sodium chloride has very important biological roles, *e.g.* in lowering the freezing point of plant fluids, regulating osmotic pressure, *etc.* There are also the vitally important natural cycles involving the three non-metals, carbon, phosphorus and nitrogen.

It is apparent that a given element can be found in radically different forms. Thus iron is a constituent of the deposits from the first and second crystallizations as well as being present extensively in the products of weathering. A selection of the chief ores of the elements follows (pp. 173–7); particular mention is made of those ores from which the element is extracted on an industrial scale and, in some cases, the important chemical reactions used in the extraction are included.

EXTRACTION

In the extraction of the pure elements from their ores, chemical, economic and metallurgical factors are all of fundamental importance. These may,

Element	Occurrence	Extraction method	Notes
HYDROGEN	Widely distributed as a constituent of water and other compounds	Small (lab.) scale: Zinc + acid Large scale: (a) $2H_2O + C$ $= CO_2 + 2H_2$ (at 1000°C) (b) $CH_4 + H_2O$ $= CO + 3H_2$ (at 1100°C) (c) Electrolysis of water (d) $4H_2O + 3Fe$ (steam) $\rightleftharpoons Fe_3O_4 + 4H_2$	
LITHIUM	*Spodumene*, $LiAl(SiO_3)_2$ *Lepidolite* (lithia mica)	Electrolysis of fused LiCl/KCl	The electropositive metals of Group I occur as water-soluble salts of strong acids and as cations in alumino-silicate rocks. Their high reactivity necessitates extraction of the metal under anhydrous conditions.
SODIUM	*Rock-salt*, $NaCl$ *Feldspar*, $NaAlSi_3O_8$ *Chile Saltpetre*, $NaNO_3$ *Borax*, $Na_2B_4O_7 . 10H_2O$	Electrolysis of fused NaOH or $NaCl/CaCl_2$	
POTASSIUM	*Carnallite*, $KCl . MgCl_2 . 6H_2O$ Various alumino-silicates *Saltpetre*, KNO_3	Electrolysis of fused $KCl/CaCl_2$	
RUBIDIUM	Associated with K and Li	Both rubidium and caesium by displacement from their chlorides by calcium: $2RbCl + Ca$ $= 2Rb + CaCl_2$	
CAESIUM	*Pollucite*, caesium aluminium silicate		
BERYLLIUM	*Beryl*, $3BeO . Al_2O_3 . 6SiO_2$ *Chrysoberyl*, $BeO . Al_2O_3$	Electrolysis of fused BeF_2/NaF or magnesium reduction of BeF_2	Be is unique in this group in occurring as a mixed oxide.
MAGNESIUM	*Carnallite*, *Magnesite*, $MgCO_3$ *Spinel*, $MgAl_2O_4$ *Olivine*, Mg_2SiO_4	Electrolysis of fused $KCl/MgCl_2$ Carbon reduction of MgO	The more electropositive elements of Group II occur as silicates and as their sparingly soluble salts. Carbon reduction can be carried out with Mg, not with the alkaline earths because a carbide is formed.
CALCIUM	*Dolomite*, $MgCO_3 . CaCO_3$ *Limestone*, $CaCO_3$ *Gypsum*, $CaSO_4$ *Fluorspar*, CaF_2 *Apatite*, $CaF_2 . 3Ca_3(PO_4)_2$	Electrolysis of fused $CaCl_2/CaF_2$	
STRONTIUM	*Strontianite*, $SrCO_3$ *Celestine*, $SrSO_4$	Electrolysis of fused halides or the aluminium reduction of oxides	
BARIUM	*Witherite*, $BaCO_3$ *Barytes*, $BaSO_4$		

Table—contd.

Element	Occurrence	Extraction methods	Notes
BORON	*Borax,* $Na_2B_4O_7.10H_2O$ *Colemannite,* $Ca_2B_6O_{11}.5H_2O$	Thermal reduction of B_2O_3 with Na, Mg, Al	Unique in Group III in occurring exclusively as an anionic constituent.
ALUMINIUM	*Bauxite,* $Al_2O_3.2H_2O$ *Cryolite,* Na_3AlF_6 Alumino-silicate rocks	Electrolytic reduction of Al_2O_3 dissolved in molten cryolite	
SCANDIUM, YTTRIUM and the heavy rare-earths, EUROPIUM to LUTETIUM	*Thortveitite,* $Sc_2Si_2O_7$ *Gadolinite* (basic silicate coloured black by iron) *Xenotime* (phosphate) *Yttrotantalite, Samarskite Fergusonite* (complex niobates and tantalates)	Electrolysis of fused chlorides	These metals of Group III A occur as silicates and phosphates. As a result of the lanthanide contraction, yttrium has the same ionic radius as the heavy lanthanons.
CERIUM and the light rare-earths, LANTHANUM to SAMARIUM	*Monazite,* phosphate *Cerite,* hydrated silicate *Orthite,* complex silicate	Electrolysis of fused chlorides	
THORIUM	*Monazite Thorite,* ThO_2	Ca reduction of ThO_2	
URANIUM	*Pitchblende,* U_3O_8 *Carnotite,* $K_2O.2UO_3.V_2O_5$	Ca or Mg reduction of UF_4	
CARBON	*Diamond, Graphite Dolomite, Chalk Limestone, Coal*	Destructive distillation of coal. Carbon also obtained as a by-product of various industrial processes	The free element is found: also combined as carbonate.
SILICON	*Quartz,* SiO_2 Many silicates and alumino-silicates	Electrothermal reduction of SiO_2 Reduction of $SiCl_4$ by Zn or hydrogen	Next to oxygen, the most abundant element.
TITANIUM	*Ilmenite,* $TiO_2.FeO$ *Rutile,* TiO_2	Reduction of $TiCl_4$ by Mg (Kroll process) or Na	Group IV A metals with a very high affinity for oxygen.
ZIRCONIUM	*Baddeleyite,* ZrO_2 *Zircon,* $ZrSiO_4$	Reduction of $ZrCl_4$ by Mg	Necessary to convert to halides and
HAFNIUM	Accompanies Zr: Hf content usually 1–2% Zr content	As for Zr	reduce in an inert atmosphere. Hf is very similar to Zr because of the lanthanide contraction.

Table—contd.

Element	Occurrence	Extraction method	Notes
VANADIUM	*Vanadinite,* $3Pb_3(VO_4)_2 . PbCl_2$ *Carnotite* *Patronite,* sulphide	Aluminothermal reduction of V_2O_5	Group V A metals with smaller affinity for oxygen than the preceding group of transition metals. V is the only metal to be found as a sulphide in this group
NIOBIUM	*Niobite,* $Fe(NbO_3)_2$ containing Ta	Sodium reduction of K_2NbF_7 or K_2TaF_7	
TANTALUM	*Tantalite,* $Fe(TaO_3)_2$ containing Nb	Electrolysis of fused K_2TaF_7 Also: $Ta_2O_5 + 5TaC = 7Ta + 5CO$	
CHROMIUM	*Chromite,* $FeO . Cr_2O_3$ *Crocoisite,* $PbCrO_4$	Reduction of Cr_2O_3 by Al or Si Also electrolysis of aqueous solutions of Cr^{III} salts	Group VI A metals which occur as mixed oxides or as part of an oxyanion.
MOLYBDENUM	*Molybdenite,* MoS_2 *Wulfenite,* $PbMoO_4$	Hydrogen reduction of MoO_3	MoS_2 is an exception.
TUNGSTEN	*Wolframite,* $FeWO_4/MnWO_4$ *Scheelite,* $CaWO_4$ *Tungstite,* WO_3	Hydrogen reduction of WO_3	Extraction method from oxide ores involves an initial roast with Na_2CO_3 to form the water-soluble Na salt.
MANGANESE	*Pyrolusite,* MnO_2 *Hausmannite,* Mn_3O_4	Reduction of Mn_3O_4 with Al or C	In Group VII A manganese is the only metal of commercial importance.
TECHNETIUM	Traces in nature; usually isolated from fission products	H_2 reduction of ammonium pertechnetate	
RHENIUM	*Molybdenite* contains up to 20 p.p.m. Re and is the chief source of this metal.	H_2 reduction of ammonium perrhenate	
IRON	*Magnetite,* Fe_3O_4 *Haematite,* Fe_2O_3 *Pyrites,* FeS_2	Reduction of oxides by CO in the blast furnace	The extraction of iron and its conversion to steels is the most important metallurgical process.
COBALT	Associated with Cu and Ni as sulphide and arsenide *Smaltite,* $CoAs_2$	Reduction of oxides by carbon or water-gas	Cobalt and nickel are much less common than iron and are usually found as low-grade ores.

Table—contd.

Element	Occurrence	Extraction method	Notes
NICKEL	Occurs in *pentlandite*, largely iron sulphide containing up to 3% Ni. *Garnierite*, silicate of Mg and Ni produced by weathering *Millerite*, NiS	Carbon reduction of oxide followed by electrolytic refining Also by Mond carbonyl process $Ni(CO)_4 \underset{60°C}{\overset{180°C}{\rightleftharpoons}} Ni + 4CO$	
RUTHENIUM RHODIUM PALLADIUM OSMIUM IRIDIUM PLATINUM	Native, *e.g.* the alloy *Osmiridium.* 0.5 p.p.m. in nickel-containing iron sulphide (main source) Rare ores: *Braggite*, PdS *Sperrylite*, $PtAs_2$	Residues from nickel carbonyl process are worked up and pure compounds of the individual elements prepared. These are then thermally decomposed: *e.g.* $PdCl_2(NH_3)_2$ to Pd and $(NH_4)_2PtCl_6$ to Pt	These are the platinum metals which have low free energies of formation for their compounds. They occur native or as easily reduced compounds.
COPPER	*Copper pyrites*, $CuFeS_2$ *Cuprite*, Cu_2O *Malachite*, $CuCO_3 . Cu(OH)_2$ Also native	Partial oxidation of sulphide ore: $2Cu_2O + Cu_2S$ $= 6Cu + SO_2$ Or acid leach with H_2SO_4 followed by electrolysis	The native metals are found. The extraction from sulphide ores can be carried out by pyro- or hydro-metallurgy.
SILVER	*Argentite*, sulphide. *Horn Silver*, AgCl Native	Sodium cyanide leach of sulphide ore. This forms $Ag(CN)_2^-$ from which Ag is precipitated by Zn	
GOLD	Native. Small amounts in many ores such as pyrites	Similar cyanide leach as for Ag	
ZINC	*Zinc blende, wurtzite*, ZnS *Calamine*, $ZnCO_3$	For Zn and Cd, the sulphides roasted to the oxides which are then reduced by C. Electrolysis of $ZnSO_4$ for Zn preparation	In Group II B, sulphide ores again pre-dominate. The metals are easily extracted from their ores.
CADMIUM	Small amounts in most zinc ores		
MERCURY	*Cinnabar*, HgS	Thermal decomposition: $HgS + O_2 = Hg + SO_2$	
GALLIUM	Small amounts in *zinc blende* and *bauxite*	By-product in the extraction of zinc or obtained by electrolysis of alkaline leachings of bauxite.	No concentrated ores of the Group III B metals are known.
INDIUM	Small amounts in *zinc blende* and *cassiterite*	In and Tl are recovered from the flue dusts of pyrites burners by electro-lysis or chemical reduction methods	
THALLIUM	Found in *pyrites*		

176

Table—contd.

Element	Occurrence	Extraction methods	Notes
GERMANIUM	Found in *zinc blende*, Rare ores are complex sulphides like *argyrodite*, $4Ag_2S.GeS_2$	H_2 reduction of GeO_2	Group IV B metals are found generally as sulphides. Tin is unusual. Electrolytic refining of tin using aqueous solution is important.
TIN	*Cassiterite*, SnO_2	Carbon reduction of SnO_2	
LEAD	*Galena*, PbS	Sulphide roasted to oxide which is then reduced by carbon	
PHOSPHORUS	*Apatite*, $CaF_2.3Ca_3(PO_4)_2$ *Chlorapatite*, $CaCl_2.Ca_3(PO_4)_2$	Electric arc reduction by carbon in presence of SiO_2 (to form calcium silicate)	Sulphide ores are again important in the heavier elements of this group.
ARSENIC	*Nickel glance*, NiAsS *Mispickel*, FeAsS	Roasting of ore in absence of air	
ANTIMONY	*Stibnite*, Sb_2S_3	Iron reduction of sulphide	The only important example of the extraction of an element by direct reduction of its sulphide.
BISMUTH	*Bismuth glance*, Bi_2S_3 *Bismuthite*, Bi_2O_3	Carbon reduction of the oxide	
SULPHUR	*Native* Also combined as sulphides and sulphates	Native S recovered by melting undergound deposits and forcing the liquid to the surface— Frasch Process	Sulphur is very abundant but selenium and tellurium are trace elements. They are recovered as by-products from other processes; for example, Se and Te are found in anode sludges from the electrolytic refining of copper.
SELENIUM TELLURIUM	Found in sulphur-bearing ores	Reduction of their compounds by SO_2	
FLUORINE	*Fluorspar*, CaF_2 *Cryolite*, Na_3AlF_6	Electrolysis of molten KF/HF mixtures	The halogens are always found as anionic constituents. Fluorine, being highly electronegative and reactive, is obtained only by electrolysis of fused, anhydrous salts. Extraction of the halogens becomes progressively easier towards the heavier end of the group.
CHLORINE	Present as chloride ion in sea-water; also solid chloride deposits	Electrolysis of brine	
BROMINE	Also found in sea-water and salt deposits	Displacement by chlorine: $MgBr_2 + Cl_2 = MgCl_2 + Br_2$	
IODINE	Less than 0·1 p.p.m. in sea-water, but concentrated in sea-weed As iodate, $NaIO_3$, in *Chilean nitrate*	Reduction of iodate with bisulphite	

177

however, often conflict. For instance, the most elegant chemical method for the preparation of an element is rarely the cheapest. Again, the particular use envisaged for a metal may determine the choice of extraction procedure. In the ensuing pages we shall deal mainly with the chemical aspects of the extraction of metals with emphasis on the exploitation of chemical differences to facilitate their separation.

The extraction of a metal from its ore generally involves three major operations; concentration of the ore, extraction of the crude metal and refining. These are discussed in turn with some examples.

Concentration of the Ore

Except for high-grade ores, this is a necessary first stage. Unwanted material can be removed by either physical or chemical methods or a combination of both. Physical methods include gravity separation and flotation processes; in some cases where the ore contains a magnetic constituent this property can be used in the concentration. Chemical methods are those of *hydrometallurgy*. This is the leaching of ores by aqueous solution to extract the required metal in the form of one of its soluble salts.

Important examples of hydrometallurgical operations are:

(*i*) the treatment of cuprous sulphide ores with dilute sulphuric acid in the presence of atmospheric oxygen to produce copper sulphate;

(*ii*) the leaching of silver ores with sodium cyanide solution, whereupon the silver is extracted as its complex, $[Ag(CN)_2]^-$;

(*iii*) the sulphuric acid or sodium carbonate leach of uranium ores followed by further purification using an ion-exchange process (p. 193);

(*iv*) the ammoniacal leach of sulphide ore containing Ni, Co and Cu under oxidizing conditions to form the metal ammine complexes;

(*v*) the precipitation of magnesium from sea-water as its hydroxide;

(*vi*) the digestion of bauxite with caustic soda under pressure to extract aluminium as soluble aluminate leaving insoluble materials as residue.

As the supplies of high-grade ores become exhausted, and greater use is made of low-grade, more complex ores, hydrometallurgical separations are being increasingly employed for preliminary concentration. Kinetic aspects are of prime importance in leaching processes and the chief disadvantage of older methods is the time-consuming nature of the operation. However, the application of the more versatile and rapid techniques of ion exchange and solvent extraction is resulting in the development of many new hydrometallurgical processes (p. 193).

Extraction of the Metal

The concentrated ore must usually be converted to a compound which is suitable for reduction to the metal. *Pyrometallurgical processes*, involving the use of high temperatures, are most widely employed for the production of the crude metal. Thermodynamic factors are of chief importance in pyrometallurgy. The kinetic aspects usually need not be considered because the use of high temperatures ensures that chemical equilibrium is rapidly reached.

178

Many oxide ores are directly reduced (smelted) to the metal. A variety of reducing agents are used, carbon being the one in most general use. Al, Si and hydrogen are other reducing agents and these may be preferred to carbon when, for instance, the metal to be isolated forms a carbide. The bulk of the impurities is removed by the addition of suitable fluxes to form a slag (p. 131).

A sulphide ore, however, is almost invariably roasted to convert it to the oxide and this is then reduced to the metal. The roasting process also removes volatile impurities such as arsenic. For thermodynamic reasons (p. 182), an oxide rather than a sulphide is used for reduction.

The highly electropositive metals, such as the alkali and alkaline-earth metals, are isolated by the electrolytic reduction of their fused halides. No suitable chemical reducing agent is available and preparation from aqueous solution is impossible because of the reactive nature of these metals. Less electropositive metals like Cr, Cu and Zn can be prepared by the electrolysis of concentrated aqueous solutions of their salts. One advantage of the electrolytic over the oxide-reduction method for extraction is the high purity of the electrolytically prepared metal.

When neither oxide reduction nor electrolysis is suitable for chemical reasons, reduction of a metal halide by reactive metals such as Mg, Na and Ca is employed. Titanium is an outstanding example of a metal which cannot be prepared by conventional methods because of the enormous affinity it has for oxygen. This, coupled with the adverse effect on the mechanical properties of the metal of quite small amounts of dissolved oxygen, led to the development of the Kroll process in which highly purified $TiCl_4$ is reduced by magnesium in an inert atmosphere. In this way, oxygen is entirely excluded from the reactants before reduction takes place and so will not be present in the metal produced. There are many technical difficulties to be overcome in the production of titanium and it is not surprising that despite the abundance of the element in the earth's crust (*Table 7.1*) the pure metal was not prepared for the first time until 1925 (by van Arkel's method, p. 181). In contrast, metals such as copper and lead are much more rare than titanium but they have been well known for centuries simply because the metals are easily extracted from accessible ores.

Factors other than purely chemical ones are usually of crucial importance in determining the choice of method of extraction. Thus it is essential to make the most economic use of all the products of an extraction process. Again, the nature of the ore has an important bearing on the least expensive route to the pure metal. For example, copper can be made from its sulphide ores by conversion of the molten sulphide to the metal by an air blast. Alternatively, particularly in the case of low-grade ores, concentration is brought about by hydrometallurgical reactions and the metal is deposited electrolytically from solution. The proposed use of the metal can also influence the choice of extraction process. This is illustrated by the cases of Cr, W and Fe. Chromium is used most extensively as a constituent of steel and, when destined for this, it is quite sufficient to prepare ferrochromium by the direct reduction of chromite $(Cr_2O_3.FeO)$ with silicon or aluminium. An important use of tungsten is in the manufacture of 'hard metal', tungsten carbide. Since only comparatively small quantities of tungsten are required, the pure metal is conveniently obtained by the reduction of WO_3 with hydrogen. In contrast,

179

the vast amounts of iron required for structural materials must be made by a process capable of application on the largest possible scale, namely carbon reduction of the oxide.

Purification of the Metal

Various refining processes are used and these will depend on the chemical nature of the metal and the impurities and on the previous history of the raw metal. Among the most important are the removal of impurities by oxidation, by electrolysis or by conversion to a volatile compound which is more readily purified. In addition, several new methods have been introduced to refine reactive and refractory metals.

Oxidative Refining.—This is usually necessary where a metal has been prepared by the reduction of its oxide. At the same time the oxides of other elements present have been reduced. Oxidative refining, using a limited amount of oxygen, is feasible when these other elements have a higher affinity for oxygen than the metal being refined. Then only the impurities are oxidized and the oxides formed are effectively separated from the metal by incorporation in a slag.

For example, when iron oxide is reduced by carbon in the blast furnace to produce pig iron, much of the impurity is removed as fusible slag but the product still contains Si, Mn, P and C. The metal is brittle because of the presence of carbon and refining is necessary to convert it to malleable iron. Oxidative refining is carried out in the Bessemer converter by blowing air through the molten iron. This oxidizes Si, Mn and C. Phosphorus is removed in this process by the addition to the converter of basic compounds such as lime to produce 'basic slag'. The carbon content of the iron is reduced by air-blasting to a figure below that required for technical purposes. In addition, some of the iron has been reoxidized. Ferromanganese, of high carbon content, is therefore added with a two-fold purpose: to increase the carbon content and to reduce the iron oxide by the manganese. The manganese oxide formed is removed as a slag. Other deoxidants have been used in place of manganese, especially silicon which also has a high affinity for oxygen.

Electrolytic Refining—The electrodeposition of pure metals from aqueous solution is important for refining a number of metals such as Cr, Cu, Sn, Ni, Zn and Ag. In the electrolytic refining of copper, for instance, castings of the crude metal are used as anodes in the electrolysis of acidified copper sulphate solution. On electrolysis, the anodes dissolve and pure copper is deposited on the cathode. The impurities which are not anodically dissolved collect at the bottom of the electrolytic cell. This is the anode sludge which is worked up for the extraction of the precious metals and for other elements such as selenium and tellurium.

Recently, fusion electrolysis has been introduced for titanium refining. Impure titanium anodes are used in an electrolyte of fused alkali metal chlorides such as the NaCl/KCl eutectic mixture, m.p. 650°C, which also contains some dissolved lower chlorides of titanium ($TiCl_2$ and $TiCl_3$). Pure titanium is deposited on the cathode as electrolysis proceeds.

Vapour-Phase Refining—This is exemplified by the Mond process for nickel. This involves the purification of nickel by forming its volatile carbonyl which

180

is then thermally decomposed. Iron can also be prepared in a very pure state via its carbonyl.

The van Arkel process, based on the formation of a volatile metal iodide, is another example. Pure compact zirconium was first prepared in 1924 by VAN ARKEL and DE BOER by the reaction at 600°C between crude zirconium and iodine vapour to form zirconium tetraiodide, ZrI_4. The vapour of this compound was allowed to diffuse on to a tungsten filament maintained at 1800°C. Decomposition occurred and pure zirconium was deposited on the filament. This method has been most effective in the preparation of those metals which are very difficult to obtain in the pure state. Besides zirconium, other metals which have been made in this way include hafnium, silicon, titanium and beryllium. Recently, the van Arkel process has been adapted for industrial preparations.

New Methods—Brief mention must be made here of the important new methods which have been developed for the refining of refractory metals. The major problems to be solved are the attainment of a sufficiently high temperature to melt the impure metal and the prevention of chemical reactions involving the metal at this temperature. The use of a vacuum arc furnace for the refining of titanium, zirconium and molybdenum is now well established. The crude metal is compacted into an electrode and this is progressively melted in an arc furnace under vacuum. Volatile impurities are boiled off during the melting. An ingot of purified metal is obtained by chilling the molten metal in a copper crucible cooled externally by water. Another recent development in this field is the use of electron bombardment in which the metal to be melted is bombarded under high vacuum by electrons from a heated tungsten filament.

One method of purification worthy of special note is that usually referred to as *zone refining*. This involves the extraction of impurities by a solidifying front and can be used for the removal from a crystalline substance of any impurity which shows a difference in its solubility in the liquid and solid states of that substance. In some ways, therefore, it is similar to fractional crystallization. The chief inorganic applications of zone refining are in the preparation of certain elements in an extremely high state of purity, particularly germanium, silicon and gallium for use as semi-conductors. Purification has reached such a stage that the impurity content is no longer detectable by normal analytical methods and must be estimated from the electrical resistivity of the material. Thus germanium has been prepared which contains as little as 10^{-7} p.p.m. of most other elements (with the exception of dissolved oxygen and hydrogen). Semi-conductors such as gallium arsenide and indium antimonide are also successfully zone refined.

THEORETICAL PRINCIPLES OF THE EXTRACTION OF METALS BY PYROMETALLURGY

The reduction of a metal oxide by another element is, in effect, the competition of both elements for the oxygen and the practical possibility of the process depends on the relative affinities of the elements for oxygen.

A quantitative comparison of relative affinities may be made by considering the free energies of formation of the oxides under standard conditions. For a reaction to proceed spontaneously at a given temperature and pressure, there must be a decrease in free energy, $-\Delta G$, in the system. ΔG is related to other thermodynamic quantities by

$$\Delta G = \Delta H - T \Delta S \qquad \qquad \text{. . . . (1)}$$

where ΔH is the change in enthalpy and ΔS is the change in entropy. ΔG can be expressed in any convenient energy units per unit of chemical change, e.g. kcal/mole.

Standard free energy values, $\Delta G°$, may be directly compared for a number of reactions. These refer to the reaction between the metal and one mole of gaseous oxygen at a partial pressure of one atmosphere and correspond with the same amount of chemical change in each case. Although the experimental methods for evaluating ΔG are outside the scope of this book, it is interesting to note the relationship with the equilibrium constant, K, of the reaction, expressed in

$$\Delta G = -RT \log_e \frac{K}{Q}$$

where R is the gas constant, T the absolute reaction temperature and Q a constant which has the same form as K but in which the activities refer to the values for the substances in the reaction. When all the reacting substances are at unit activity, $Q=1$ and $\Delta G = \Delta G°$.

Equation (1) indicates that $\Delta G°$ is dependent on T and there is very nearly a linear relationship between them. *Figure 7.1* demonstrates this for a number of oxides. This is the graphical representation of free energy which was first used by H. J. T. ELLINGHAM and it provides a sound basis for discussing the preparation of the elements by oxide reduction.

It is significant that most of the plots slope upwards from left to right, that is, $\Delta G°$ becomes less negative as the temperature rises. The slope is given by

$$\left(\frac{\partial \Delta G°}{\partial T} \right)_p = -\Delta S°$$

and the change in $\Delta G°$ corresponds with the entropy loss resulting from the disappearance of one mole of gaseous oxygen. Entropy is a measure of the randomness of a given state: solids therefore have low entropies and the entropy of any material increases on fusion or evaporation with the result that gases have comparatively large entropies. For this reason a marked increase in slope is often evident at the boiling point of the metal. Thus the curve for calcium shows an abrupt change in slope at 1490°C (the boiling point of the metal). Above this temperature the plot represents the free energy change of the reaction between gaseous calcium and oxygen to form solid calcium oxide. The production of 1 mole of oxide therefore involves the disappearance of 2 moles of gaseous reactants. Below 1490°C the same amount of calcium oxide is formed when only 1 mole of gaseous material (oxygen) is consumed. The entropy loss in the reaction is therefore greater above than below the boiling-point of calcium. When other transitions such as phase changes or melting occur, the entropy changes are generally much smaller and the change in slope is correspondingly less.

The more negative the $\Delta G°$ value for oxide formation at a given temperature the more difficult it is to reduce the metal oxide concerned. When the plot for one metal lies below that for another, the first metal is thermodynamically capable of reducing the oxide of the second.

As a consequence of this the representative and A sub-group elements of Groups II, III and IV can reduce many metal oxides. Aluminium and silicon are used extensively for such purposes.

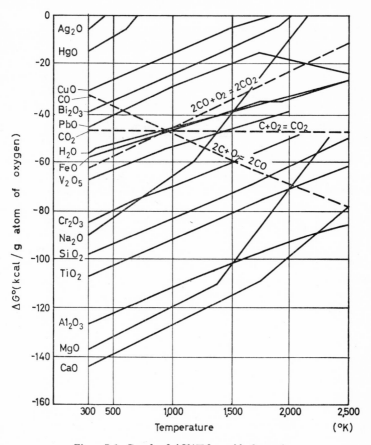

Figure 7.1. Graph of $\Delta G°/T$ for oxide formation

The particular utility of carbon as a reducing agent can be understood by reference to the change in $\Delta G°$ as T increases for the oxidation of carbon to carbon monoxide. $\Delta G°$ becomes more negative, that is, the trend is opposite to that shown generally by metal oxides. This is due to the increase in entropy which accompanies the reaction

$$2\,C \text{ (solid)} + O_2 \text{ (gas)} \rightleftharpoons 2\,CO \text{ (gas)}$$

wherein 2 moles of gaseous product are obtained for every mole of gaseous oxygen consumed. The plot shows that at temperatures around 2000°C carbon is thermodynamically capable of reducing almost all metal oxides.

183

The alternative reaction possible between carbon and oxygen is

$$C + O_2 \rightleftharpoons CO_2$$

which becomes the more important at lower temperatures. CO_2 is the main product below 710°C, CO above this temperature. In the region of 710°C, the equilibrium represented by

$$C + CO_2 \rightleftharpoons 2CO$$

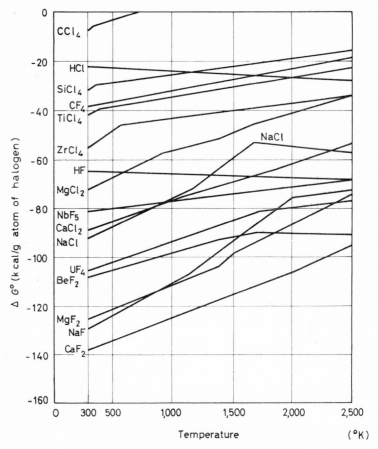

Figure 7.2. Graph of $\Delta G°/T$ for halide formation

determines the proportions of each gas present. The plot for

$$2CO + O_2 \rightleftharpoons 2CO_2$$

shows that carbon monoxide is an effective reducing agent only at temperatures below 700°C.

The same thermodynamic treatment is applicable to metal/sulphur reactions. The Ellingham plots for these have not been reproduced here because, with the sole exception of antimony, no metals are prepared industrially by the direct

184

reduction of their sulphides. The free energies of formation of most metal sulphides are greater than those for H_2S and CS_2, carbon disulphide being in fact an endothermic compound, and so neither hydrogen nor carbon is a suitable reducing agent. Hence the common practice to roast sulphide ores to the corresponding oxides prior to reduction.

The $\Delta G°/T$ plots for a number of metal chlorides and fluorides are shown in *Figure 7.2.* The salient features of these plots are the same as those for oxide formation. In the case of chlorides, however, carbon cannot be used as reducing agent, and hydrogen has only a few applications, for example, in the reduction of $SiCl_4$. Recourse must generally be made to reactive electropositive metals such as magnesium or sodium, as in the production of zirconium and titanium from their tetrachlorides.

There are also several metals, in particular uranium, beryllium and niobium, which are made from their fluorides by calcium or magnesium reduction. *Figure 7.2* shows clearly the thermodynamic reason for choice of these metals as reducing agents.

SUGGESTED REFERENCE FOR FURTHER READING

GIBSON, D. T. 'The terrestrial distribution of the elements', *Quart. Rev. chem. Soc., Lond.*, 3 (1949) 263.

8

SOLVENT EXTRACTION AND ION EXCHANGE

THESE are two modern techniques which have proved to be very effective in the accomplishment of separations which are much more difficult to realize by classical methods such as fractional crystallization or precipitation. Both solvent extraction and ion-exchange procedures are widely applied on a laboratory scale for analytical purposes and on the plant scale for the purification of materials of industrial importance.

The advantages which these techniques possess over classical methods include (*i*) a high degree of selectivity in suitable circumstances, (*ii*) ease and simplicity of operation, (*iii*) the ability to concentrate minute amounts of material and to separate minor from major constituents and (*iv*) speed of operation (this applies more particularly to solvent extraction).

The main features of each technique will now be outlined, together with examples of some of the more important applications.

SOLVENT EXTRACTION SYSTEMS

The theoretical basis of solvent extraction is the *Nernst Partition Law*. This states that at equilibrium and at a constant temperature, the ratio of the concentration of a solute in two immiscible liquids is a constant. Although strictly true only for ideal dilute solutions, many substances obey this law, for example, iodine distributed between carbon tetrachloride and water.

Ionic compounds, as a general rule, are not soluble in organic solvents but unless the lattice energy is high, show appreciable solubility in water and other solvents of high dielectric constant. Solution in water is accompanied by hydration of the cations and anions.

In contrast, covalent compounds show preferential solubility in organic solvents. Hence it is found that solvent extraction from an aqueous solution into an immiscible organic solvent can take place provided that an uncharged species is formed. This may either be a neutral molecule or an ion pair.

Several types of solvent extraction systems can be recognized and these are divisible into three broad classes:

1. Metal Chelates

When an organic solvent containing a chelating reagent HR is shaken with an aqueous solution of a metal salt, the metal M^{n+} may be partly or completely extracted into the organic phase if an uncharged chelated complex MR_n is formed. The equilibrium reactions established in the two-phase system are summarized in *Figure 8.1*. It should be noted that the reagent and its metal complex are usually much more soluble in the organic phase than in the aqueous solution: also, as *Figure 8.1* indicates, the extent to which the reagent dissociates and hence the proportion of metal which is complexed depends on the pH.

186

Typical examples of metal chelate solvent extraction systems are the inner complexes formed by 8-hydroxyquinoline, acetylacetone, dithizone and dimethylglyoxime (p. 142). When the metal ion and/or its complex are coloured, the solvent extraction of the complex can be utilized in analytical procedures for the metal.

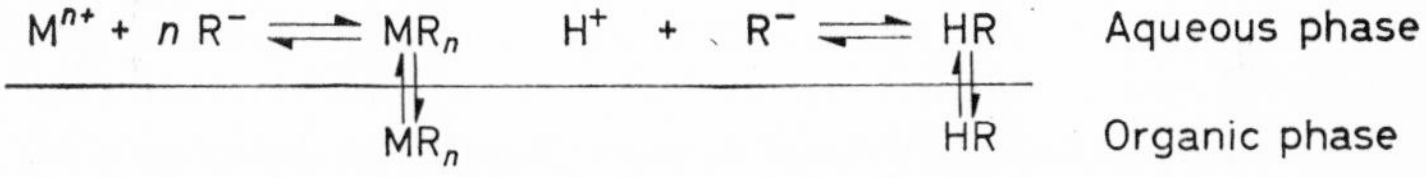

$$M^{n+} + n\,R^- \rightleftharpoons MR_n \qquad H^+ + R^- \rightleftharpoons HR \qquad \text{Aqueous phase}$$

$$MR_n \qquad\qquad\qquad\qquad HR \qquad \text{Organic phase}$$

Figure 8.1. The extraction of a metal chelate

2. Ion Association

(a) The metal may be incorporated into a large cation or anion. This, in association with an ion of opposite charge, constitutes an ion pair which may be readily extracted by an organic solvent. Examples of ion pairs are tetraphenylarsonium perrhenate, $(C_6H_5)_4\,As^+.ReO_4^-$, and permanganate, $(C_6H_5)_4As^+.MnO_4^-$. These are formed by reaction between the appropriate metal compound in aqueous solution and tetraphenylarsonium chloride dissolved in a non-reactive solvent such as chloroform.

(b) A very important type is that in which the organic solvent plays a major role in the extraction processes. For instance, displacement by solvent molecules of co-ordinated water from the cation and anion occurs during these extractions. It has been known for many years that uranyl nitrate, $UO_2(NO_3)_2$, is extracted from nitric acid solutions by diethyl ether. The hydrated species, $UO_2(NO_3)_2.6H_2O$, in the aqueous phase becomes $UO_2(NO_3)_2.2[(C_2H_5)_2O].2H_2O$ in the organic phase. Other solvents beside diethyl ether have been used, including derivatives of phosphoric acid such as tri-n-butyl phosphate $(C_4H_9O)_3P{=}O$.

An ion-associaton system of this class is more complicated than either 1 or 2(a) because more than one complex may be formed and extracted. Thus in the uranyl nitrate system, the trinitrato-anionic complex $[UO_2(NO_3)_3]^-$ is known as well as the dinitrato complex, $UO_2(NO_3)_2$.

Another well-known example is the extraction of iron (III) chloride. This is extracted by ethers and other oxygen-containing solvents from aqueous solutions containing appreciable concentrations of hydrochloric acid. In such solutions, iron is present largely as the tetrachloro-ferrate (III) ion, $[FeCl_4]^-$. It is believed that the major species extracted by ether is the solvated hydrogen acid, $HFeCl_4$. One molecule of ether is associated with the proton and two with the iron thus:

$$(C_2H_5)_2O{\rightarrow}H^+.Fe[(C_2H_5)_2O]_2Cl_4^-$$

Other species which must be considered in this extraction system are lower chloro-complexes of Fe^{III} in the aqueous phase and polynuclear complexes (those which contain more than one metal atom per molecule) in the organic phase.

Many other metal nitrates, halides and other salts can be solvent-extracted under suitable conditions and a number of important applications are known.

(c) Recent developments have been associated with the use, in an inert solvent such as xylene or kerosene, of organic reagents of high molecular weight which contain either an acidic or a basic group in the molecule. For example, di(2-ethylhexyl) hydrogen phosphate contains one acidic hydrogen atom and it also possesses two long hydrocarbon chains which promote solution in organic solvents. This reagent in xylene effectively extracts uranium from aqueous sulphate, chloride or phosphate solutions and is akin to cation-exchange materials (p. 190) in its behaviour. Basic properties are associated with high molecular weight amines such as tris(6-methylheptyl)amine. In a suitable solvent, this compound will extract simple or complex anions from acid aqueous solutions and thus acts as a liquid anion-exchanger.

3. Covalent Compounds

This class includes a diversity of substances such as the halogens (chlorine, bromine and iodine), sulphur dioxide, the tetroxides of osmium and ruthenium, mercuric chloride, germanium tetrachloride, etc. These are extracted by hydrocarbon or halogenated hydrocarbon solvents. The process of extraction is closer to physical solution than in the classes 1 and 2.

APPLICATIONS OF SOLVENT EXTRACTION

The Purification of Nuclear Fuels

The most important large-scale uses of this technique are in the processing of fuels for nuclear reactors.

Metallic uranium is to date the most widely used nuclear fuel. This contains the fissile isotope ^{235}U. In order to utilize fully the ^{235}U content of uranium it is necessary periodically to remove the irradiated fuel elements from the reactor, to separate the fission products and ^{239}Pu (formed from ^{238}U) and to re-constitute the fuel rods with purified uranium. The fission products are valuable as a source of radioactive isotopes and ^{239}Pu is itself an important nuclear fuel.

The approximate composition of natural uranium after an irradiation corresponding to the energy release of 1000 megawatt-days per ton is: U, 99·8 per cent; Pu, 0·08 per cent; fission products, 0·08 per cent. Solvent extraction procedures have proved to be the most successful for the isolation of pure uranium and plutonium from such a mixture.

The process carried out at Windscale (Cumberland) by the U.K.A.E.A. is based on the preferential extraction of plutonyl and uranyl nitrates, $PuO_2(NO_3)_2$ and $UO_2(NO_3)_2$ respectively, by an organic solvent. The chief stages are:

(i) Dissolution of the irradiated fuel in nitric acid. This oxidizing solvent produces U^{VI} and Pu^{VI}.

(ii) Extraction of U^{VI} and Pu^{VI} by an immiscible organic solvent. Dibutyl carbitol ('Butex') was originally used but it has been superseded by tri-n-butyl phosphate ('TBP'). Uranyl and plutonyl nitrates, together with some nitric acid, are extracted from aqueous solution, leaving almost all the fission products behind:

$$UO_2^{2+}(aq) + 2NO_3^-(aq) + 2TBP(org) = UO_2(NO_3)_2 . 2TBP(org)$$

Nitric acid is co-extracted as the $1:1$ solvate—$HNO_3 . TBP$.

(*iii*) Neutralization of nitric acid in the TBP phase and reduction of Pu^{VI} to Pu^{III} by ferrous sulphamate. U^{VI} is unaffected.

(*iv*) Extraction of Pu^{III} from the TBP phase by aqueous 8 M ammonium nitrate (containing a small amount of nitric acid).

(*v*) Oxidation of the aqueous phase containing Pu^{III} with sodium dichromate. Then the Pu^{VI} formed is extracted by fresh TBP from nitric acid solution as before, leaving behind the remainder of the fission products.

(*vi*) Back-extraction of the separate TBP solutions of $UO_2(NO_3)_2$ and $PuO_2(NO_3)_2$ into dilute aqueous acid. This gives two aqueous solutions containing purified uranium and plutonium respectively. These are then worked up to obtain the metals themselves.

The whole of the above process is operated on a continuous basis with constant recirculation of solvents and solutions.

The Separation of Zirconium and Hafnium

These two elements invariably occur together in nature and are noted for their great chemical resemblance to each other. Many attempts have been made to achieve a separation and these have received fresh impetus from the demand of the atomic energy industry for hafnium-free zirconium. This metal and its alloys have good corrosion resistance and a low absorption for neutrons. Both these properties are desirable when the material is to be used inside a nuclear reactor, either for structural purposes or to contain the radioactive fuel elements. Hafnium, in contrast, is a powerful neutron absorber.

Several solvent extraction processes are used on a large scale to effect the separation. In one method, hafnium thiocyanate, $Hf(SCN)_4$, is preferentially extracted from HCl solutions by isobutyl methyl ketone. Another process depends on the preferential extraction of zirconium from nitrate solutions using TBP.

The Separation of Niobium and Tantalum

Niobium and tantalum are another pair of metals which are very difficult to separate by classical methods. Successful solvent extraction procedures have, however, been developed. For example, tantalum is extracted to a greater extent than niobium from HF/HCl solutions by methyl isobutyl ketone. Both niobium and tantalum form fluoro-complexes: in aqueous solutions containing moderate concentrations of HF (1 to 3 M) Ta^V is present largely as $[TaF_7]^{2-}$ and Nb^V is present as $NbOF_5$. $[NbF_7]^{2-}$ is formed to an appreciable extent only at high HF concentrations. It is probable that the preferential extraction of tantalum is related to the greater ease of formation and extraction of the acido-complex H_2TaF_7 compared with H_2NbF_7.

LIQUID METAL SYSTEMS

Silver is distributed between immiscible molten lead and zinc phases with a partition coefficient of about 300 in favour of the zinc phase. This solvent extraction system was the basis of the Parkes process (1850) for the desilverization of lead which was in use for many years in this country.

Recent investigations into the use of a liquid metal as an extractant have been with the aim of devising a more direct method for the re-processing of irradiated uranium than the aqueous/organic solvent process. A liquid-metal extraction process would have the chief advantage of the preservation of the metallic state throughout. The two most promising metals for the extraction of plutonium from irradiated uranium are silver and magnesium. Silver is the better extractant but the subsequent separation of the silver and plutonium presents difficulties owing to the high boiling point of silver. Magnesium extracts plutonium to a lesser extent than does silver but it can be readily removed afterwards because of its relatively high volatility. Neither metal, however, is very selective for the separation of fission product activity from either the uranium or plutonium. Another problem which must be solved is the provision of a suitable containing material for the liquid metals. Tantalum metal, coated with suitable ceramic material to reduce corrosion, appears to be the most promising to date.

ION EXCHANGE

An ion-exchange material is an insoluble substance containing anions or cations which are exchangeable with ions in a surrounding solution without physical change in the structure of the ion-exchange material.

Certain naturally occurring alumino-silicates, the zeolites, show the property of ion exchange. Synthetic zeolites, whose main use is in water softening, have also been made. Dissolved calcium and magnesium salts are responsible for the hardness of water. The softening process involves the removal of the metal ions. This can be carried out by allowing the hard water to percolate through a bed of zeolitic exchanger in the sodium form. Replacement of the calcium ions in water by sodium ions takes place according to:

$$Ca^{2+} + 2Na^+(Z^-) \rightleftharpoons 2Na^+ + Ca^{2+}(Z^-)_2$$

where (Z^-) represents the zeolite. Magnesium ions are replaced by a similar reaction. If percolation is continued, a stage is reached when all the sodium ions on the exchanger have been replaced by calcium. The exchange material may then be regenerated for further water softening by washing with a concentrated solution of sodium chloride. This procedure reverses the above equation.

The first synthetic organic cation exchangers were produced in 1935 by the sulphonation of various coals and soon afterwards ion-exchange resins were synthesized by condensation reactions like that between phenol and formaldehyde. These resins incorporate acidic groups like sulphonic, $—SO_3H$, in strongly acid resins, and carboxyl, —COOH, in weakly acid resins. Hydrogen ions can be displaced by other cations:

$$R.SO_3H + NaCl \rightleftharpoons RSO_3Na + HCl$$
$$2R.SO_3Na + Ca^{2+} \rightleftharpoons (RSO_3)_2Ca + 2Na^+$$

Anion-exchange resins are condensation products containing basic quaternary ammonium groups and replaceable OH^- ions. Examples of the anion-exchange process are:

$$R.N(CH_3)_3OH + NaCl \rightleftharpoons R.N(CH_3)_3Cl + NaOH$$
$$2R.N(CH_3)_3Cl + SO_4^{2-} \rightleftharpoons [R.N(CH_3)_3]_2SO_4 + 2Cl^-$$

To be of practical use, an ion-exchange resin must be resistant to chemical and physical breakdown and insoluble in any solvent used. These properties are gained by the careful control of the conditions of manufacture.

The great success of these materials in effecting difficult separations is due to their different affinities for various ions. For example, the order of affinities, obtained in 0·1 N aqueous chloride solution at 25°C, of some simple ions for a sulphonic cation-exchanger is:

$$Li^+ < H^+ < Na^+ < K^+ < Cd^{2+} < Rb^+ < Cs^+ < Mg^{2+} < Cu^{2+} < Co^{2+}$$
$$< Ca^{2+} < Sr^{2+} < Ba^{2+} < Al^{3+} < Th^{4+}$$

The greater the charge, the more firmly bound is the ion and the greater the tendency for it to displace one of lower charge from the resin. For two ions of equal charge, the larger one is the more strongly held by the resin.

Ion-exchange materials are applied to an ever-increasing extent both in the laboratory and on an industrial scale and some of the more important uses are described below.

1. The Demineralization of Water

Complete removal of dissolved salts can be brought about by the use of both types of exchanger. Thus the aqueous solution can be passed first through a bed of cation-exchanger in the hydrogen form to convert the salts to the corresponding free acids. The acids may then be removed on an anion-exchanger. Alternatively, the process can be carried out by passing the solution through a 'mixed-bed' of resin which contains both anion- and cation-exchanger.

2. Separations by Ion-Exchange Chromatography

These are most conveniently achieved by sorption of the mixture of ions to be separated on a column of resin material followed by the elution (removal) from the column by washing with an aqueous solution of suitable reagents.

(a) *The rare earths*—The history of the discovery of the rare earths is characterized by the application of improved techniques of identification and separation resulting in the further subdivision of what had hitherto been considered as homogeneous substances. Spectroscopic analysis was of major importance in the characterization of the rare-earth metals. The close similarity of the rare earths to one another posed difficult problems in their

191

separation and up to 15 years ago they could only be separated by the repetition of the time-consuming procedures of fractional precipitation or crystallization of their salts. In a few cases it was possible to utilize valency states different from the group valency of 3. Thus Ce^{III} can be oxidized to Ce^{IV} and then resembles a Group IV rather than a Group III metal; Eu^{III}, Sm^{III} and Yb^{III} can all be reduced to the divalent state in which they show resemblances to the alkaline earths.

Arising from intensive research on atomic energy projects during World

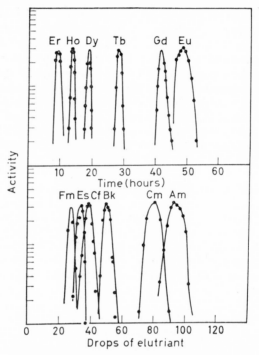

Figure 8.2. The elution of tripositive lanthanide ions (upper diagram) and tripositive actinide ions (lower diagram) from Dowex-50 cation-exchange resin using ammonium citrate/citric acid eluant of pH 3·35 at 87°C (Diagram from KATZ, J. J. and SEABORG, G. T. *The Chemistry of the Actinide Elements*, Methuen, London, 1957)

War II, a chromatographic separation of the lanthanides was worked out using ion-exchange resins. The tripositive ions are strongly sorbed by a cation-exchange resin: La^{3+}, the largest, is most strongly held; Lu^{3+}, the smallest, is least strongly held. Elution by HCl therefore removes Lu^{3+} first and La^{3+} last. The separation is not good, however, particularly between the heavier lanthanides, but is markedly improved by the addition of a complexing agent such as a citrate to the eluting solution. The citrate ion complexes most strongly with the heaviest metals and least strongly with the lightest. When elution is carried out using an ammonium citrate/citric acid buffer, the partial separation effected by the resin is greatly enhanced by complex-formation in solution. Other complexing agents used in the aqueous phase include ethylenediaminetetracetic acid (EDTA, p. 145). As much as 80 per cent of an element is obtained in a high state of purity from a single passage through the exchange column. *Figure 8.2* illustrates the chromatographic separation of the lanthanides. In this way it has proved possible for the first time to prepare and study the properties of kilogram quantities of many of the rare-earth metals in a pure state.

(*b*) *The transuranic elements*—Ion-exchange resins have also been of great value in the isolation of the artificially prepared transuranic elements. For example, berkelium (97) is produced by the bombardment of americium (95) with α-particles from a cyclotron. Curium (96) and fission products are obtained at the same time. The most effective means of purifying berkelium is by elution from a cation-exchange resin, using a citrate buffer. *Figure 8.2* demonstrates that complete separation from Cm and Am is achieved.

Many other separation procedures involving cation-exchange resins have been devised. A number of other separations are possible using an anion-exchange resin—usually a strongly basic one—which sorbs metals as complex anions. These are then successively eluted with a mixture of aqueous HF and HCl. In this way, niobium and tantalum, and zirconium and hafnium have been separated.

3. The Production of Uranium Concentrates

Uranium is widely distributed but deposits of high-grade ore are rare. At the present time the major part of the uranium supply comes from ores which have a uranium content as low as 0·1 per cent. Ion exchange is very important in the working-up of these low-grade ores for the preparation of uranium concentrates.

Physical methods of concentration are used for the initial removal of un-wanted materials. Then the ore is chemically treated either by an acid leach using dilute sulphuric acid or by an alkaline leach using sodium carbonate solution.

The acid leach is carried out in the presence of an oxidizing agent such as MnO_2 or $NaClO_3$ to ensure that the uranium originally present (usually as U_3O_8) is converted completely to U^{VI}. In the leach liquor, the uranium is is present in the form of complex anions such as $[UO_2(SO_4)_2]^{2-}$ and $[UO_2(SO_4)_3]^{4-}$. These will exchange readily for other ions on an anion-exchange resin. Uranium is one of the few elements to form strong anionic complexes in sulphate solutions and so many impurities are removed by the sorption of uranium from such solutions by an anion-exchanger.

The carbonate leach is more selective than the acid extraction because most metal carbonates are insoluble in water and do not form soluble complexes. High temperatures or pressures are needed, however, in order to speed up the solution process.

A typical ion-exchange column for use in uranium concentration is 7 ft. in diameter, 12 ft. high and contains about 7 tons of resin. For sorption from acid leach solutions a three-column system is employed. Two columns are used to remove uranium from the leach liquors, whilst the third is being eluted with $1M$ NH_4NO_3. After removal of uranium from the third column, the resin is regenerated with sulphuric acid and is re-used in the next sorption cycle. The prime advantage of the ion-exchange process is that concentration of the uranium in solution is achieved at the same time as the removal of impurities.

SUGGESTED REFERENCES FOR FURTHER READING

DAWSON, J. K., and LONG, G. *Chemistry of Nuclear Power*, Newnes, London, 1959.

DUNCAN, J. F., and LISTER, B. A. J. 'Ion exchange', *Quart. Rev. chem. Soc., Lond.*, 2 (1948) 307.

IRVING, H. M. N. H. 'Solvent extraction', *Quart. Rev. chem. Soc., Lond.*, 5 (1951) 200.

MARSH, J. K. 'The separation of the lanthanons', *Quart. Rev. chem. Soc., Lond.*, 1 (1947) 126.

MARTIN, F. S., and HOLT, R. J. W. 'Liquid–liquid extraction in inorganic chemistry', *Quart. Rev. chem. Soc., Lond.*, 13 (1959) 327.

9

THE COMPARATIVE CHEMISTRY OF THE REPRESENTATIVE ELEMENTS

HYDROGEN

THE hydrogen atom has the electron configuration $1s^1$. The properties of the element may be compared either with those of the alkali metals, since H^+ is formed like Li^+, Na^+, *etc.* by the loss of one electron, or else with the halogens, since like them the hydrogen atom can attain the configuration of an inert gas by the acquisition of one electron to form the hydride ion H^- or by forming one covalent bond. Although certain analogies are possible with both groups, there are many unique aspects of hydrogen chemistry and so the element is generally considered on its own.

Table 9.1. The properties of hydrogen

Electron configuration	$1s^1$		
Ionization potential (kcal/g atom)	313·6		
Electron affinity (kcal/g atom)	17·3		
Electronegativity	2·1		
Ionic radius (Å) H^+	$\sim 10^{-5}$		
H^-	2·1		
Isotopes	^1_1H	^2_1H	^3_1H
Atomic weights	1·0081	2·0147	3·0061

As indicated in *Table 9.1*, three isotopes exist: hydrogen (H), deuterium (D) and tritium (T). Of these, only the first two are important in nature, the relative abundance ratio being of the order of 6000:1 in favour of the lighter isotope. The third isotope occurs to only about one part in 10^{17} of ordinary hydrogen and is generally prepared by nuclear bombardment of the light elements.

The diatomic molecule (H_2) is found in two forms existing in equilibrium, namely *ortho*- and *para*-hydrogen; these differ from each other in the direction of nuclear spin. In the former, spins are parallel but in the latter they are opposed. At room temperature and above, the ratio of *ortho* to *para* is 3:1 whereas at low temperatures (about 20°K) the equilibrium lies almost entirely in favour of the *para* form. Conversion of *ortho* to *para* may be catalysed by absorption on to activated charcoal. The two forms have slightly different physical properties. A similar situation arises in the case of the deuterium molecule.

Chemically, hydrogen is characterized by the formation of binary covalent hydrides and the hydride ion. The unipositive oxidation state is shown in combination with the more electronegative elements such as chlorine and bromine to form the polar molecules HCl and HBr. The hydride ion is formed only in combination with the most electropositive elements such as

195

lithium and sodium. In solution chemistry, molecules like HCl are ionized and the solvated proton is formed by the attraction of the extremely small H^+ ion, with its associated high charge density, for the solvent molecules. In aqueous solution the oxonium ion is formed. This is conventionally written as H_3O^+ though there are almost certainly more water molecules attached to the proton than this simple formulation would suggest.

The covalency of hydrogen is limited to one because only two electrons can be accommodated in the first quantum shell. There are, however, certain instances where a hydrogen atom is to be found between two atoms being covalently bound to the first atom and joined by hydrogen bonding to the second. Hydrogen bonding, as previously mentioned (p. 69) is only observed where hydrogen is in combination with the most electronegative elements. This bond is responsible for association in hydrogen fluoride, water and liquid ammonia and dictates the structure of crystals of ice, oxy-acids, ammonium salts and many minerals.

Compounds

Hydrides

This is the general name assigned to compounds formed between hydrogen and other elements of the Periodic Table, though to be dogmatic this should only be applied to compounds formed with elements of lower electronegativity. From a consideration of the type of bonding that occurs in these compounds, three classes may be distinguished.

(a) *The Ionic Hydrides*—These are typified by the compounds formed with the Group I A and II A elements, except magnesium and beryllium, at elevated temperatures. The presence of the hydride ion H^- is demonstrated by electrolysis of the molten hydride when hydrogen is formed at the anode. This is best accomplished with LiH since the thermal stability decreases from LiH to CsH and CaH_2 to BaH_2.

As ionic compounds, these hydrides are characterized by high melting points and boiling points and are electrically conducting in the fused state. The alkali metal hydrides possess the sodium chloride structure but the structures of the hydrides of the alkaline earth metals are more complex.

Vigorous hydrolysis occurs with the formation of hydrogen and the corresponding hydroxide:

$$H^- + H_2O = H_2 + OH^-$$

Reducing properties are exhibited at high temperatures; thus sodium hydride will reduce Fe_3O_4 to metallic iron and carbon dioxide to sodium formate:

$$NaH + CO_2 = NaCOOH$$

At room temperature, however, this reducing property is lost; it appears, therefore, that thermal dissociation of the hydride must be a necessary step in these reactions.

(b) *The Covalent Hydrides*—The representative elements of Groups IV, V, VI and VII form mononuclear hydrides where the element exhibits the group valency. These compounds, except water and a few others, are gaseous under normal conditions. The stability of the hydrides within any one group

196

decreases as the atomic number increases, those formed by the more metallic elements in particular are extremely unstable although there is evidence for the existence of hydrides such as PbH_4 and BiH_3.

With the members of Group III B, the simplest hydrides formed are of the polynuclear type, *e.g.* B_2H_6, Ga_2H_6 and $(AlH_3)_n$. In these compounds, which are electron deficient, multicentre bonds are present (p. 207).

A number of polynuclear hydrides are also formed by certain other elements: these include the lighter elements of Group IV B, which give rise to hydrocarbons, silanes, germanes; and nitrogen and oxygen, which form hydrazine and hydrogen peroxide respectively.

The preparation of the hydrides may be effected by a variety of methods:

(i) Direct combination of the elements, *e.g.* H_2O, NH_3 and HF.
(ii) Reduction of certain compounds in the presence of hydrogen, *e.g.* AsH_3 and SbH_3.
(iii) Electrolytic reduction, *e.g.* SnH_4.
(iv) Hydrolysis of metal borides, carbides and similar compounds.
(v) Reduction of halides by lithium aluminium hydride, *e.g.* SiH_4, GeH_4 and SnH_4.

(*c*) *Interstitial Hydrides*—The uptake of hydrogen by palladium metal is a well-known characteristic of the metal. This is accomplished by absorption of the hydrogen into the interstices of the metallic lattice, the resultant composition approximating to $PdH_{0.6}$. Non-stoichiometric formulae are found for most compounds of this group, thus zirconium forms $ZrH_{1.92}$ and titanium forms a compound $TiH_{1.73}$, though the use of different pressures and temperatures of reaction may cause variations in the exact proportion of hydrogen. A close similarity is found between the hydrides and the parent metal; thus they are involatile and metallic in character. The absorption of hydrogen causes an expansion of the metal lattice as indicated by the lower density of the hydride.

Although the more basic of the lanthanide elements form hydrides of similar non-stoichiometric constitution, *e.g.* $LaH_{2.76}$, $CeH_{2.7}$ and $PrH_{2.9}$, their heats of formation are comparable with the salt-like hydrides. Again, their densities are less than that of the parent metal.

Certain metallic hydrides do possess stoichiometric formulae, *e.g.* a hydride of copper, obtained by the reduction of Cu^{2+} by the hypophosphite ion at 70°C, has the formula CuH, though accurate measurements show there is a very slight hydrogen deficiency. Hydrides of composition NiH_2, CoH_2, FeH_2 and CrH_3 may be prepared by reaction between the anhydrous metal chloride in ether with phenyl magnesium bromide and hydrogen.

DEUTERIUM

Evidence for the existence of this isotope was first obtained when the examination of residues from large quantities of liquid hydrogen by spectral techniques showed shifts in the spectral lines of the Balmer series. These shifts could only be explained by the assumption that an isotope of hydrogen with mass two was present (UREY, BRICKWEDDE and MURPHY, 1931).

This is the more accessible of the heavy isotopes and is obtained by a process of fractional electrolysis of water. This involves repeated electrolyses until at the later stages deuterium is obtained at the cathode in fairly high proportions. The cathode gases are burned and returned to the cell and eventually a residue of heavy water, D_2O, is left. Deuterium may then be obtained by any one of the processes used to prepare hydrogen from water.

Chemically, deuterium is indistinguishable from hydrogen but there are significant differences in the physical properties, as shown in *Table 9.2*.

Table 9.2. Comparison of physical properties of hydrogen and deuterium

Property	Hydrogen (H_2)	Deuterium (D_2)
Boiling point (°C)	−252·6	−249·4
Melting point (°C)	−259·2	−254·4
Latent heat of fusion (cal/mole)	28·0	52·3
Vapour pressure (mm Hg) (at b.p. of H_2)	760	250

Compounds of deuterium may be prepared by reactions involving D_2O; thus ND_3 may be obtained by reacting magnesium nitride with D_2O, and SO_3 reacts with heavy water to form D_2SO_4.

Rapid exchange takes place between ionizable hydrogen and ionizable deuterium, but covalently bound deuterium does not appear to take part in exchange reactions unless hydrogenation catalysts are present. Because of these exchange properties deuterium finds considerable application in the study of mechanisms of reactions and as an isotopic indicator.

TRITIUM

This isotope was discovered during mass spectrometric investigations of deuterium-enriched hydrogen; its occurrence in ordinary water is minute and generally it is prepared by one of a number of nuclear reactions.

Deuteron bombardment of deuterium compounds leads to the following reaction:

$$^2_1H + ^2_1H \longrightarrow ^3_1H + ^1_1H$$

Another method of production involves the bombardment of beryllium by deuterons:

$$^2_1H + ^9_4Be \longrightarrow ^3_1H + 2^4_2He$$

Neutron bombardment of certain lithium or boron isotopes produces tritium:

$$^1_0n + ^{10}_5B \longrightarrow ^3_1H + 2^4_2He$$

$$^1_0n + ^6_3Li \longrightarrow ^3_1H + ^4_2He$$

This isotope of hydrogen is radioactive, being a weak β-emitter, with a half-life of approximately 12·5 years.

GROUP 0—THE INERT GASES

The elements constituting this group of the Periodic Table are helium (He), neon (Ne), argon (Ar), krypton (Kr), xenon (Xe) and radon (Rn).

All are monatomic gases characterized by high volatility and a short liquid range. With the exception of helium, which has the electron configuration $1s^2$, all the other elements of the group have a completely filled p shell of electrons. These complete shells of electrons, which have high ionization potentials, have appeared to be chemically inert until quite recently, hence the name inert gases. Because, however, a number of xenon compounds have now been prepared, together with two krypton fluorides, the term *noble gases* is to be preferred. Extraction of all except helium and radon is carried

Table 9.3. *The properties of the inert gases*

	He	Ne	Ar	Kr	Xe	Rn
Atomic number	2	10	18	36	54	86
Electron configuration	$1s^2$	$2s^2 2p^6$	$3s^2 3p^6$	$4s^2 4p^6$	$5s^2 5p^6$	$6s^2 6p^6$
Melting point (°C)	−272·1*	−248·6	−189·4	−156·6	−111·5	−71·0
Boiling point (°C)	−268·98	−246·0	−185·9	−152·9	−107·1	−65·0
Ionization potential (kcal/g atom)	566·8	497·2	363·4	322·8	279·7	247·9
Atomic radius (Å)	0·93	1·12	1·54	1·69	1·90	

* At 25 atmospheres pressure

out by fractional distillation of liquid air. Isotopes of radon are formed during certain radioactive disintegrations and helium is a product of radioactive decay —the alpha particles take up two electrons to form the helium atom. Helium gas is thus associated with minerals that contain alpha emitters, *e.g.* pitchblende; production is effected in the U.S.A. from natural gases by liquefaction of all except helium.

Some physical properties of the inert gases are given in *Table 9.3*.

Compounds

Until very recently, no chemical compounds of the inert gases were known. In discharge tubes species such as He_2^+ and HeH^+ have been observed: under these excited conditions the s electrons in helium are unpaired and one is excited to a higher energy state.

Physical trapping of atoms of the inert gases may occur in crystal lattices. Thus argon, krypton and xenon atoms become trapped in quinol when the latter substance is crystallized from water under considerable pressure of the inert gas. The empirical formulae of these solids, known as *clathrate compounds*, are (3 quinol. IG), the inert gas being encaged by three quinol molecules linked by hydrogen bonding.

Hydrates and deuterates have been obtained for the heaviest of the inert gases, *e.g.* $Xe.6H_2O$; with the lighter elements these are formed only under pressure.

More recently, a number of stoichiometric compounds, such as $XePtF_6$ and XeF_4, have been made for the first time and currently the synthesis of further inert gas compounds is of great interest (see p. 282). The existence of compounds between the inert gases and electronegative elements is not really surprising when ionization potential data is considered: thus the first ionization potential of xenon is very close to that of bromine and is appreciably less than that of hydrogen (see p. 43).

Because of their unreactive character, these elements, particularly argon, are useful as inert atmospheres where experimentation is not possible in the presence of air. Both neon and argon find application in the electronics field and liquid helium is used as a coolant.

GROUP I—REPRESENTATIVE ELEMENTS

The elements of this group, lithium (Li), sodium (Na), potassium (K), rubidium (Rb), caesium (Cs) and francium (Fr), the first series of representative elements, have one s electron in the new quantum shell after the inert-gas core. A consideration of their ionization potentials shows that this electron is but loosely held and the group, as a whole, therefore, is characterized by the great tendency to form monovalent cations. The electropositive character is the highest of the known elements and the metals are thus extremely reactive. The ease of loss of the outermost electron determines the chemical properties of the metals to a large extent: thus the reaction with water increases with vigour from lithium to caesium. The metals exhibit a high degree of conductivity and are soft and readily fusible. In the vapour state a small proportion of diatomic molecules is present. The atoms are held together by a weak covalent bond formed by the overlap of the s orbitals.

Table 9.4. The properties of the alkali metals

	Li	Na	K	Rb	Cs	Fr
Atomic number	3	11	19	37	55	87
Electron configuration	$2s^1$	$3s^1$	$4s^1$	$5s^1$	$6s^1$	$7s^1$
Melting point (°C)	179·1	97·5	63·5	39·0	28·5	
Boiling point (°C)	1340	885	775	690	670	
Ionization potential (kcal/g atom)	124·3	118·4	100·0	96·3	89·3	
Atomic radius (Å)	1·23	1·57	2·03	2·16	2·35	
Ionic radius (Å)	0·60	0·95	1·33	1·48	1·69	
Ionic mobility × 10⁵ (cm²/sec volt)	40·1	51·9	76·2	79·2	79·6	

Compounds

Hydrides

All the metals of the group form hydrides of the type MH by direct combination which requires increasingly higher temperatures from lithium to caesium. These are ionic compounds (p. 196), the most stable being lithium hydride, and all have the sodium chloride lattice.

Hydrolysis results in the formation of the corresponding hydroxide with liberation of hydrogen. Electrolysis in the fused state yields hydrogen at the anode as expected for the presence of H^-.

In addition to these simple hydrides a number of complex hydrides are also known, for example $LiBH_4$ and $LiAlH_4$. Like the simple hydrides, these are good reducing agents. $LiBH_4$ has the constitution of a salt with Li^+ and BH_4^- ions in the lattice.

200

Nitrides

The ease of formation of the nitrides falls with increasing atomic number and only lithium nitride is capable of formation by heating the metal in nitrogen. The remaining alkali metals form nitrides by reaction with activated nitrogen but the products are frequently contaminated by azide formation.

Extreme sensitivity is shown to moisture, with hydrolysis to ammonia and the hydroxide.

Oxides

Lithium and sodium show distinct differences from the other metals of the group in their reaction with oxygen.

Burning of lithium in excess oxygen leads to the formation of the monoxide Li_2O, whereas under the same conditions sodium yields mainly the peroxide Na_2O_2. With the remaining metals this reaction results in the formation of the superoxides MO_2. Small amounts of the superoxide are often found as impurity in commercial samples of sodium peroxide and this imparts a yellow colour to the otherwise white solid. Normally, sodium superoxide is obtained by reacting the peroxide with oxygen under pressure and at elevated temperatures.

Special methods are employed for the preparation of the less stable oxides. Thus K_2O_2 is obtained by passing oxygen into solution of the metal in liquid ammonia at about $-60°C$. The monoxides of the heavier metals are obtained by heating the metal with the nitrate:

$$e.g. \quad 10K + 2KNO_3 = 6K_2O + N_2$$

The superoxides, all highly coloured, were for some time thought to have the dimeric formula M_2O_4. Such a formulation would require them to be diamagnetic, whereas paramagnetism is exhibited corresponding to the presence of one unpaired electron as required by the ion O_2^-. This ion may be formulated as below, with one three-electron bond as well as the single electron-pair bond; or better from the molecular-orbital approach, as O_2 plus one electron in a π^*2p orbital.

$$:\!\overset{\cdot}{O}\!\cdot\cdot\cdot\!\overset{\cdot}{\underset{\cdot\cdot}{O}}\!:^{-}$$

The presence of O_2^- is supported by x-ray data on the solids which are found to have a distorted NaCl structure (O_2^- replacing Cl^-).

Rapid reaction with water occurs with all the oxides and results in the formation of the hydroxides:

$$2Na_2O_2 + 2H_2O = 4NaOH + O_2$$
$$2KO_2 + 2H_2O = 2KOH + H_2O_2 + O_2$$

In addition to these oxides, rubidium and caesium are reported to form sesquioxides Rb_2O_3 and Cs_2O_3. Investigations have shown that there are correctly formulated as mixed superoxides–peroxides, *e.g.* $Rb_2O_2.2RbO_2$.

Furthermore the reaction of ozonized oxygen with the hydroxides in the solid state or with the metals in liquid ammonia yields the ozonides MO_3. The stability of these compounds increases with increasing atomic number and the formation of LiO_3 is extremely doubtful. Paramagnetism is exhibited by the ozonides and they are characterized by high colouration and great reactivity.

Slow decomposition to the superoxide and oxygen occurs on standing and rapid hydrolysis is effected by moisture.

Halides

With the exception of certain lithium halides, the alkali metal halides are essentially ionic in their constitution. The thermal stability of the halides increases with increasing atomic number of the metal atom and decreasing atomic number of the halogen atom.

Except for CsCl, CsBr and CsI, the crystal structure is that of sodium chloride with 6 co-ordination of the ions. For the caesium halides, 8 co-ordination is exhibited.

A general survey of the salts of the alkali metals shows them to be more soluble in water and other polar solvents than the corresponding salts of other metals. The degree of solvation in solution diminishes from lithium to caesium as demonstrated by the ionic mobilities of the individual ions (*Table 9.4*); lithium, because of the high positive charge density in the ion, shows the greatest tendency to hydrate. Sodium chloride shows less tendency to hydrate, although a dihydrate has been prepared by crystallization of a saturated solution of the salt at less than 0°C. Hydration persists in the solid state where some 75 per cent of lithium and sodium salts are found to be hydrated. For the heavier metals this percentage drops to 25 per cent for potassium salts and for rubidium and caesium only one salt is found to be hydrated, this being the ferrocyanide. Evidence suggests that for salts of potassium, rubidium and caesium the hydration is associated with the anion rather than the cation.

A number of alkali metal complexes have been obtained with organic molecules, for instance salicylaldehyde will complex with all the group members. In these complexes the co-ordination of lithium is invariably 4 but the other alkali metals exhibit both 4 and 6 co-ordination.

Peculiarities of Lithium

Because of its small ionic size, comparable with that of magnesium, lithium shows distinct differences from the lower group members and in fact strongly resembles magnesium in its chemical behaviour. Several instances of this are:

(*a*) Lithium is the only member of the group to form a nitride by direct combination with nitrogen. Similarly, the ready combination with carbon to form a carbide is an analogy with magnesium.

(*b*) The carbonate is relatively unstable thermally and the bicarbonate cannot be isolated from aqueous solution.

(*c*) The solubilities in water of the compounds of lithium as a whole resemble those of magnesium; thus the chloride, bromide and iodide all have high solubility but the fluoride, carbonate, phosphate and oxalate are only slightly soluble.

Francium

Until 1946 the gap in the Periodic Table at element 87 had defied filling, but it was then established that the element arose from a branch chain decay of ^{227}Ac by alpha emission, the main decay (98·8%) of which is by electron emission to ^{227}Th. Characterization of the chemical properties of francium is made difficult by the problem of the short half-life (21 min) of the longest-lived isotope ^{223}Fr which decays to ^{223}Ra, but it appears to fit into the alkali metal group and in its precipitation reactions shows a strong resemblance to caesium.

Several other isotopes are known and these all have shorter half-lives than ^{223}Fr; the three longest-lived after ^{223}Fr are ^{212}Fr, ^{222}Fr and ^{221}Fr, with respective half-lives of 19·3, 14·8 and 4·8 minutes.

GROUP II—REPRESENTATIVE ELEMENTS

This group contains beryllium (Be), magnesium (Mg); the alkaline earths calcium (Ca), strontium (Sr) and barium (Ba); the radioactive element radium (Ra).

With the elements of this group there are two valency electrons contained in a completed s quantum shell. The loss of these electrons with the formation of the dipositive oxidation state becomes easier with increasing atomic number, but, unlike the members of Group I A, the chemistry of this family is not completely dominated by the chemistry of the cations. Covalent character is

Table 9.5. *The properties of the Group II representative elements*

	Be	Mg	Ca	Sr	Ba	Ra
Atomic number	4	12	20	38	56	88
Electron configuration	$2s^2$	$3s^2$	$4s^2$	$5s^2$	$6s^2$	$7s^2$
Melting point (°C)	1280	650	850	760	710	
Boiling point (°C)	1500	1100	1490	1380	1640	
Ionization potential						
(kcal/g atom) 1st	214·9	176·3	140·9	131·2	120·1	
2nd	419·9	346·6	273·7	254·4	230·6	
Atomic radius (Å)	0·89	1·36	1·74	1·91	1·98	
Ionic radius (Å) M^{2+}	0·31	0·65	0·99	1·13	1·35	

predominant in the compounds of the first member, beryllium, which, because of its small size and high nuclear charge, shows distinct anomalies in its behaviour and in many instances shows a diagonal relationship to aluminium. The ease of loss of the valency electrons is again the governing factor in the chemistry of the group. The reaction with cold water is vigorous for the alkaline-earth metals but for magnesium attack is only readily effected by hot water and beryllium remains inert even at elevated temperatures.

The general physical properties of the elements are summarized in *Table 9.5*.

Compounds

Hydrides

As the group is descended there is an increase in reactivity towards hydrogen. Beryllium and magnesium show only a slight tendency to react with hydrogen but calcium, strontium and barium react to form the saline hydrides MH_2 at high temperatures. Compared with the alkali metal hydrides, those of calcium, strontium and barium are more thermally stable, but they are similar in behaviour on hydrolysis and electrolysis and hence contain the H^- ion.

Nitrides

On heating, all the group members react with nitrogen forming the nitrides of general formula M_3N_2. Heating the metals in ammonia results in the formation of the same compounds. The stability of the nitrides falls with increasing atomic number. Hydrolysis results in the formation of ammonia and the corresponding hydroxide.

Oxides

Reaction between oxygen and the metals takes place on heating to form the normal oxides, MO. In the case of calcium, strontium and barium these may be obtained also by the thermal decomposition of the corresponding carbonates at very high temperatures.

The oxides, except BeO, have the ionic sodium chloride lattice; beryllium oxide, mainly covalent, has the crystal structure of wurtzite.

Peroxides, MO_2, of the alkaline earth metals are known, the most stable being that of barium which is obtained in the reaction between barium and oxygen at high temperatures and under pressure. The calcium and strontium peroxides may be precipitated as octahydrates by adding hydrogen peroxide to alkaline solutions of calcium and strontium salts. Acidification of the peroxides yields H_2O_2 and this reaction has been used in the preparation of hydrogen peroxide from BaO_2.

Beryllium oxide is inert towards hydrolysis but the remaining oxides of the group hydrolyse with the formation of the corresponding hydroxides which are strong bases. Compared with the alkali metal hydroxides, these are relatively much less soluble. Thermal stability increases from magnesium to barium; barium hydroxide is sufficiently stable to be heated to fusion without decomposition to the oxide.

Halides

Beryllium halides are essentially covalent in their behaviour having low melting points, appreciable volatility and showing no electrical conductivity in the fused anhydrous state. The compounds with any particular halogen show an increase in ionic character with an increase in cationic radius (see p. 50) and the halides of any particular metal show an increase in ionic character for a decrease in anionic radius.

The fluorides of the group have higher lattice energies than the other halides and are consequently less soluble in water. The solubility of the other halides decreases from magnesium to barium. Hydrate formation is characteristic of the halides and attempts to dehydrate by heating often result in the formation of the basic halide by the loss of hydrogen halide; this tendency decreases from magnesium to barium.

Complexes

Beryllium has a great tendency to increase its covalency to the maximum of four by sp^3 hybridization in the formation of tetrahedral complexes such as BeF_4^{2-}. Organic complexes of beryllium are well characterized, in particular compounds with β-diketones and monobasic acids, *e.g.* acetic acid, are typical of the complexes with oxygen as donor atom.

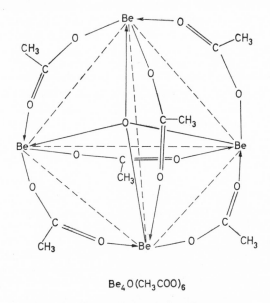

Acetylacetone complex of Be^{II}

With the monobasic carboxylic acids, 'basic' complexes are formed of which the best known is basic beryllium acetate $Be_4O(CH_3COO)_6$. In this compound tetrahedral symmetry is exhibited as shown in *Figure 9.1*. A central oxygen atom is tetrahedrally surrounded by four beryllium atoms and six acid groups are along the edges of the beryllium tetrahedron thus giving a set of 4 co-ordinate beryllium atoms.

$$Be_4O(CH_3COO)_6$$

Figure 9.1. Structure of basic beryllium acetate

For the remainder of the group, weak β-diketone and β-keto ester complexes are formed. Complexes with ethylenediaminetetracetic acid are, however, far more stable and better characterized; the formation of such complexes is used in the quantitative estimation of the metal ions (p. 146).

GROUP III—REPRESENTATIVE ELEMENTS

This group comprises the elements boron (B), aluminium (Al), gallium (Ga), indium (In) and thallium (Tl). The electron configuration is ns^2np^1 and the group valency is three. In addition, lower valency states are obtained and the univalent state in particular becomes of increasing importance as the group is descended; with thallium it is the most important state.

The chemistry of the group may be conveniently divided into that of boron and aluminium on the one hand and that of gallium, indium and thallium on the other.

BORON AND ALUMINIUM

Some general properties of these two elements are given in *Table 9.6*. The high ionization potentials for the formation of the tripositive cations means that bonding in the three-valent state will be mainly covalent. The formation of

Table 9.6. The properties of boron and aluminium

		B	Al
Atomic number		5	13
Electron configuration		$2s^2 2p^1$	$3s^2 3p^1$
Melting point (°C)		2030	660
Boiling point (°C)		3930	2450
Ionization potential	1st	191·3	138·0
(kcal/g atom)	2nd	580·0	434·0
	3rd	874·4	655·8
Atomic radius (Å)		0·80	1·25
Ionic radius (Å) M^{3+}		(0·20)	0·50

three covalent bonds leaves the atoms two short of a completed octet. A great tendency to accept two more electrons and hence increase the number of electrons to eight is shown by both elements.

Compounds

Hydrides

Both boron and aluminium form hydrides of the covalent type.

In the case of boron, several hydrides have been prepared (*Table 9.7*). These were originally investigated by STOCK who obtained a mixture of them

Table 9.7. Physical properties of the boron hydrides

Formula	B_2H_6	B_4H_{10}	B_5H_9	B_5H_{11}	B_6H_{10}	$B_{10}H_{14}$
Name	Diborane	Tetra-borane	Stable penta-borane	Unstable penta-borane	Hexa-borane	Deca-borane
Melting point (°C)	−165·5	−120	−46·6	−123	−65	+99·7
Boiling point (°C)	−92·5	+18	+48	+63		+213

by the acid hydrolysis of magnesium boride Mg_3B_2. This results mainly in the formation of B_4H_{10} and small quantities of the others. At least six volatile hydrides are known and these have attracted much attention because of their reactions and the difficulty experienced in devising suitable structural formulae for them.

Diborane, B_2H_6, is the simplest of the boron hydrides and several methods are available for its preparation:

(*i*) The reaction between boron trichloride or trifluoride and lithium aluminium hydride in ethereal solution.

(*ii*) Sparking of boron trichloride with hydrogen.

and (*iii*) The reduction of boron trifluoride with lithium hydride in ether

$$6\,LiH + 8\,BF_3.Et_2O = 6\,LiBF_4 + B_2H_6 + 8\,Et_2O$$

Higher hydrides may be obtained by pyrolysis of diborane. At 100–120°C the main products of pyrolysis are B_4H_{10} and B_5H_{11}.

Diborane is spontaneously inflammable, especially in damp air, and decomposes to boric acid and hydrogen in the presence of alkali.

With hydrogen chloride, B_2H_5Cl is formed which slowly decomposes to BCl_3 and diborane.

The reaction with excess ammonia at high temperatures yields borazene, $B_3N_3H_6$, a compound somewhat similar to benzene, which has a ring structure of alternate boron and nitrogen atoms.

Structure of the Boron Hydrides

The lowest of the boron hydrides is a dimer, B_2H_6, and this immediately poses problems as to the electronic structure of the molecule. The least number of electron-pair bonds necessary to hold eight atoms together is seven, but in diborane the number of valency electrons is only twelve. Diborane is thus said to be electron-deficient.

Physical evidence suggests that the two boron atoms are bridged by two hydrogens. Various attempts have been made to explain this bridging via hydrogen. PITZER has attempted to describe it in terms of a protonated double bond in which the two bridge hydrogens are situated at the points of

greatest electron density in a double bond similar to that in ethylene. Although this is a reasonably simple approach, it has the drawback of suggesting that the bridge hydrogens should have acidic properties whereas the chemistry of diborane suggests that they react as H^-.

A more convincing approach envisages the boron atom as sp^3 hybridized and forming two molecular orbitals over the boron atoms and the bridge hydrogen atoms. These three-atom orbitals are bent and are frequently referred to as 'banana' bonds, each contains two electrons, one from hydrogen and one from boron:

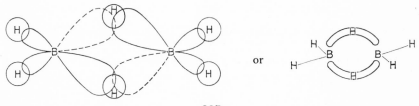

207

The structures of the higher hydrides also pose similar difficulties and for more details of the structures of these molecules the student is referred to more advanced texts.

Aluminium forms a solid polymeric hydride of formula $(AlH_3)_n$ by treatment of lithium hydride with aluminium chloride. The presence of excess lithium hydride leads to the formation of lithium aluminium hydride, $LiAlH_4$. No dimeric hydride has been obtained and the structure of the polymer is not exactly known.

Besides the complex aluminium hydrides, complex boron hydrides are known. Those of the alkali metals are ionic in character but aluminium borohydride is covalent, being a colourless liquid boiling at 45°C. Both the AlH_4^- and BH_4^- ions are unstable in the presence of water and the alkali metal salts of both are useful reducing agents.

Oxides

Boron oxide, B_2O_3, is the product of combustion of boron in oxygen though it also results as the product of dehydration of orthoboric acid, H_3BO_3, via the intermediate formation of metaboric acid, HBO_2, and tetraboric acid, $H_4B_2O_7$. Of these acids, the salts most commonly encountered are those of HBO_2 and $H_4B_2O_7$. The orthoborate ion has a planar structure like NO_3^- and the metaborate ion in $NaBO_2$ has the structure

$$
\begin{bmatrix}
& & O & & \\
& & | & & \\
& & B & & \\
& \diagup & & \diagdown & \\
O & & & & O \\
| & & & & | \\
B & & & & B \\
\diagup & \diagdown & & \diagup & \diagdown \\
O & & O & & O
\end{bmatrix}^{3-}
$$

Boron oxide shows a resemblance to silica in physical properties and has the property of forming complex glasses with other metal oxides.

Aluminium oxide, Al_2O_3, is obtained either by heating the metal in air or by dehydration of the hydrated oxides. This oxide is amphoteric in behaviour and exists in several crystalline modifications. When formed at very high temperatures, a variety of Al_2O_3 is obtained that is extremely resistant to attack, needing fusion with $NaHSO_4$ to dissolve it.

Halides

Boron forms the halides BF_3, BCl_3, BBr_3 and BI_3. The method of formation of the last three is by reduction of the oxide with carbon in the presence of the appropriate halogen at high temperatures. The action of HF on B_2O_3 is used to prepare the fluoride.

All four trihalides are covalent molecules existing as triangular monomers in the vapour phase. Hydrolysis occurs to orthoboric acid:

$$4BF_3 + 3H_2O = H_3BO_3 + 3HBF_4$$

$$BX_3 + 3H_2O = H_3BO_3 + 3HX \quad (X = Cl, \text{ Br or I})$$

All the trihalides behave as acceptor molecules, in particular nitrogen and oxygen are common donor atoms; typical complexes formed are

$$F_3B\leftarrow\!\!-NH_3 \quad \text{and} \quad F_3B\leftarrow\!\!-OEt_2$$

Aluminium similarly forms all four trihalides and, of these, the fluoride is ionic. The chloride, bromide and iodide exist as dimeric molecules both in the vapour phase and in solution of solvents such as benzene. This dimerization occurs by bridging through the halogen atoms as shown. The dimeric molecules are easily broken down by reaction with donor molecules such as ethers:

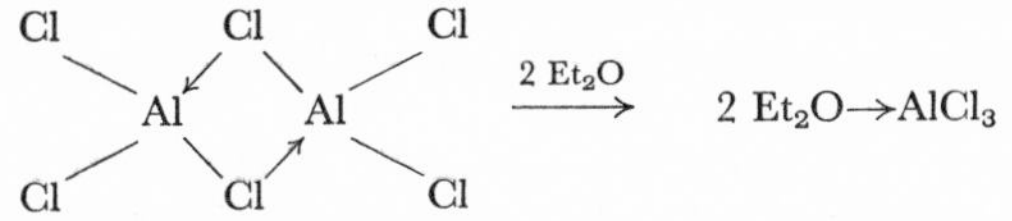

Complex fluoroborates and fluoroaluminates are well known, *e.g.* KBF_4 and Na_3AlF_6.

Complexes

Both boron (III) and aluminium (III) form complexes with β-diketones such as acetylacetone (ac.ac). Aluminium gives the trichelate complex $Al(ac.ac)_3$, whereas boron trihalides react in a different manner to form such complexes as $B(ac.ac)F_2$ (shown below) and $[B(ac.ac)_2]^+ Cl^-$.

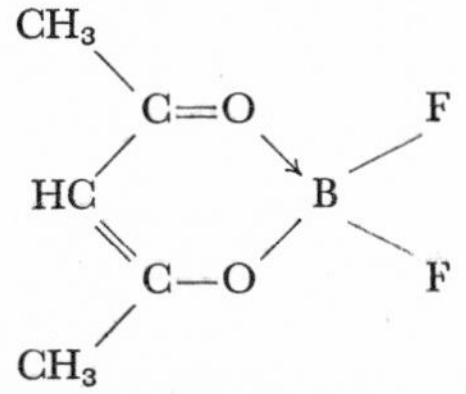

Aluminium (III) also forms complexes with such reagents as oxalic acid, and 8-hydroxyquinoline (see p. 142).

GALLIUM, INDIUM AND THALLIUM

All three elements have three electrons in the outermost shell and exhibit the group valency. Indium also shows a valency of one, though this is unstable with respect to oxidation to indium (III). Thallium (III) compounds are strong oxidants and rapidly decompose to the corresponding thallium (I) compounds, a striking example of the inert pair effect.

The characteristic properties of the three elements are given in *Table 9.8*.

The compounds of gallium are similar to those of aluminium; the oxide is less acidic than Al_2O_3.

In the case of indium, the oxide is even more basic than Ga_2O_3, but compounds of indium (III), on the whole, tend to resemble those of gallium (III). The formation of a number of indium (I) compounds shows some increased inertness of the outermost *s* electrons.

Table 9.8. The properties of gallium, indium and thallium

		Ga	In	Tl
Atomic number		31	49	81
Electron configuration		$3d^{10}4s^24p^1$	$4d^{10}5s^25p^1$	$5d^{10}6s^26p^1$
Melting point (°C)		29·8	156·2	303·6
Boiling point (°C)		2240	2050	1470
Ionization potential	1st	138·4	133·4	140·8
(kcal/g atom)	2nd	473·0	434·2	470·9
	3rd	705·6	643·4	684·9
Atomic radius (Å)		1·25	1·50	1·55
Ionic radius (Å)	M^{3+}	0·62	0·81	0·95
	M^+			1·44

Both gallium and indium form compounds of empirical formula MCl_2, where the metal is apparently in the divalent state. Physical evidence points to the formulation of these chlorides as $M^I(M^{III}Cl_4)$, since if M^{2+} were present paramagnetism would be expected, and the compounds are in fact diamagnetic.

Thallium forms two series of compounds. The thallic, Tl^{III}, compounds show certain resemblances to Ga^{III} and In^{III}. The oxide is completely basic in behaviour. Thallous, Tl^I, compounds show a strong resemblance to both lead (II), with which Tl^I is isoelectronic, and to silver (I). In addition, there are certain resemblances to the alkali metals; thus, the oxide and hydroxide are strong bases.

GROUP IV—REPRESENTATIVE ELEMENTS

This group shows a pronounced change from non-metallic to metallic character as the atomic number increases. Carbon (C) has non-metallic properties, silicon (Si) and germanium (Ge) are semi-conductors, whilst tin (Sn) and lead (Pb) are usually regarded as true metals. Allotropy is shown by carbon and tin. Physical data of the elements are summarized in *Table 9.9*.

Table 9.9. The properties of the Group IV representative elements

	C	Si	Ge	Sn	Pb
Atomic number	6	14	32	50	82
Electron configuration	$2s^22p^2$	$3s^23p^2$	$4s^24p^2$	$5s^25p^2$	$6s^26p^2$
Melting point (°C)		1410	937	232	327
Boiling point (°C)	3850 (subl.)	2680	2830	2687	1751
Electronegativity (Pauling)	2·5	1·8	1·8	1·8	1·8
Atomic radius (Å)	0·77	1·17	1·22	1·41	1·54
Ionic radius (Å) M^{2+}			0·93	1·12	1·20
M^{4+}		0·41	0·53	0·71	0·84

The outermost electron shell is four short of the next inert-gas configuration. The gain of four electrons by one atom appears to be energetically impossible except with carbon in the ionic carbides of strongly electropositive metals. Alternatively, four covalent bonds are formed, as in the hydrides MH_4, the tetrafluorides MF_4, and the tetrachlorides MCl_4, which are known for all five elements. These molecules are tetrahedral and the central atom is therefore sp^3 hybridized. Covalent bond formation of this type is the dominant feature in carbon and silicon chemistry but with the heavier elements account must also be taken of the formation of positive ions.

For Ge, Sn and Pb both the $+2$ and $+4$ oxidation states are well known. The $+2$ state of Ge and Sn are reducing but dipositive Pb is stable. Pb in the $+4$ state has strong oxidizing properties and readily reverts to the $+2$ state. There is, in fact, a well-defined increase in the stability of the $+2$ state in going from Ge to Pb and a corresponding decrease in the stability of the tetravalent state. In the formation of Sn^{2+} and Pb^{2+} ions we have good examples of the inert-pair effect. However, in combination with very electronegative elements, for example, in the dioxides SnO_2 and PbO_2 which have the rutile structure, the tetrapositive ions Sn^{4+} and Pb^{4+} respectively are found.

Carbon, as a first short period element, shows marked differences from the remaining members of the group.

Firstly, the carbon atom is covalently saturated; in other words the second quantum shell is completely filled whenever it is joined by four covalent bonds to other atoms. The maximum covalency of Si and the other elements is six because here d orbitals are available for bonding. In this way, we can account for the inertness of the carbon tetrahalides towards water compared with the ready hydrolysis shown by the tetrahalides of the succeeding elements. The first stage in hydrolysis is the co-ordination of a water molecule followed by the elimination of hydrogen halide from the complex:

$$\begin{array}{c} X \quad X \\ \diagdown \diagup \\ Si \\ \diagup \diagdown \\ X \quad X \end{array} + H_2O = \begin{array}{c} X \quad X \\ \diagdown \diagup \\ Si \leftarrow OH_2 \\ \diagup \diagdown \\ X \quad X \end{array} = \begin{array}{c} X \quad X \\ \diagdown \diagup \\ Si \\ \diagup \diagdown \\ X \quad OH \end{array} + HX$$

and it is apparent that the carbon tetrahalides, with no vacant orbital on the carbon, cannot react in this way. Silicon halides are hydrolysed to SiO_2 irreversibly but hydrolysis is incomplete with the halides of the heavier elements of the group and may be suppressed by the addition of the appropriate hydrogen halide:

$$SiCl_4 + 2H_2O \rightarrow SiO_2 + 4HCl$$
$$GeCl_4 + 2H_2O \rightleftharpoons GeO_2 + 4HCl$$
$$SnCl_4 + 2H_2O \rightleftharpoons SnO_2 + 4HCl$$

Secondly, carbon–carbon bonds are stronger than bonds between like atoms formed by the other members of the group. Numerous carbon compounds are known in which two or more carbon atoms are covalently bound together and this property of forming links with itself (catenation), coupled with the high stability of carbon–hydrogen bonds, is responsible for the immense range of organic compounds. Silicon forms much stronger bonds with fluorine, oxygen and chlorine than with itself or hydrogen (*Table 9.10*) and in contrast to the hydrocarbons the silicon compounds which contain Si—Si or Si—H bonds are generally very reactive. Thus only a few hydrides of silicon, the silanes, are known (SiH_4 to Si_6H_{14}) and these are spontaneously inflammable in air and rapidly decomposed by water. The silanes are analogous to the straight-chain paraffins and, from Si_2H_6 onward contain Si—Si bonds. Catenation is also found to a limited extent in the germanes (GeH_4 to Ge_5H_{12}) but not in compounds of tin and lead.

Table 9.10. *Energies of bonds involving either carbon or silicon*

Bond	Energy (kcal/mole)	Bond	Energy (kcal/mole)
C—H	98·7	Si—H	76
C—C	82·6	Si—Si	53
C=C	145·8		
C≡C	199·6		
C—O	85·5	Si—O	108
C—F	116	Si—F	135
C—Cl	81	Si—Cl	91
C—Br	68	Si—Br	74
C—I	52	Si—I	56

Lastly, carbon is the only element of the group to form stable multiple bonds with itself (*Table 9.10*) and other elements. As a result, there are many carbon compounds which have no analogy elsewhere in the group. Examples are the cyanides (—CN), cyanates (—CNO), thiocyanates (—CNS) and unsaturated organic compounds: also the molecular compounds carbon sub-oxide, C_3O_2, carbon monoxide, CO, and carbon disulphide, CS_2.

Compounds

Hydrides

The formation of volatile hydrides is a property associated mainly with non-metals and carbon is the supreme example. Compared with the enormous number of hydrocarbons, only a few silanes and germanes are known, and the weakly electropositive metals tin and lead form only stannane (SnH_4) and plumbane (PbH_4).

For details of the preparation of hydrocarbons, reference must be made to a textbook of organic chemistry. A mixture of the silanes is obtained when magnesium silicide, Mg_2Si, is hydrolysed with aqueous acid or ammonium bromide/liquid ammonia (p. 126). SiH_4 alone is prepared by the reduction of $SiCl_4$ with $LiAlH_4$ in diethyl ether at 0°C. GeH_4 and SnH_4 are made by similar reactions. The formation of PbH_4 has been demonstrated by the addition of a dilute acid to an alloy of magnesium and thorium-B (radio-active [212]Pb). The production of a volatile hydride of lead is shown by the transfer of radioactivity to the vapour phase.

The thermal stability of the tetrahydrides falls off steadily with increasing molecular weight. The stability towards water, however, follows the sequence:

$$CH_4 \quad > \quad GeH_4 \quad > \quad SnH_4 \quad > \quad SiH_4$$

| stable | unattacked by 33% alkali | unattacked by 15% alkali | quantitative decomposition by water |

This and other chemical evidence has led other workers to dispute Pauling's electronegativity values for Group IV as it is very unlikely that such great differences in reactivity as are shown by SiH_4, GeH_4 and SnH_4 are consistent with the identical values of electronegativity assigned by him to the three elements concerned (*Table 9.9*). ALLRED and ROCHOW have suggested an alternation of electronegativities in this group:

$$C = 2\cdot6; \quad Si = 1\cdot9; \quad Ge = 2\cdot0; \quad Sn = 1\cdot93; \quad Pb = 2\cdot45$$

These values apply to compounds in which the element is sp^3 hybridized and forms 4 covalent bonds. The order of increasing ease of hydrolysis of the tetrahydrides is seen to be that of decreasing electronegativity. The hydrolysis of SiH_4, for example, occurs easily and is catalysed by OH^- ion. It may therefore proceed by co-ordination of OH^- to the silicon (this carries a fractional positive charge because it is less electronegative than hydrogen) followed by the formation of molecular hydrogen from the proton of water and one of the negatively charged hydrogen atoms in the SiH_4 molecule. This process is less likely to occur when the central atom is any of the other elements of this group because of their greater electronegativities and hence their smaller attraction for the OH^- ion.

Oxides

(a) *Dioxides*—Some properties of these are summarized in *Table 9.11*.

CO_2 is conveniently displaced from a carbonate by treatment with dilute acid. It is slightly soluble in water to give a solution of carbonic acid:

$$H_2O + CO_2 \rightleftharpoons H_2CO_3 \overset{H_2O}{\rightleftharpoons} H_3O^+ + HCO_3^-$$

The transition in structure type from the molecular CO_2 to the three-dimensional SiO_2 is clearly illustrated by the boiling points of the two compounds. The electronic description of the CO_2 molecule has been given earlier (p. 64).

Table 9.11. The dioxides of the Group IV representative elements

Compound	Melting point (°C)	Boiling point (°C)	Structure	Properties
CO_2		−78·5 (subl.)	Molecular	Acidic
SiO_2	1710	2590	3 dimensional lattice (quartz, tridymite and cristobalite)	Acidic
GeO_2	1116	1200	Ionic: rutile (quartz above 1030°C)	Amphoteric
SnO_2		1900 (subl.)	Ionic: rutile	Amphoteric
PbO_2	752 (decomp. under 1 atm pressure of O_2)		Ionic: rutile	Amphoteric

All three forms of SiO_2—quartz, tridymite and cristobalite—occur in nature. Like CO_2, silica has acidic properties and reacts with basic oxides and carbonates at high temperature to give silicates.

The hydrolysis of $SiCl_4$ (p. 211) or the addition of acids to alkali metal silicate solutions gives hydrated silica. This can be dried to an amorphous powder (silica gel), containing about 4 per cent water. Its main use is as a drying agent and as a catalyst support.

GeO_2 and SnO_2 are prepared by treatment of the element with concentrated nitric acid: PbO_2 is made by the electrolytic oxidation of Pb^{II} salts or the reaction of Cl_2 or Br_2 with an alkaline solution of lead acetate. PbO_2 is the chief constituent of the anode of the charged lead accumulator. It is an effective oxidizing agent, liberating Cl_2 from HCl and oxidizing Mn^{2+} in acid solution to MnO_4^-. It cannot be classed as a peroxide because H_2O_2 is not liberated from PbO_2 by acid.

All five dioxides have acidic properties and the derived oxy-acids or their salts are known. In the case of C, Si and Ge, only the salts have been isolated. These are the carbonates (containing CO_3^{2-}), the silicates (p. 104) and the germanates (both meta-, GeO_3^{2-}, and ortho-salts, GeO_4^{4-}). SnO_2 on fusion with alkali gives rise to a water-soluble stannate, for example Na_2SnO_3. The addition of acid causes precipitation of hydrated stannic oxide, α-stannic acid. This dissolves easily in more concentrated acid, but it ages on standing to an unreactive insoluble form, β-stannic acid. The loss in reactivity is believed to be due to a progressive increase in the size of colloidal particles. PbO_2 similarly interacts with alkali to form plumbates. These and the stannates have been shown by x-ray analysis to contain 6 co-ordinated metal atoms. For instance, the hydrated salt potassium metastannate, $K_2SnO_3.3H_2O$, should more properly be formulated as $K_2Sn(OH)_6$.

(b) *Monoxides*—CO can be made by the interaction of carbon and carbon dioxide at high temperatures (p. 184). It behaves as a neutral compound. The metallic carbonyls (p. 161) are important derivatives. The electronic structure of CO has been discussed earlier.

The evidence for a monoxide of silicon is not conclusive. SiO appears to be formed around 1300°C when a mixture of SiO_2 and Si is vaporized under reduced pressure.

GeO is made by the reduction of Ge^{IV} in solution using hypophosphorous acid, H_3PO_2. The preparation must be carried out in an inert atmosphere because rapid oxidation back to the tetrapositive state would otherwise occur. SnO, obtained when the metal is heated with a limited supply of air is similarly oxidized to SnO_2. PbO (litharge) is formed when lead is heated in air.

The monoxides of Ge, Sn and Pb are amphoteric with basic properties increasing in importance as the atomic number of the metal increases. They are the parent compounds both of the normal salts of Ge^{II}, Sn^{II} and Pb^{II} and of the oxy-acid salts known as the germanites (GeO_2^{2-}), stannites (SnO_2^{2-}) and plumbites (PbO_2^{2-}).

(c) *Other Oxides*—Carbon is unique in forming a suboxide C_3O_2. This is a gaseous compound formed when malonic acid is heated with P_2O_5. It polymerizes readily on heating and behaves towards water as the anhydride of malonic acid. The molecule is linear, a chain of three carbon atoms being terminated at each end by an oxygen atom. The molecular structure is usually represented in terms of multiple bonds between the atoms with non-localized π-bonds as an important feature (*cf.* the structure of CO_2, p. 64).

Two other oxides of lead are known. Pb_3O_4 (red lead) is made by heating litharge in air to 450°C. This is formulated as $(Pb^{II})_2Pb^{IV}O_4$. Pb_2O_3, made when a soluble lead (II) salt is treated with a plumbate, also contains lead in two valency states—$Pb^{II} Pb^{IV}O_3$.

Halides

(a) *Tetrahalides* (MX_4)—All possible ones have been made except the tetrabromide and tetraiodide of lead. The non-existence of these is attributed to the strong oxidizing properties of Pb^{IV} which would at once convert a heavy halide ion to free halogen. Preparative methods are illustrated by the tetrachlorides:

CCl_4 is made by chlorination of CS_2. $SiCl_4$ and $GeCl_4$ are prepared by heating the dioxide and carbon in chlorine. $SnCl_4$ is obtained by direct chlorination of the metal. $PbCl_4$ is formed as an unstable yellow liquid by the reaction between PbO_2 and concentrated HCl.

The tetrafluorides of C, Si and Ge are gaseous at ordinary temperatures: SnF_4 and PbF_4 are involatile solids, subliming at 705°C and melting at 600°C respectively. The other tetrahalides are generally volatile liquids or easily melted solids. CBr_4 and CI_4 are unstable: this is related to the steric difficulty of forming four bonds between the small carbon atom and the large halogen atoms.

A hexafluoro-complex of Si is known, namely $[SiF_6]^{2-}$. This is produced when SiF_4 is hydrolysed:

$$SiF_4 + 2H_2O = SiO_2 + 4HF$$

then $\qquad\qquad SiF_4 + 2F^- \ \rightleftharpoons [SiF_6]^{2-}$

Other complex hexahalide ions are $[GeF_6]^{2-}$, $[GeCl_6]^{2-}$, $[SnF_6]^{2-}$, $[SnCl_6]^{2-}$, $[SnBr_6]^{2-}$, $[SnI_6]^{2-}$, $[PbF_6]^{2-}$, $[PbCl_6]^{2-}$ and $[PbBr_6]^{2-}$.

(b) *Catenated halides*—Carbon forms a large number of fluorocarbons, compounds which are noted for their chemical stability. They are made by the electrolytic generation of fluorine in the presence of hydrocarbons. Under these conditions, replacement of H by F takes place. Several chlorocarbons are also known, for example C_2Cl_6, C_3Cl_8 and C_4Cl_{10}, but these are much less stable than the corresponding fluorine compounds.

Silicon also forms a number of catenated halides:

$$Si_2F_6, \ Si_2Cl_6, \ Si_2Br_6 \ \text{and} \ Si_2I_6;$$

$$Si_3Cl_8, \ Si_4Cl_{10}, \ Si_5Cl_{12}, \ Si_6Cl_{14} \ \text{and} \ Si_{10}Cl_{22}.$$

Here the chloro-compounds are the most numerous and the most stable. Direct reaction between the halogen and a Ca–Si alloy at elevated temperatures serves as a preparative method. These halides are easily soluble in organic solvents and hydrolysis results in the removal of all halogens to give, as one of the chief products, silico-oxalic acid, $H_2Si_2O_4$.

Ge_2Cl_6 appears to be the only similar compound formed by the elements following Si.

(c) *Dihalides* (MX_2)—These are formed by Ge, Sn and Pb. Generally they have greater ionic character in the solid state than the tetrahalides; for instance, their volatility is much less.

$GeCl_2$ is obtained when $GeCl_4$ is heated with Ge. $SnCl_2$ is prepared by

215

heating the metal in HCl. $PbCl_2$ has a low solubility in water and is readily made by precipitation from aqueous solution.

The germanium halides and $SnCl_2$ appear to be polymeric in the vapour state. For example, vapour density measurements on the vapour of $GeCl_2$ have indicated association and it has been suggested that bridged molecules of the type

$$\begin{array}{ccccccccc}
\text{Cl} & & \text{Cl} & & \text{Cl} & & \text{Cl} & & \text{Cl} \\
\diagup & \searrow \diagup & & \searrow \diagup & & \searrow \diagup & & \searrow \diagup & \\
\text{Ge} & & \text{Ge} & & \text{Ge} & & \text{Ge} & & \text{Ge} \\
\diagup & \diagup & & \diagup & & \diagup & & \diagup & \\
\text{Cl} & \text{Cl} & & \text{Cl} & & \text{Cl} & & \text{Cl} &
\end{array}$$

are present.

Silicones

These are polymeric organic compounds containing silicon which find many applications because of their remarkable stability to chemical attack or thermal decomposition.

Silicones are prepared as follows:

(i) Reaction between alkyl or aryl halides and a copper–silicon alloy at about 300°C. This produces alkyl or aryl halogen silanes—$SiRX_3$, SiR_2X_2 and SiR_3X (R=alkyl or aryl, X=halogen).

(ii) Hydrolysis to silicols:

$$SiR_2X_2 + 2H_2O = SiR_2(OH)_2 + 2HX$$

$$SiR_3X + H_2O = SiR_3(OH) + HX$$

(iii) Condensation of silicols to silicones by heating or by the action of acids:

$$2HO{-}\underset{\underset{R}{|}}{\overset{\overset{R}{|}}{Si}}{-}OH = HO{-}\underset{\underset{R}{|}}{\overset{\overset{R}{|}}{Si}}{-}O{-}\underset{\underset{R}{|}}{\overset{\overset{R}{|}}{Si}}{-}OH + H_2O$$

Further condensation extends the chain. The chain length is controlled by the proportion of SiR_3X present, for condensation with this terminates the chain. The presence of $SiRX_3$ in the reactants produces cross-linked silicones.

The extent of cross-linking and the nature of the alkyl or aryl group determine the properties of the silicones. The water-clear mobile liquids contain short chains or rings. The viscous liquids or rubber-like solids are composed of much longer chains and the silicones resins contain three-dimensional networks.

Silicones are water-repellent and thermally and electrically insulating. These properties lead to their widespread industrial use.

GROUP V—REPRESENTATIVE ELEMENTS

Nitrogen (N) and phosphorus (P) are non-metals. Metallic properties first become significant when the underlying shell of 18 electrons is present, that is, with arsenic (As) and antimony (Sb) and bismuth (Bi) which are increasingly metallic. Three elements of this group show allotropy (p. 83) and the

Table 9.12. The properties of the Group V representative elements

	N	P	As	Sb	Bi
Atomic number	7	15	33	51	83
Electron configuration	$2s^2 2p^3$	$3s^2 3p^3$	$4s^2 4p^3$	$5s^2 5p^3$	$6s^2 6p^3$
Melting point (°C)	−210	44·1 (white)		630·5	271
Boiling point (°C)	−195·8	280·5 (white)	610 (subl.)	1380	1450
Electronegativity	3·0	2·1	2·0	1·9	1·9
Atomic radius (Å)	0·74	1·1	1·21	1·41	1·52
Ionic radius (Å) M^{3+}			0·69	0·90	1·20

variations in melting and boiling points reflect the changes in the structural units present in the elements (*Table 9.12*).

Each atom is three electrons short of the configuration of the nearest inert gas. Nitrogen gains three electrons in forming the nitride ion N^{3-}, found in the ionic nitrides of lithium and Group II metals. The electronegativity of the remaining elements of the group is insufficient for them to form triply charged anions. Thus the bonding in metallic phosphides and arsenides is largely covalent.

Alternatively, the electronic shell is completed when the element forms three covalent bonds, as in the hydrides MH_3, and in most of the trihalides. The compound containing the most electropositive Group V element and the most electronegative halogen, BiF_3, has salt-like properties and hence contains the Bi^{3+} ion. The tripositive cation is probably also present in the salts of strong acids such as $Bi(ClO_4)_3.5H_2O$ and $Sb_2(SO_4)_3$ but does not appear to be stable in the presence of water because hydrolysis occurs to bismuthyl (BiO^+) and antimonyl (SbO^+) salts. The formation of M^{3+} by the later members of the group is another example of the inert-pair effect.

The first member (nitrogen) shows differences from the other elements. The atom is restricted to a maximum covalency of four (as in the ammonium ion) because only four orbitals are available for bonding. The heavier elements all have vacant d orbitals which can be used in bonding and show an extra valency of 5 and a maximum covalency of six. As examples, we may quote the electronic configurations of the phosphorus atom by itself and in various chemical combinations:

The later Group V elements (P onwards) can thus show oxidation states of -3 (in MH_3), $+3$ (in MCl_3) and $+5$ (in MCl_5). Additional states arise in the case of N and P, frequently because of the formation of multiple bonds. The covalency maximum of 6 is shown in ions such as $[AsF_6]^-$, $[SbCl_6]^-$ and $[Sb(OH)_6]^-$.

Nitrogen

Four-fifths of the atmosphere consists of nitrogen but the element is not of great abundance in the combined state in the earth's crust. This is a striking illustration of the stability of molecular nitrogen and many nitrogen compounds are in fact endothermic with respect to nitrogen itself. Nitrogen forms diatomic molecules in which the atoms are held together by a triple bond ($N\equiv N$), the strength of which is shown by the magnitude of the dissociation energy, 225·8 kcal/mole. Molecular nitrogen is therefore chemically rather inert at ordinary temperatures.

Direct reaction with hydrogen to form ammonia is favoured by high pressures and relatively low temperatures:

$$N_2 + 3H_2 \rightleftharpoons 2NH_3 + 22 \text{ kcal}$$

This reaction is the basis of the Haber process.

Combination with oxygen to produce NO, nitric oxide, takes place to a slight extent at high temperatures, although even at 3200°C the yield of NO is only 4·4 per cent.

Nitrogen reacts directly with many other elements at high temperatures. Ionic nitrides are formed by Li, by all Group II metals and by Th (Th_3N_4). These react readily with water to form metal hydroxides and ammonia and their composition and properties are consistent with the presence of N^{3-} ions. Volatile covalent nitrogen compounds are formed with the non-metals H, C, F, Cl and O. Also non-volatile covalent substances are known for the elements of the boron group (except Tl) and for Si and P. Boron nitride, BN, is of interest because it has the same hexagonal structure as graphite. A number of transition metal nitrides are known—these are of an interstitial nature.

Compounds

Hydrides (MH_3)

These are formed by all five elements.

Ammonia and its derivatives are of great chemical importance. NH_3 acts as a weak base in aqueous solution (p. 122). It combines with protonic acids to yield ammonium salts. These salts strongly resemble the alkali metal salts in their solubilities and structures (the radius of NH_4^+ is 1·43 Å compared with that of Rb^+ of 1·48 Å). Ammonium compounds are thermally unstable and the products of decomposition are dependent on the nature of the anion present. If it cannot be reduced, ammonia is formed:

$$NH_4Cl \rightleftharpoons NH_3 + HCl$$

If the anion has oxidizing properties, an oxidation product of NH_3 is obtained:

$$NH_4NO_2 = N_2 + 2H_2O$$

$$NH_4NO_3 = N_2O + 2H_2O$$

Many complexes are known in which NH_3 acts as a ligand molecule. Metal amides, containing NH_2^- ions, are formed primarily by the representative elements of Groups I and II. Preparation is effected by heating the metal in gaseous NH_3.

Ammonia is relatively stable towards many oxidizing agents. It reacts with atmospheric oxygen above 500°C in the presence of a platinum catalyst to form NO. This is the first stage in the production of nitric acid from ammonia (Ostwald process).

Hydrazine, N_2H_4, and hydroxylamine, NH_2OH, are two important derivatives of NH_3. Hydrazine is prepared by the oxidation of NH_3:

$$NH_3 + NaOCl = NH_2Cl + NaOH$$

$$NH_2Cl + NH_3 + NaOH = H_2N.NH_2 + NaCl + H_2O$$

Hydroxylamine can be made by the electrolytic reduction of low concentrations of nitrate ion in 50 per cent H_2SO_4 at an amalgamated lead cathode:

$$HO.NO_2 + 6e^- + 6H^+ = HO.NH_2 + 2H_2O$$

Both compounds are bases but they are weaker bases than ammonia. The following equilibrium constants illustrate this:

$$NH_3 + H_3O^+ \overset{k_1}{\rightleftharpoons} NH_4^+ + H_2O \quad k_1 = 1.8 \times 10^{-5}$$

$$N_2H_4 + H_3O^+ \overset{k_2}{\rightleftharpoons} N_2H_5^+ + H_2O \quad k_2 = 8.5 \times 10^{-7}$$

$$NH_2OH + H_3O^+ \overset{k_3}{\rightleftharpoons} NH_3OH^+ + H_2O \quad k_3 = 6.6 \times 10^{-9}$$

Phosphine, PH_3, is made by reaction of phosphonium iodide, PH_4I, with alkali:

$$PH_4I + H_2O = PH_3 + H_3O^+ + I^-$$

PH_4I itself is prepared by the interaction of white phosphorus and iodine in carbon disulphide solution, followed by evaporation of the solvent and treatment of the residue with small amounts of water. PH_3 and its derivatives are generally less stable than NH_3 and its derivatives. Phosphine is also a weaker base and a stronger reducing agent than NH_3.

PH_3 and substituted phosphines form a large number of co-ordination compounds, especially with the platinum group of metals. In these complexes the lone pair on the phosphorus atom is donated to the metal. An additional process which increases the stability of the complex is π-bonding involving the d orbitals of the phosphorus atom (p. 149). PH_3 is thus acting as an electron donor as well as an electron acceptor whereas NH_3 can act only as an electron donor because N has no vacant d orbitals.

Diphosphine, P_2H_4, is the analogue of N_2H_4, and is formed in small amounts when phosphine is prepared.

AsH_3, SbH_3 and BiH_3 are increasingly unstable and have strong reducing properties. The existence of BiH_3 (bismuthine) can be demonstrated using a radioactive isotope of the metal. This is incorporated in a Bi–Mg alloy, which forms BiH_3, a volatile compound detectable by its radioactivity, on treatment with acid.

The ammonia molecule is pyramidal with an H—N—H bond angle of 106°45'. In the hydrides of the other elements of this group the H—M—H angle is much smaller: PH_3, 93°50'; AsH_3, 91° 35'; SbH_3, 91°30'. This decrease is associated with a decrease in the electronegativity of the central atom. In passing from NH_3 to PH_3 for example, the bonding pairs of electrons are less strongly attracted by the phosphorus than by the nitrogen atom. As a result the repulsion between the lone pair on the central atom and the bonding pairs becomes relatively more important and the bond angle closes up. It is interesting to note that for AsH_3 and SbH_3 the bond angle is very close to that expected (90°) for bonds involving pure p orbitals. An alternative interpretation of the observed decrease in bond angle in the trihydrides is therefore that the nitrogen atom in NH_3 is sp^3 hybridized whilst the orbitals used in bonding by the heavier atoms show an increasing amount of p character.

The thermal stability and basic strength of the hydrides is greatly increased by the replacement of hydrogen by groups of lower electronegativity, such as alkyl groups. For example, tetra-alkyl ammonium hydroxides have similar properties to the caustic alkalis. The organic derivatives of phosphine and the hydrides of As and Sb are similarly more stable than the parent hydrides.

Oxides and Oxy-acids

The binary compounds between nitrogen and oxygen provide more examples of multiple bond formation. The five well-characterized oxides are: N_2O,

Table 9.13. The oxides of nitrogen and phosphorus

Compound	Physical state (at 20°C)	Structure	Properties
N_2O	gas	molecular	neutral oxide
NO	gas	molecular	neutral oxide
N_2O_3	gas	molecular	acid anhydride
N_2O_4	liquid (b.p. 21·1 °C)	molecular	acid anhydride
N_2O_5	solid	ionic	acid anhydride
P_4O_6	solid (m.p. 23·8 °C)	molecular	acid anhydride
P_4O_{10}	solid	molecular; hexagonal	acid anhydride
$(P_4O_{10})_x$	solid	polymeric; orthorhombic 1	acid anhydride
$(P_4O_{10})_x$	solid	polymeric; orthorhombic 2	acid anhydride
$(PO_2)_n$	solid	—	acid anhydride

NO, N_2O_3, N_2O_4 and N_2O_5. These correspond with the formal oxidation states for nitrogen of +1, +2, +3, +4 and +5 respectively. Physical properties are summarized in *Table 9.13*.

220

Nitrous oxide, N_2O, is prepared by the thermal decomposition of NH_4NO_3 (p. 219). It is formally the anhydride of hyponitrous acid, $H_2N_2O_2$, but it does not react with water to form this. It is a linear molecule and its structure may be described in terms of the resonating forms

$$\overset{-}{N}=\overset{+}{N}=O \quad \text{and} \quad N\equiv\overset{+}{N}-\overset{-}{O}$$

Since N_2O is isoelectronic with CO_2, the electronic descriptions of the two are similar.

Nitric oxide, NO, is synthesized directly from the elements. It is a neutral molecule which has remarkable stability considering that it contains an odd number of electrons. NO dimerizes to the diamagnetic N_2O_2 in the liquid state. The molecular-orbital description of the NO molecule has been given earlier (p. 60).

Dinitrogen trioxide, N_2O_3, is prepared by the reduction of nitric acid with As_2O_3. It reacts with water to form nitrous acid HNO_2, and is accordingly classed as an acid anhydride. It behaves at room temperature as a mixture of NO and NO_2; association to the diamagnetic N_2O_3 molecules is more extensive the lower the temperature. Resonance structures of the type

$$\overset{-}{O}\diagdown \quad \diagup O$$
$$\overset{+}{N}-N$$
$$\diagup \qquad \diagdown$$
$$O \qquad O$$

have been suggested.

Dinitrogen tetroxide, N_2O_4, the mixed anhydride of HNO_2 and HNO_3, is prepared by reaction of NO with O_2 or by the heating of heavy metal nitrates:

$$2\,Pb(NO_3)_2 = 2\,PbO + 4\,NO_2 + O_2$$

Increasing use is made of this oxide as a solvent medium for inorganic reactions (p. 129). In the vapour state, dissociation to the brown NO_2 monomer takes place to an extent which depends on the temperature. Like NO, NO_2 is paramagnetic (it contains 17 valency electrons) and its structure has been described in terms of resonance between

$$\overset{x+}{N} \qquad\qquad \overset{x+}{N}$$
$$\diagup \quad \diagdown \qquad \text{and} \qquad \diagup \quad \diagdown$$
$$O \qquad O^- \qquad \qquad {}^-O \qquad O$$

or of localized σ-bonds and a delocalized π-bond.

Dinitrogen pentoxide, N_2O_5, is the anhydride of nitric acid, from which it may be prepared by dehydration using P_4O_{10}. It is molecular in the vapour state but the solid has been shown to have an ionic structure, being composed of nitronium, NO_2^+, and nitrate, NO_3^-, ions.

The three best-known oxy-acids of nitrogen are given in *Table 9.14*, together with their characteristic properties.

The nitrite, NO_2^-, and nitrate, NO_3^-, ions are angular and planar respectively. Their shapes may be interpreted as follows. In NO_2^- the nitrogen atom is sp^2 hybridized, two of the hybrids forming a σ-bond with each oxygen

8* 221

Table 9.14. The oxy-acids of nitrogen and phosphorus

Acid	Formula	Oxidation state	Properties
Hyponitrous	$H_2N_2O_2$	$+1$	Unstable, weak, dibasic and reducing
Nitrous	HNO_2	$+3$	Unstable, weak, monobasic and oxidizing
Nitric	HNO_3	$+5$	Strong, monobasic and oxidizing
Hypophosphorous	H_3PO_2	$+1$	Strong, monobasic and strongly reducing
Orthophosphorous	H_3PO_3	$+3$	Moderately strong, dibasic and strongly reducing
Hypophosphoric	$H_4P_2O_6$	$+4$	Moderately strong, tetrabasic. No reducing properties and resists oxidation
Orthophosphoric	H_3PO_4	$+5$	Moderately strong and tribasic. Stable

Also known for phosphorus are the condensed acids:
  Pyrophosphorous $(H_4P_2O_5)$ and metaphosphorous $(HPO_2)_n$;
  Pyrophosphoric $(H_4P_2O_7)$ and metaphosphoric $(HPO_3)_n$, where $n = 3, 4, 6$ *etc.*
Three per-acids are known:
  Peroxonitric acid HNO_4, peroxomonophosphoric acid, H_3PO_5, and peroxodiphosphoric acid, $H_4P_2O_8$.

and the third containing the lone pair. The valency octet around nitrogen is completed by the formation of one non-localized π-bond:

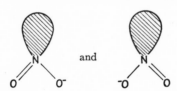

In NO_3^- the nitrogen is again sp^2 hybridized and it forms three σ-bonds and one non-localized π-bond:

It is interesting to note that the anions BO_3^{3-}, CO_3^{2-} and NO_3^-, which contain a first short period element as central atom, are all planar. The oxy-anions of the second period elements are tetrahedral (SiO_4^{4-}, PO_4^{3-}, SO_4^{2-} and ClO_4^-). In NO_3^-, the π-bond must involve a p electron from the nitrogen and so the number of σ-bonds is restricted to three. In PO_4^{3-}, d orbitals are available for π-bonding and four tetrahedrally distributed σ-bonds are formed. Another

222

difference between the oxy-anions of the first and second short periods is that carbonates and nitrates are found only as mononuclear ions, but condensed anions are easily formed by silicates and phosphates.

The oxides of phosphorus show very little resemblance in their physical properties to those of nitrogen. This is because in its compounds with oxygen phosphorus tends to form polymeric structures.

Phosphorus (III) oxide, P_4O_6, is the chief product when the element is burned in a limited supply of air. It is the anhydride of phosphorous acid, H_3PO_3. The structural unit is a molecule with four P atoms at the apices of a tetrahedron, each P atom being joined to the other three by oxygen bridges. The P—O bond length is 1·65 Å.

P_4O_6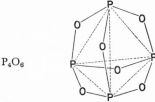

Phosphorus (V) oxide, P_4O_{10}, is the product of combustion of the element in excess air. It is the anhydride of phosphoric acid, H_3PO_4. This oxide is polymorphic and at least three crystalline and two amorphous forms have been recognized. One of the crystalline polymorphs contains discrete P_4O_{10} molecules (this molecule is also present in the vapour of the oxide). These are related to P_4O_6 by the addition of an extra oxygen to each phosphorus. The four additional oxygen atoms are bound more firmly than the other six. The evidence for this comes from the shorter P—O distance of 1·39 compared with 1·62 Å for the bond between P and the bridging O. The shorter bonds therefore appear to be multiple and so in P_4O_{10} the valency shell of the phosphorus atom must be expanded beyond 8 electrons.

P_4O_{10}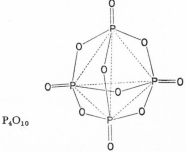

The other two crystalline forms are orthorhombic and have polymeric structures. Each P atom is tetrahedrally surrounded by four O atoms and three of these are shared with adjacent tetrahedra to give sheet polymers of infinite extent. One of these polymorphs has interlocking rings containing 6 P and 6 O atoms: the second contains larger rings of 10 P and 10 O atoms. The P—O bonds in such crystals are largely covalent.

$(PO_2)_n$, commonly called phosphorus tetroxide, is made by heating P_4O_6 in vacuo above 210°C. Its properties suggest that it also has a polymeric structure.

Several oxy-acids of phosphorus are known. Their properties are summarized in *Table 9.14*.

In a systematic approach to these compounds it is of value to consider how they arise by the replacement of successive hydrogen atoms with oxygen in the phosphonium cation, PH_4^+.

$$
\begin{array}{ccccc}
\underset{\text{PH}_4{}^+}{\overset{+}{\text{H}-\overset{\displaystyle H}{\underset{\displaystyle H}{P}}-\text{H}}}
&
\underset{\substack{\text{Phosphine}\\\text{oxide}}}{\text{H}-\overset{\displaystyle H}{\underset{\displaystyle H}{P}}-\text{O}}
&
\underset{\substack{\text{Hypo-}\\\text{phosphite}}}{\overset{-}{\text{H}-\overset{\displaystyle H}{\underset{\displaystyle O}{P}}-\text{O}}}
&
\underset{\text{Phosphite}}{\overset{2-}{\text{O}-\overset{\displaystyle H}{\underset{\displaystyle O}{P}}-\text{O}}}
&
\underset{\text{Phosphate}}{\overset{3-}{\text{O}-\overset{\displaystyle O}{\underset{\displaystyle O}{P}}-\text{O}}}
\end{array}
$$

As oxygen replaces hydrogen around the phosphorus atom there is a change from basic to acidic properties. The number of hydrogen atoms combined with oxygen determines the basicity of the acid for the P—H group shows no tendency to lose a proton. This is in accordance with the much lower electronegativity of P compared with O. Also it is evident that reducing properties are possessed by the acid if it contains a P—H bond.

The structures of all the phosphoric acids are based on PO_4 tetrahedral units. Discrete PO_4^{3-} ions occur in orthophosphates, whilst in pyro- and tri-phosphate ions, two and three tetrahedra respectively are attached by shared oxygens.

Pyrophosphate (left, charge $4-$) and Triphosphate (right, charge $5-$) structures.

In metaphosphates, the process of sharing of oxygens has gone further with the formation of ring structures:

Metaphosphate (ring structure, charge $3-$).

These processes may be summarized by the equations:

$$2\,HPO_4^{2-} = P_2O_7^{4-} + H_2O$$
$$H_2PO_4^- + 2\,HPO_4^{2-} = P_3O_{10}^{5-} + 2\,H_2O$$
$$x\,H_2PO_4^- = (PO_3)_x^{x-} + x\,H_2O$$

The above reactions do not occur when orthophosphates are acidified but are brought about by heating. A wide range of polyphosphate ions, of either chain or ring structure, exists in the crystalline phosphates.

The oxides of As^{III} and Sb^{III} correspond with P_4O_6. As_4O_6, prepared by burning arsenic in air, has a similar structure, being composed of tetrahedral molecules. Sb_4O_6 is made by reaction between $SbCl_3$ and Na_2CO_3. It is dimorphic. One form consists of discrete Sb_4O_6 molecules: the other is composed of double chains:

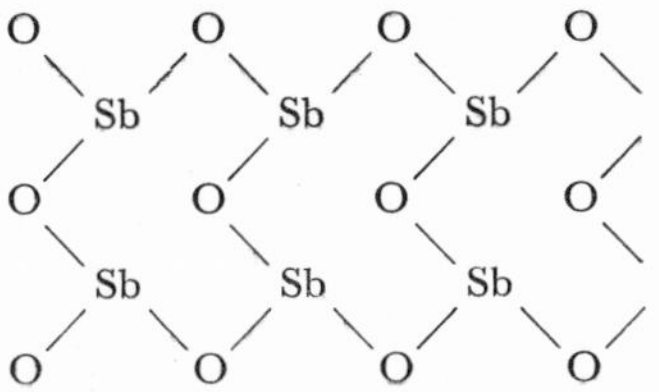

These two oxides are amphoteric giving rise to As^{III} and Sb^{III} compounds on reaction with strong acids and to arsenite (AsO_3^{3-}) and antimonite (SbO_3^{3-}) with alkalis.

Bismuth trioxide, Bi_2O_3, has basic properties only and crystallizes in several forms. One of these is cubic and has an ionic structure. The trend of non-metallic to metallic character of the elements is therefore accompanied by a change from molecular to polymeric to ionic structure for the lower oxides.

As_2O_5 and Sb_2O_5 are prepared by oxidation of the elements with nitric acid. Their structures are unknown. These are oxidizing agents and they have pronounced acidic character, as shown by reactions with alkali to form arsenates (AsO_4^{3-}) and antimonates $[Sb(OH)_6]^-$ respectively. The change from tetrahedral to octahedral co-ordination by oxygen takes place on passing from As to Sb.

Bismuthates containing Bi^V are known and have powerful oxidizing properties. The pentoxide has not been obtained as a pure compound.

Halides

Two series of compounds, the tri- and penta-halides, are known for phosphorus and the heavier elements. Trihalides only are formed by nitrogen because its covalency maximum is four.

NF_3, prepared by the electrolysis of molten ammonium hydrogen fluoride, NH_4HF_2, is a colourless gas (b.p. $-129°C$) which is notable for its stability and resistance to hydrolysis.

NCl_3, made by electrolysis of saturated ammonium chloride solution, is an unstable yellow oil which is readily decomposed by water. The electronegative nitrogen atom acts as an electron-pair donor towards the hydrogen of water and hydrolysis proceeds with the successive replacement of Cl by H atoms:

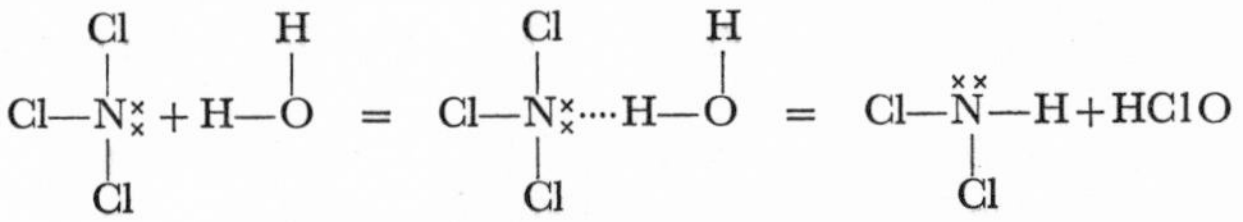

$$NHCl_2 + H_2O = NH_2Cl + HClO$$
$$NH_2Cl + H_2O = NH_3 + HClO$$

The tribromide and triiodide of nitrogen have been prepared only in the form of their very unstable ammoniates, such as $NBr_3 . 6NH_3$.

225

The remaining elements each form the four binary trihalides and a number of mixed trihalides (PF_2Cl, $PFCl_2$, PF_2Br, $PFBr_2$ and $SbBrI_2$). The binary compounds, with the exception of the ionic BiF_3 (m.p. 727°C), are all covalent molecular substances. Hydrolysis of the phosphorus and arsenic trihalides occurs with the production of the corresponding oxy-acid. Here, the P or As atom acts as an electron-pair acceptor and its valency shell is expanded to 10 electrons by accepting a lone pair from the oxygen atom of water. For example,

$$Cl-\underset{\underset{Cl}{|}}{\overset{\overset{H}{|}}{P^{\times}_{\times}}} + \overset{\times}{\underset{\times\times}{\times}}O-H \;=\; Cl-\underset{\underset{Cl}{|}}{\overset{\overset{Cl}{|}}{P}}\overset{\overset{H}{|}}{\underset{\times\times}{\diagup}}O-H \;=\; P(OH)Cl_2 + HCl$$

$$P(OH)Cl_2 + H_2O = P(OH)_2Cl + HCl$$
$$P(OH)_2Cl + H_2O = P(OH)_3 \;+ HCl$$

The trihalides of antimony and bismuth (except BiF_3) are reversibly decomposed to form insoluble compounds containing antimonyl (SbO^+) and bismuthyl (BiO^+) cations.

$$BiCl_3 + H_2O \rightleftharpoons BiOCl + 2HCl$$

The covalent trihalides form pyramidal molecules. The shape arises from a tetrahedral arrangement of three bonding and one non-bonding pairs of electrons around the central atom. The compounds are generally poor conductors of electricity in the liquid state in accordance with their covalent character. AsF_3 and SbF_3 are exceptional in that they show, in the fused state, a specific conductivity similar to that of BrF_3 and IF_5. This is attributed to self-ionization:

$$2AsF_3 \rightleftharpoons AsF_2^+ + AsF_4^-$$

Phosphorus pentachloride is the best-known of the pentahalides. It is a solid at ordinary temperatures which undergoes thermal decomposition:

$$PCl_5 \rightleftharpoons PCl_3 + Cl_2$$

This dissociation has been thoroughly studied as an outstanding example of a reversible reaction. In the vapour state PCl_5 exists as a trigonal bipyramidal molecule and the phosphorus atom is accordingly sp^3d hybridized (PF_5, AsF_5, $SbCl_5$ and PF_3Cl_2 also have the same molecular shape). In the fused state the compound shows very little electrical conductivity but greater conductivity is shown by its solutions in polar solvents. This is due to the presence of $[PCl_4]^+$ and $[PCl_6]^-$ ions. Solid PCl_5 has an ionic lattice containing these two ions.

Phosphorus pentabromide, PBr_5, also has an ionic structure in the solid state: in this case the ions present are $[PBr_4]^+$ and Br^-. The ion $[PBr_6]^-$ is known to be present in solutions of PBr_5 in a polar solvent such as methyl cyanide.

Antimony pentachloride, $SbCl_5$, is prepared by the chlorination of $SbCl_3$, but the corresponding pentachloride of arsenic is unknown. The bonding in a pentahalide involves a d orbital of the Group V atom, and the formation of such a compound requires the promotion of an electron from an s or a p orbital of lower energy. There is an appreciably larger energy difference between the $4d$ and the $4s$ and $4p$ orbitals in arsenic than between the corresponding orbitals in the third quantum shell in phosphorus or the fifth quantum shell in antimony. As a result, arsenic is more reluctant to show pentavalency than either phosphorus or antimony.

The cation $AsCl_4^+$ is known, being present in the compound $AsCl_5 . PCl_5$ (correctly formulated as $AsCl_4^+ PCl_6^-$). Also known are the ionic compounds $AsCl_4^+ SbCl_6^-$ and $AsCl_4^+ AsF_6^-$. Indeed, recent studies on the halides of Group V have shown how important ions of this type are in their chemistry.

The pentabromides and pentaiodides of As, Sb and Bi are not formed owing to the oxidizing tendencies of the $+5$ state of these three elements.

Phosphonitrilic Halides

These are the polymeric compounds containing P, N and a halogen; they show several unusual features in their properties and structure.

The chlorides are synthesized by the reaction between PCl_5 and NH_4Cl in an inert solvent such as *sym*-tetrachloroethane.

$$n\,PCl_5 + n\,NH_4Cl = (PNCl_2)_n + 4n\,HCl$$

Removal of the solvent by distillation *in vacuo* followed by fractional distillation under reduced pressure yields first of all the trimer, $[PNCl_2]_3$, and then the tetramer, $[PNCl_2]_4$.

These are acid chlorides which undergo hydrolysis with the replacement of some or all of the chlorines by hydroxyl groups. As they are insoluble in water, hydrolysis is best carried out by shaking their ethereal solutions with water. $[PN(OH)_2]_3$ is obtained from $[PNCl_2]_3$ and $[PN(OH)_2]_4 . 2H_2O$ from $[PNCl_2]_4$.

The trimer has a planar ring composed of alternate P and N atoms. The P—N bonds are all equal in length and much shorter (1·65 Å) than the single P—N bond length observed in other compounds (1·78 Å). This suggests that resonance must occur between the structure

and a second structure in which the three double bonds are in the alternative positions. The $[PNCl_2]_3$ ring accordingly has 'aromatic' character and the chemical reactions of the trimer have been interpreted on this basis.

$[PNCl_2]_4$ is also a cyclic polymer containing alternate P and N atoms in a puckered 8-membered ring.

Other polymers of higher molecular weight have been isolated from the reaction mixture of PCl_5 and NH_4Cl. These appear to be linear. Further polymerization takes place on heating phosphonitrilic chlorides to 250° to 350°C with the production of a rubber-like polymer of high molecular weight.

Practical applications of this are limited by the chemical reactivity of the chlorine atoms.

Phosphonitrilic fluorides and bromides have been synthesized but no iodides have been reported.

GROUP VI—REPRESENTATIVE ELEMENTS

These elements—oxygen (O), sulphur (S), selenium (Se), tellurium (Te) and the radioactive polonium (Po)—show systematic changes in chemical properties with increase in atomic number. Thus O and S are non-metals, Se and Te are semi-conductors and Po has metallic character. The structure of the elements changes strikingly from diatomic molecules, through ring and chain molecules to a metallic lattice (p. 83).

The electronic configuration common to all is two short of that of the nearest inert gas. In many of their compounds the atoms attain a completed octet of electrons. There are several ways in which this can take place.

(a) The divalent anion X^{2-} is formed by gaining two electrons. This is an endothermic process, hence the positive sign for electron affinity in *Table 9.15*;

Table 9.15. The properties of the Group VI representative elements

	O	S	Se	Te	Po
Atomic number	8	16	34	52	84
Electron configuration	$2s^2 2p^4$	$3s^2 3p^4$	$4s^2 4p^4$	$5s^2 5p^4$	$6s^2 6p^4$
Melting point (°C)	−218·9	118·95*	217·4†	449·8	
Boiling point (°C)	−182·96	444·6	684·8	1390	
Electronegativity	3·5	2·5	2·4	2·1	
Electron affinity, kcal/g atom (formation of X^{2-})	+152·9	+94·5	+101		
Atomic radius (Å)	0·74	1·04 (S$_8$)	1·17	1·37	1·52
Ionic radius (Å) X^{2-}	1·40	1·84	1·98	2·21	

* For monoclinic sulphur   † For grey selenium

whilst energy is released by the acquisition of the first electron, the addition of the second is opposed by Coulombic repulsion and requires the absorption of a greater amount of energy. Compounds containing X^{2-}, namely oxides, sulphides, *etc.*, are considered later.

(b) The anions OH^- and SH^- are formed. The hydroxide ion, OH^-, is much more stable than the hydrosulphide, SH^- (for example, hydroxides are stable but hydrosulphides are decomposed to H_2S by boiling their aqueous solution). Compounds containing SeH^- or TeH^- have not been isolated.

(c) Two covalent bonds are formed as in the hydrides H_2O, H_2S, H_2Se and H_2Te; hydrogen peroxide, H_2O_2, and persulphides, H_2S_2, *etc.*; the halides OF_2, SCl_2, *etc.*; and organic derivatives such as the ethers R_2O and thioethers R_2S. The allotropy shown by S and Se is attributable to ring or straight-chain structures wherein each atom is covalently bound to two neighbours. Sulphur in particular shows a marked tendency for catenation and there are many sulphur compounds which have no analogy elsewhere in the group. These include the polysulphur dichlorides, S_nCl_2 where $n=3$ to 6, and the thionic acids, $H_2S_nO_6$ where $n=2$ to 6. Selenium has a smaller tendency to form compounds with Se—Se bonds. Thus Se_2Cl_2 is less stable than S_2Cl_2 and there are no Se analogues of the thionic acids.

(d) The formation of one double bond. The property is shown by oxygen in many compounds. For instance,

phosgene,

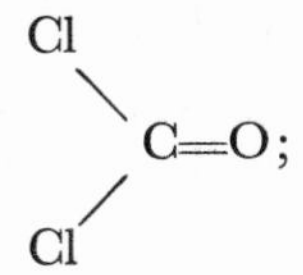

$$\begin{array}{c} Cl \\ \diagdown \\ \diagup \\ Cl \end{array} C{=}O ;$$

urea,

$$\begin{array}{c} NH_2 \\ \diagdown \\ \diagup \\ NH_2 \end{array} C{=}O ;$$

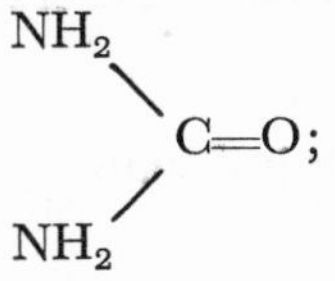

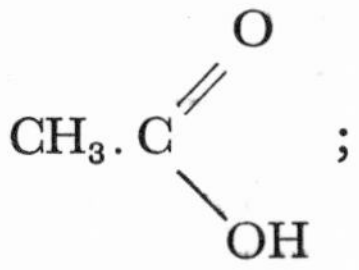

acetic acid,

$$CH_3 . C \diagup\!\!\!\!\diagup\, O \atop \diagdown OH \;;$$

the sulphoxides,

$$\begin{array}{c} R \\ \diagdown \\ \diagup \\ R \end{array} S{=}O ;$$

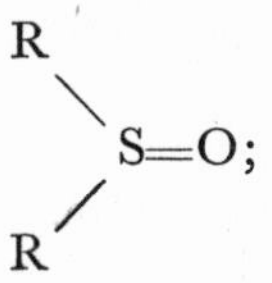

and the sulphones,

$$\begin{array}{c} R \\ \diagdown \\ \diagup \\ R \end{array} S \diagup\!\!\!\diagup\, O \atop \diagdown\!\!\!\diagdown\, O$$

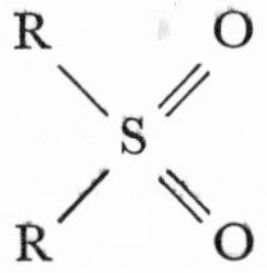

A number of sulphur compounds are also known, such as

thiourea,

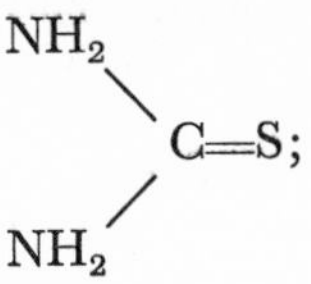

$$\begin{array}{c} NH_2 \\ \diagdown \\ \diagup \\ NH_2 \end{array} C{=}S ;$$

and ethanethionic acid,

$$CH_3 . C \diagup\!\!\!\!\diagup\, S \atop \diagdown OH$$

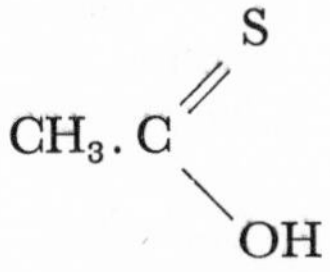

(e) The acceptance of a pair of electrons donated by another atom. The tendency for this to occur diminishes as the group is descended, that is, as the electronegativity decreases. With oxygen, this behaviour is found in the amine and phosphine oxides, $R_3N{\to}O$ and $R_3P{\to}O$ respectively. In aqueous solution alkali metal sulphides can react with sulphur to form polysulphide ions which may be regarded as formed by the donation of an electron pair from S^{2-} to an S atom to complete the valency octet of the latter. Polyselenides and polytellurides are produced in a similar way and can be formulated in like manner.

Oxygen is a first short period element and hence is restricted to a covalency maximum of 4. Basic beryllium acetate, Be_4O $(CH_3COO)_6$, is an example of 4-covalent oxygen (p. 205). More commonly, oxygen has a covalency of 3, as in the oxonium ion H_3O^+. Here the oxygen atom forms two covalent bonds with the hydrogens and uses a lone pair for co-ordination of the proton.

S, Se and Te can form up to 6 covalent bonds by the expansion of the valency shell to include d orbitals. Examples are the hexafluorides, SF_6, SeF_6 and TeF_6:

	$3s$	$3p$			$3d$	
Ground state of S	↑↓	↑↓	↑	↑		
Excited state	↑	↑	↑	↑	↑	↑
S in SF_6	↑↓	↑↓	↑↓	↑↓	↑↓	↑↓

These three elements can show a variety of oxidation states, namely -2, $+2$, $+4$ and $+6$. The best known compounds are those in which the Group VI element shows an oxidation state of $+4$ or $+6$ in combination with oxygen or the halogens.

There is some evidence for the formation of cations by the heavy elements of this group. Thus both Te^{4+} and Po^{4+} ions exist in the ionic dioxides, TeO_2 and PoO_2. Po is more electropositive than Te and tends to form a normal salt, for instance $Po(SO_4)_2$, whereas only the basic salt is known with Te, $TeO.SO_4$. The formation of tetrapositive ions by Te and Po shows the persistence of the inert pair effect into this Group.

Compounds

Hydrides

Four of general formula H_2X are known—H_2O, H_2S, H_2Se and H_2Te.

H_2S is prepared by the decomposition of a metallic sulphide with acid: H_2Se and H_2Te are formed when metallic selenides and tellurides respectively are hydrolysed.

The volatility increases sharply from H_2O to H_2S because of association in water by hydrogen bonding (p. 70). In this group only oxygen is sufficiently electronegative to show this property in its compounds. The hydrides of the remaining elements show the increase in m.p. and b.p. with molecular weight, which is normally shown in any series of homologous compounds.

The thermal stability falls off markedly with increase in molecular weight. The heats of formation are: H_2O, $+68.35$; H_2S, $+4.8$; H_2Se, -18.5; H_2Te, -34.2 kcal/mole. The acid strengths increase in the same direction, that is as the size of the anion XH^- increases and hence as its power of attaction for a proton decreases. Accordingly, H_2S is an acidic solute in water.

The molecules are V-shaped with the following inter-bond angles:

$$H_2O, 104° 30'; \quad H_2S, 92° 20'; \quad H_2Se, 91°$$

The decrease in angle as the electronegativity of the Group VI element decreases can be interpreted, as for the Group V hydrides, in terms of the repulsion between electron pairs which results in increasing deviation from the tetrahedral angle. Alternatively, it appears to be perfectly adequate to describe the bonding in H_2Se and H_2S as involving pure p orbitals of the Se and S atoms repectively.

Oxides, sulphides, selenides and tellurides are derivatives of the hydrides. The oxides of most metals are ionic and show basic properties. The oxides of electropositive metals such as the alkali and alkaline earth elements react vigorously with water to give alkaline solutions. The oxide ion is very strongly basic, and has a powerful affinity for the proton. The oxides of metals showing higher valencies have high lattice energies and as a result are often sparingly soluble in water. These compounds will usually dissolve in acidic solutions because the high concentration of protons necessary to effect solution is then available. For instance TiO_2, insoluble in water, is slowly dissolved by hot strong sulphuric acid. The oxides of the more electronegative elements are often characterized by amphoteric properties and insolubility in aqueous media. Fusion under alkaline or acid conditions is then necessary to render them soluble. Acidic properties predominate in the case of transition metal oxides in which the metal shows a high oxidation state and for the oxides of non-metals. A few 'neutral' oxides like CO, N_2O and NO are exceptional.

Sulphides of the alkali and alkaline-earth metals have ionic structures and are decomposed by water thus:

$$S^{2-} + H_2O \rightleftharpoons OH^- + SH^-$$

On boiling, $\qquad SH^- + H_2O = OH^- + H_2S \uparrow$

A number of other sulphides, for example Al_2S_3, Cr_2S_3 and SiS_2, are also readily hydrolysed. Sulphides of the heavy metals, in contrast, have extremely low solubilities in water and some are not even decomposed by mineral acid. Hence the great utility of H_2S as a reagent in qualitative analysis for the precipitation of the sulphides of Pb, Cu, Cd, Bi, Hg, Sb, Sn and As from acid solution.

Where a metal oxide has an ionic structure, the corresponding sulphide may often have a layer lattice due to the greater polarizability of S^{2-}. For example, TiO_2 and SnO_2 have the rutile structure but TiS_2 and SnS_2 have the cadmium iodide structure.

Alkali metal selenides and tellurides are ionic and resemble the corresponding sulphides in their properties. Heavy metal selenides and tellurides have many similarities to the sulphides of these elements.

O and S form other molecular hydrides. These are hydrogen peroxide (H_2O_2), hydrogen persulphide (H_2S_2) and a series of hydrogen polysulphides (H_2S_3 to H_2S_8) containing chains of sulphur atoms.

H_2O_2 is made by electrolytic oxidation of ammonium sulphate/sulphuric acid solution. Peroxodisulphuric acid, $H_2S_2O_8$, is first formed and this is hydrolysed to H_2O_2:

$$2SO_4^{2-} = S_2O_8^{2-} + 2e^-$$
$$H_2S_2O_8 + 2H_2O = 2H_2SO_4 + H_2O_2$$

Hydrogen peroxide has a variety of uses—as an oxidizing agent in organic synthesis, a bleaching agent and a rocket fuel. The chief advantage of this over other oxidizing agents is that its only by-product is water and so, in organic preparative work, the recovery of a product of high purity is facilitated. The H_2O_2 molecule is dihedral, that is, the two O—H bonds are not in the same

231

plane (*Figure 9.2*). This is the most stable configuration because the repulsion between the lone pairs on the two oxygen atoms is a minimum. Here it is assumed that only oxygen *p* orbitals are used in bonding. Repulsion between the lone pairs is greatest when the *p* orbitals containing them, one on each oxygen atom, are parallel and least when the orbitals are at right angles.

Important derivatives of H_2O_2 include the ionic peroxides, formed by the alkali and alkaline-earth metals and containing the peroxide ion, O_2^{2-} (p. 204), and the peroxo-acids and their salts, formed by the representative elements and transition metals of Groups IV, V and VI; for instance, peroxonitric acid, HNO_4, peroxomonosulphuric acid, H_2SO_5, and peroxotitanic acid, H_4TiO_5. These compounds are chiefly of note for their strong oxidizing properties.

H_2S_2 and the polysulphides are prepared by the addition of acid to an aqueous solution of sulphur in alkali metal sulphides. A water-insoluble

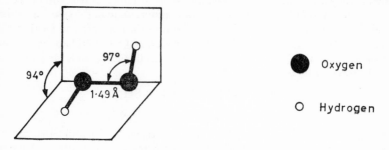

Figure 9.2. The hydrogen peroxide molecule

yellow oil is obtained and this may be fractionally distilled under reduced pressure to give individual sulphides. The H_2S_2 molecule is similar to H_2O_2 in its shape.

Oxides and Oxy-acids

The binary compounds with oxygen are:

S_2O	—	TeO	PoO
S_2O_3	—	—	—
SO_2	SeO_2	TeO_2	PoO_2
SO_3	SeO_3	TeO_3	—
S_2O_7	—	—	—
SO_4	—	—	—

The most important are the dioxides and trioxides.

SO_2 is prepared by burning sulphur or sulphides in air. It is a reducing agent, itself being converted to SO_3. SO_2 is a molecular oxide and the S—O bonds are essentially double. The angular shape of the molecule—

—is attributable to sp^2 hybridization of the sulphur. Two hybrid orbitals are used to form σ-bonds with each oxygen and the third contains a lone pair. Two π-bonds are also formed. The S atom therefore has ten electrons in its outermost shell.

SeO_2, made by burning Se in air, is a solid subliming at 315°C. It is easily reduced to elementary Se and so finds uses as an oxidizing agent. In the solid state it has a chain-like structure:

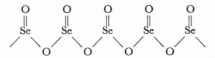

TeO_2, prepared by the combustion of Te, has oxidizing properties. It is a solid which is much less volatile than SeO_2 and has the ionic rutile structure. The dioxides thus illustrate clearly the transition from a covalent to an ionic structure as the electronegativity of the Group VI element decreases. SO_2 and SeO_2 have acidic properties and TeO_2 is amphoteric, in accordance with this trend.

Of the three trioxides, SeO_3 is the most difficult to prepare and this compound is one example of the reluctance of Se to show its maximum oxidation state in combination with oxygen.

SO_3 is made by heating SO_2 in oxygen to 400°C in the presence of a catalyst. It condenses at 44·8°C and freezes at 16·8°C to a colourless ice-like solid. This is γ-SO_3 which appears to be a ring-shaped trimer, S_3O_9. Two other modifications are known, α- and β-SO_3, and these also appear to be polymeric.

SeO_3 is prepared by the oxidation of SeO_2 with oxygen in a high-frequency electrical discharge. It is a white solid, m.p. 118°C, resembling SO_3.

TeO_3 is obtained by dehydration of telluric acid, H_6TeO_6. It is a non-volatile solid, thermally very stable. SeO_3 and TeO_3 structures are unknown.

The following oxy-acids are derived from the above-mentioned oxides:

Table 9.16.

Parent oxide	Oxy-acid	Basicity	Properties
SO_2	Sulphurous, H_2SO_3	Weak, dibasic	Reducing
SeO_2	Selenous, H_2SeO_3	Weak, dibasic	Oxidizing
TeO_2	Tellurous, H_2TeO_3	Weak, dibasic	Oxidizing. Tends to polymerize
SO_3	Sulphuric, H_2SO_4	Strong, dibasic	Weak oxidizing agent
SeO_3	Selenic, H_2SeO_4	Strong, dibasic	Very strongly oxidizing
TeO_3	Telluric, H_6TeO_6	Very weak, dibasic. Orthotellurates such as Ag_6TeO_6 are known	Strongly oxidizing. Tends to polymerize

In the case of the oxides of S and Se, the oxy-acids are prepared by reaction of the parent oxide with water. Te oxides are sparingly soluble in water and the oxy-acids are best made by direct oxidation of the element.

The sulphite ion is pyramidal and the sulphate is tetrahedral. The bonding between sulphur and oxygen has been the subject of great speculation and to explain the observed equivalence of the S—O bond lengths in both ions, resonance between a number of different structures has been proposed. The S—O bond length in SO_2 and SO_3 is 1·44 Å and in these molecules the bonds are regarded as essentially double in character. (A single S—O bond, as found in potassium ethyl sulphate, $K . SO_3 . O . C_2H_5$, is appreciably longer—1·60 Å). In the sulphate ion in hydrazine sulphate, $N_2H_4 . H_2SO_4$, the S—O bond length is 1·49 Å. The bond thus is intermediate between a single and a double bond and this is consistent with Pauling's formulation of SO_4^{2-} as a resonance hybrid between such structures as:

$$
\begin{array}{cccc}
\overset{\displaystyle O^-}{\underset{\displaystyle O^-}{^-O-\overset{+}{S}=O}}
&
\overset{\displaystyle O^-}{\underset{\displaystyle O^-}{O=\overset{-}{S}=O}}
&
\overset{\displaystyle O^-}{\underset{\displaystyle O}{O=\overset{-}{S}=O}}
&
\overset{\displaystyle O}{\underset{\displaystyle O}{O=\overset{2-}{S}=O}}
\end{array}
$$

The molecular-orbital description is in terms of 4 σ-bonds (hence the tetrahedral shape) and two non-localized π-bonds. Similar descriptions have been put forward for the sulphite ion, either a resonance hybrid or the sulphur atom, in a state of sp^3 hybridization, forming 3 σ-bonds, 1 non-localized π-bond and carrying one lone pair of electrons:

In addition to H_2SO_3 and H_2SO_4, a number of other sulphur oxy-acids are known. In some cases the free acid has been made; in others, only the salts are known. Some interrelations of these acids are summarized in *Figure 9.3*.

The thionic acids have the general formula $H_2S_nO_6$ where n is 2 to 6. The ions all contain unbranched chains of S atoms, for example, the pentathionate ion, $S_5O_6^{2-}$, is

$$
\left(
\begin{array}{c}
\text{O} \qquad \text{S} \qquad \text{S} \qquad \text{O} \\
\diagdown \diagup \qquad \diagdown \diagup \qquad \diagdown \diagup \\
\text{O}-\text{S} \qquad \text{S} \qquad \text{S}-\text{O} \\
\diagup \qquad\qquad\qquad\qquad \diagdown \\
\text{O} \qquad\qquad\qquad\qquad \text{O}
\end{array}
\right)^{2-}
$$

Pyrosulphite, $S_2O_5^{2-}$, dithionite, $S_2O_4^{2-}$, thiosulphite, $S_2O_2^{2-}$ and thiosulphate, $S_2O_3^{2-}$, ions all contain S—S bonds:

$$
\left(
\begin{array}{c}
\text{O} \qquad\qquad \text{O} \\
\diagdown \qquad\quad \diagup \\
\text{S}-\text{S}-\text{O} \\
\diagup \qquad\quad \diagdown \\
\text{O} \qquad\qquad \text{O}
\end{array}
\right)^{2-}
\qquad
\left(
\begin{array}{c}
\text{S} \\
| \\
\text{S} \\
\diagup | \diagdown \\
\text{O} \;\; \text{O} \\
\text{O}
\end{array}
\right)^{2-}
$$

$$\qquad\qquad S_2O_5^{2-} \qquad\qquad\qquad\qquad S_2O_3^{2-}$$

Pyrosulphate, $S_2O_7^{2-}$, is produced by the condensation of two sulphate ions:

$$2SO_4^{2-} + 2H^+ \rightleftharpoons H_2O + S_2O_7^{2-}$$

In the ion, one oxygen is shared by two sulphur atoms:

$$\left(\begin{array}{c} O \qquad O \qquad O \\ \diagup \qquad \diagdown \diagup \qquad \diagup \\ O-S \qquad S-O \\ \diagdown \qquad \diagdown \\ O \qquad O \end{array} \right)^{2-}$$

$$S_2O_7^{2-}$$

Finally, two peroxoacids are known. Peroxomonosulphuric acid, H_2SO_5, is formally derived from H_2SO_4 by the replacement of one oxygen by a peroxo-group, —O—O—. Peroxodisulphuric acid, $H_2S_2O_8$, is a condensed oxy-acid

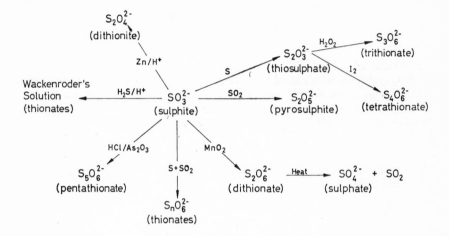

Figure 9.3. Interrelationships of the oxy-acids of sulphur

in which the sulphur atoms are joined by the peroxo-group. The peroxodisul-phate ion, $S_2O_8^{2-}$, is

$$\left(\begin{array}{c} O \qquad O \qquad S-O \\ \diagdown \qquad \diagup \diagdown \qquad \diagup \\ O-S \qquad O \qquad O \\ \diagdown \\ O \end{array} \right)^{2-}$$

Oxy-Halides

SO$_2$ reacts with PCl$_5$ to form thionyl chloride, SOCl$_2$. This is a colourless liquid, b.p. 75°C. It reacts with several fluorides to form thionyl fluoride,

SOF_2, and with HBr at low temperatures to give the unstable bromide, $SOBr_2$. SOF_2 is slowly hydrolysed but $SOCl_2$ is immediately decomposed:

$$SOCl_2 + H_2O = SO_2 + 2HCl$$

Use of this reaction has been made to prepare anhydrous metal chlorides.

The $SOCl_2$ molecule is pyramidal: the S atom is sp^3 hybridized, forming 3 σ-bonds and carrying one lone pair—

Analogous selenyl halides, $SeOX_2$ (X=F, Cl or Br) have been prepared.

SO_2 combines with chlorine in the presence of an organic catalyst such as camphor or acetic acid to form sulphuryl chloride, SO_2Cl_2. This is a low-boiling liquid which is almost completely dissociated to SO_2 and Cl_2 in the vapour phase at 100°C. It is readily hydrolysed:

$$SO_2Cl_2 + 2H_2O = 2HCl + H_2SO_4$$

The molecule is a distorted tetrahedron. The S atom (sp^3 hybridized) forms 4 σ- and 2 π-bonds:

$$\underset{\underset{O}{\parallel}}{\overset{\overset{O}{\parallel}}{\underset{Cl}{\overset{S1}{\diagup}}\diagdown Cl}}$$

Halides

The binary halides of S, Se and Te are:

S_2F_2	S_2Cl_2	S_2Br_2	—
—	Se_2Cl_2	Se_2Br_2	—
SF_2	SCl_2	—	—
—	$SeCl_2$	$SeBr_2$	—
—	$TeCl_2$	$TeBr_2$	—
SF_4	SCl_4	—	—
SeF_4	$SeCl_4$	$SeBr_4$	—
TeF_4	$TeCl_4$	$TeBr_4$	TeI_4
SF_6	—	—	—
SeF_6	—	—	—
TeF_6	—	—	—
S_2F_{10}	—	—	—
Te_2F_{10}	—	—	—

The lower halides of the types A_2X_2, AX_2 and AX_4 are formed by direct union of the elements. They are molecular, covalent compounds which are chemically reactive and are readily hydrolysed. S_2Cl_2 has a non-planar structure similar to that of H_2O_2. The boiling points of the di- and tetra-halides of Te are relatively high and $TeCl_4$ conducts electricity in the fused state. This could be evidence of ionic character or of self-ionization according to

$$2\,TeCl_4 \rightleftharpoons TeCl_3^+ + TeCl_5^-$$

The hexafluorides are all highly exothermic compounds and SF_6 is particularly noted for its resistance to chemical attack. As the electronegativity of the central atom decreases, the hexafluoride becomes more reactive. Thus, even at red heat, SF_6, is unattacked by O_2, NH_3 and many other chemical substances. SeF_6 reacts with ammonia above 200°C:

$$SeF_6 + 2\,NH_3 = N_2 + Se + 6\,HF$$

and TeF_6 is decomposed slowly by water at room temperature:

$$TeF_6 + 6\,H_2O = H_6TeO_6 + 6\,HF$$

The molecules are regular octahedra.

Nitrogen Compounds

The binary compounds of oxygen with nitrogen have been discussed in Group V.

A number of interesting sulphur compounds is known in which sulphur and nitrogen are combined. The reaction between S_2Cl_2 and ammonia gives rise to the ring compound, tetrasulphur tetranitride, S_4N_4. This is an orange-yellow solid, m.p. 178°C, which is hydrolysed in alkaline solution:

$$2\,S_4N_4 + 6\,OH^- + 9\,H_2O = 2\,S_3O_6^{2-} + S_2O_3^{2-} + 8\,NH_3$$

Reduction with tin (II) chloride or dithionite results in the formation of tetrasulphur tetraimide, $S_4(NH)_4$. In both these sulphur compounds, 8-membered rings are present:

The S_4N_4 ring is non-planar with the S atoms forming a distorted tetrahedron and the 4 N atoms lying in one plane. Electronically, this compound is a resonance hybrid, all the S atoms being exactly equivalent.

The S_4N_4 ring can be easily cleaved into two molecules of disulphur dinitride. For example, on treatment with ammonia, the ammoniate, $S_2N_2.NH_3$ (or $H_2N.SN.SNH$), is produced. A number of metallic derivatives of this is known such as $Pb(NS)_2$, $Tl(NS)_2$ and $Cu(NS)_2$. Complex compounds of formula $M(NS)_2$ are obtained from S_4N_4 and metals of Group VIII by the interaction between the nitride and the appropriate metal carbonyl in an inert solvent.

A second sulphur imide, heptasulphur imide, S_7NH, is also found in small quantities amongst the reaction products of S_2Cl_2 and NH_3. Structurally this compound is related to the S_8 ring. The hydrogen atom can be replaced by a number of metals, by acetyl and benzoyl groups and by the sulphonic acid group, $—SO_3H$.

$$
\begin{array}{ccc}
S—S—S \\
| \quad\quad | \\
S \quad\quad S \\
| \quad\quad | \\
S—N—S \\
H
\end{array}
\qquad S_7NH
$$

The other elements of Group VI do not form compounds of this type.

Polonium

This radioactive element occurs as an intermediate in the various decay series (p. 9).

It is made by neutron irradiation of ^{209}Bi:

$$^{209}_{83}Bi \; (n, \gamma) \; ^{210}_{83}Bi \rightarrow \, ^{210}_{84}Po + \, ^{0}_{-1}e$$

^{210}Po decays by α-emission and has a half-life of 138·4 days. Its high specific activity means that the handling of the element in quantity is hazardous.

The element itself is a soft, low-melting metal which resembles lead in appearance. It is dimorphic, and cubic and rhombohedral modifications are known. In this respect Po behaves as a true metal. The compounds of polonium which have been prepared include PoO, PoO_2, various halides ($PoCl_2$, $PoCl_4$, $PoBr_2$, $PoBr_4$ and PoI_4) and the sulphates $(PoO_2)SO_3$ and $Po(SO_4)_2$.

The general properties of polonium confirm its classification as the most electropositive element in Group VI B.

GROUP VII—REPRESENTATIVE ELEMENTS

The halogens are the non-metals fluorine (F), chlorine (Cl), bromine (Br), iodine (I) and the radioactive element, astatine (At). Physical and chemical data are summarized in *Table 9.17*.

The atomic number of each halogen is one less than that of the nearest inert gas. A completed octet of electrons is reached by a halogen atom X either by accepting one electron to give the halide ion X^-, as in the formation of ionic halides, or by forming a covalent bond with another atom, as in the diatomic halogen molecules X_2 and the halides of hydrogen and other non-metals.

The valency of fluorine is restricted to one because there is no possibility of expanding the second quantum shell to contain more than eight electrons. In the other halogens, however, one or more d orbitals in the outermost shell can be used in bonding. For example, a pair of electrons in a p orbital may be split up and one promoted to a vacant d orbital. This gives an excited state of the atom which has three unpaired electrons and is therefore capable of forming three covalent bonds. Similarly, by the involvement of the two remaining

Table 9.17. The properties of the halogens

	F	Cl	Br	I	At
Atomic number	9	17	35	53	85
Electron configuration	$2s^2 2p^5$	$3s^2 3p^5$	$4s^2 4p^5$	$5s^2 5p^5$	$6s^2 6p^5$
Melting point (°C)	−223	−102	−7·3	114	
Boiling point (°C)	−187	−34·6	58·8	184·4	
Electron affinity (kcal/g atom)	−80·2	−85·1	−79·5	−72·6	
Ionization potential (kcal/g atom)	401·5	300	272·9	241·0	
Electronegativity	4·0	3·0	2·8	2·5	
Atomic radius (Å)	0·64	0·99	1·14	1·35	
Ionic radius (Å)	1·36	1·81	1·95	2·16	
Dissociation energy (D) for $X_2 = 2X$ (kcal/mole)	37	58	46	36	

pairs of electrons in the valency shell of the halogen, valencies of five and seven can be shown. The energy necessary to split up the electron pairs and to promote electrons to higher energy levels is available from the energy released when covalent bond formation occurs.

The higher valencies of iodine, for example, are illustrated by the formation of various compounds with another halogen. The electronic configurations of some of these are given in *Table 9.18.*

Table 9.18. The electronic configuration of iodine in various compounds

Valency sub-shell	5s	$5p_x$ $5p_y$ $5p_z$	5d 5d 5d
I	1↓	1↓ 1↓ 1	
I in ICl	1↓	1↓ 1↓ 1↕	
I in ICl₃	1↓	1↓ 1↕ 1↕	1↕
I in IF₅	1↓	1↕ 1↕ 1↕	1↕ 1↕
I in IF₇	1↕	1↕ 1↕ 1↕	1↕ 1↕ 1↕

Although fluorine shows the greatest tendency to form a negative ion, its electron affinity is less than that of chlorine. This is a consequence of the unusually low heat of dissociation of the F_2 molecule; this quantity and the electron affinity are interrelated by the appropriate Born–Haber cycle (p. 45).

The high values of the first ionization potential are in accordance with the observation that cationic species are not encountered with either fluorine or chlorine. There is a considerable body of experimental evidence to support the existence of uni- and tri-positive iodine, and it has recently been reported that, in suitable non-aqueous solvents, bromine may also give rise to compounds in which it appears to be tripositive.

Fluorine is the most electronegative element. One property associated with it is the occurrence of hydrogen bonding in a number of its compounds. For example, hydrogen fluoride behaves as an associated substance due to the presence of hydrogen bonds (the m.p. and b.p. of HF are $-83°C$ and $+19·4°C$ respectively compared with the values of $-111·4°C$ and $-85°C$ for HCl).

Another result of the high electronegativity of fluorine is that metal fluorides are predominantly ionic. The chloride ion, being the larger, is more readily polarized than fluoride and, as a result, the fluoride and chloride of the same metal often have quite different structures (p. 101). Similarly, the iodide ion is more polarizable than the bromide ion and this accounts for the fact that, whilst AgF, AgCl and AgBr have the sodium chloride structure, AgI has that of zinc blende, a structure typical of compounds with appreciable covalent character (p. 97).

The value for the dissociation energy of F_2 is unexpectedly small. The data for Cl_2, Br_2 and I_2 indicate a steady decrease in stability of the molecule as the size of the halogen atom increases and one would, indeed, expect the covalent bond between two large atoms to be weak because of the relatively small region of overlap possible between the two big bonding orbitals. One would predict, by extrapolation of the data for the heavier halogens, the greatest stability of all for the F_2 molecule. The observed weakness of the bond in F_2 is attributable to the repulsion between non-bonding pairs of electrons which becomes important for small atoms. Supporting evidence for this hypothesis is found in the low values for the dissociation energies of hydrazine and hydrogen peroxide (21 and 35 kcal respectively) where similar repulsion effects would be expected.

Fluorine is remarkable for its great chemical reactivity and this may be attributed to the ease of breakage of the F—F bond. In contrast, the bonds between fluorine and many other elements are noteworthy for their great stability. Thus the C—F bonds in fluorinated hydrocarbons and the S—F bonds in SF_6 are extremely resistant to attack.

Fluorine can also bring out the maximum valency of other elements with which it is combined, for example in IF_7 and SF_6. In an exothermic reaction between two elements, the energy released in bond formation must be more than sufficient to break up the reacting molecules and to raise the atoms to excited valency states prior to chemical combination. The reaction between sulphur and fluorine may be represented by a sequence of (hypothetical) steps in which the isolated atoms are formed from solid sulphur and molecular fluorine and then combined to form SF_6:

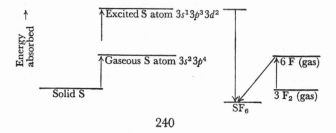

The F_2 molecule is more easily dissociated than Cl_2 and hence the formation of a chlorine atom requires more energy than the formation of a fluorine atom. As a result, SF_6 is known but the highest chloride of sulphur is SCl_4.

Reactions of the Halogens

They are all chemically reactive and combine directly with many other elements to form the halides. Various reactions are possible between the halogens and water. In the cases of chlorine, bromine and iodine the hypohalous acid is formed, for example,

$$Cl_2 + H_2O \rightleftharpoons H^+ + Cl^- + HOCl$$

The equilibrium constants for this type of reaction are $4 \cdot 8 \times 10^{-4}$, 5×10^{-9} and 3×10^{-13} for HOCl, HOBr and HOI respectively. No oxy-acids exist for fluorine and oxidation of the water takes place:

$$2F_2 + 2H_2O \rightleftharpoons 4HF + O_2$$

Some H_2O_2 and oxygen difluoride, OF_2, are produced in secondary reactions. With iodine, the reaction

$$4H^+ + 4I^- + O_2 \rightleftharpoons 2I_2 + 2H_2O$$

is important and acid solutions of an iodide are slowly oxidized by oxygen to iodine.

The oxidizing properties of the halogens decrease with increase in atomic number. A lighter halogen will always displace a heavier halogen from its simple anion. An important application of this property is in the extraction of bromine from sea-water by means of the reaction:

$$2Br^- + Cl_2 = 2Cl^- + Br_2$$

Compounds

Hydrogen Halides

These are prepared by direct combination between the elements or by displacement from their salts by a less volatile acid:

$$CaF_2 + H_2SO_4 = CaSO_4 + 2HF$$

HBr and HI are often made by hydrolysis of a phosphorus trihalide:

$$PX_3 + 3H_2O = H_3PO_3 + 3HX$$

Their stability decreases as the size of the halogen increases as shown by the energy required to rupture the hydrogen–halogen bond. This varies as follows: HF, 135; HCl, 103; HBr, 87; HI, 71 kcal/mole. HF is very stable and cannot be chemically oxidized to fluorine in aqueous solution, hence the industrial preparation of this halogen by the electrolysis of an anhydrous fluoride melt (p. 177). Chlorine can be made by the action of strong oxidizing agents like MnO_2 and $KMnO_4$ on HCl. Bromine is even more readily formed from HBr; the weak oxidizing action of concentrated sulphuric acid is

241

sufficient to form bromine as well as HBr on reaction with a metallic bromide.

The hydrogen halides all act as acids in aqueous solution: approximate values for their dissociation constants are HF, 6.7×10^{-4}; HCl, 10^7; HBr, $>10^7$; HI, $>10^7$. In dilute solution, HF acts as a weak acid but in concentrated solution, over the range 5 to 15 M, it behaves as a much stronger acid. Conductivity measurements on the more concentrated solutions have indicated that the predominant anion is F_2H^-. The striking difference between HF and the other hydrogen halides is due largely to the very high dissociation energy of the HF molecule, the unusually low electron affinity of fluorine and the extensive hydrogen bonding shown by HF in aqueous solution.

Oxides and Oxy-acids

Binary compounds between oxygen and the halogens are:

OF_2	Cl_2O	Br_2O	I_2O_4
O_2F_2	ClO_2	BrO_2	I_4O_9
O_3F_2	ClO_3	BrO_3	I_2O_5
—	Cl_2O_7	—	I_2O_7*

The best-known of the three fluorides is oxygen difluoride, OF_2, which is formed when fluorine is passed through dilute aqueous caustic soda. It reacts with excess alkali to liberate oxygen but no hypofluorite has been isolated. This is because the F^- ion is a very stable species in solution: an oxy-ion containing fluorine is not formed as this would imply the presence of an F—O bond with at least some sharing of electrons and the great electronegativity of fluorine militates against this.

The oxides of chlorine are endothermic with chlorine heptoxide, Cl_2O_7, being the least unstable. They all react with water to produce oxy-acids:

$$Cl_2O + H_2O = 2HClO$$
$$2ClO_2 + H_2O = HClO_2 + HClO_3$$
$$2ClO_3 + H_2O = HClO_3 + HClO_4$$
$$Cl_2O_7 + H_2O = 2HClO_4$$

ClO_2 and ClO_3 are of theoretical interest because they are both paramagnetic, each molecule containing one unpaired electron (p. 67).

The oxides of bromine are also unstable and have strong oxidizing properties. In composition they correspond with the oxides of chlorine but no analogue of Cl_2O_7 is known.

The oxides of iodine are solid involatile substances which are not comparable with the oxides of the lighter halogens in their chemical properties. Iodine pentoxide, I_2O_5, is the only true oxide. This is a white solid, stable up to 300°C, which decomposes without melting and is believed to have a polymeric structure. It can be prepared by the dehydration of iodic acid, HIO_3. The other two binary oxygen compounds are not regarded as simple acid anhydrides. Thus I_2O_4 is insoluble in water and reacts very slowly with alkali:

$$3I_2O_4 + 6KOH = KI + 5KIO_3 + 3H_2O$$

* Probable constitution of the orange solid obtained by reaction between periodic acid and 65% oleum.

242

and I_4O_9 reacts to give a mixture of iodate and iodine. These compounds are usually formulated as iodates, I_2O_4 as $IO^+IO_3^-$, and I_4O_9 as $I^{3+}(IO_3)_3$.

The oxy-acids, known either in the free state or as their salts, are:

HClO	HBrO	HIO
$HClO_2$	—	—
$HClO_3$	$HBrO_3$	HIO_3
$HClO_4$	—	HIO_4, H_3IO_5, H_5IO_6 and $H_4I_2O_9$

The acids, like the oxides, have oxidizing properties. The three hypohalous acids, HXO, may be made in the form of their salts by the direct action of halogen on cold aqueous alkali. The acids are less stable than their salts and the stability and the acid strength both decrease as the size of the halogen increases. Many practical applications of the oxidizing properties of the hypohalites are known, for example, sodium hypochlorite, NaOCl, is used as a bleaching agent and as a reagent in volumetric analysis.

Chlorous acid, $HClO_2$, and the chlorites are not very stable. The free acid in solution decomposes readily:

$$8\,HClO_2 = 6\,ClO_2 + Cl_2 + 4\,H_2O$$

The salts, chlorites, are active oxidizing agents.

Free chloric, $HClO_3$, and bromic, $HBrO_3$, acids exist only in solution and concentration causes decomposition. The alkali metal salts are conveniently prepared by direct reaction between the halogen and hot aqueous alkali. Iodic acid, HIO_3, can be prepared as a stable, white crystalline solid by the oxidation of iodine with chloric acid solution:

$$HClO_3 + I_2 \ = HIO_3 + ICl$$
$$HClO_3 + ICl = HIO_3 + Cl_2$$

Although perchloric acid, $HClO_4$, is stable in dilute cold aqueous solutions, it has strong oxidizing properties in hot concentrated solutions. It is a remarkably strong acid and many of its salts are freely soluble in water. The K^+, NH_4^+, Rb^+ and Cs^+ salts are sparingly soluble and are of analytical importance.

Neither perbromic acid nor its salts are known. It is not easy to explain why this is so because chlorine and bromine are so similar in many other ways.

Several periodic acids have been prepared. Orthoperiodic acid, H_5IO_6, can be made by the action of a strong oxidizing agent such as peroxodisulphate or hypochlorite on an iodate. This contains 6-covalent iodine:

$$\begin{array}{c} O \\ HO \diagdown \| \diagup OH \\ I \\ HO \diagup | \diagdown OH \\ OH \end{array}$$

On heating, H_5IO_6 loses water to give firstly pyroperiodic acid, $H_4I_2O_9$, then metaperiodic acid, HIO_4, and finally it decomposes to iodic acid. These changes may be represented as the removal of water from the pentahydrate of

243

the hypothetical oxide I_2O_7, although there is no evidence for the formation of the anhydrous oxide at any stage.

$$2H_5IO_6 \xrightarrow[\text{reduced pressure}]{80°C} H_4I_2O_9 \xrightarrow{100°C} 2HIO_4 \xrightarrow{138°C} 2HIO_3 + O_2$$
$$(I_2O_7.5H_2O) \qquad\qquad (I_2O_7.2H_2O) \qquad (I_2O_7.H_2O)$$

The Interhalogens

These are binary compounds of the type AB_n where $n = 1, 3, 5$ or 7. They are usually prepared by direct reaction between the elements. When n is 3, 5 or 7, excess of halogen B must be present in the reaction mixture. The known interhalogens are listed in *Table 9.19*. Some of these compounds are

Table 9.19. The interhalogens

Compound	Physical state (at 20°C)	Stability
ClF	gas	Stable to at least 250°C
BrF	gas	Complete decomp. to Br_2, BrF_3 and BrF_5 at 50°C
BrCl	gas	Instability prevents accurate determination of m.p. and b.p.
ICl	solid	Decomp. $\sim 97°C$
IBr	solid	Decomp. $\sim 42°C$
ClF_3	gas	Stable
BrF_3	liquid	Stable
IF_3	solid	Decomp. above $-35°C$
ICl_3	solid	Complete dissociation to ICl and Cl_2 at 77°C
ClF_5	—	Stable solid below $-195°C$
BrF_5	liquid	Stable to at least 460°C
IF_5	liquid	Stable to at least 400°C
IF_7	gas	Stable to at least 500°C
AtI	—	—

not well-characterized because of their instability, thus accurate physical data is not available for BrF and BrCl, and because of the radioactivity of astatine, little is known about AtI. While many of the compounds containing fluorine are colourless, those containing two of the heavier halogens are coloured and the colour becomes more pronounced the greater the molecular weight (as with the halogens themselves).

The interhalogens are noted for their great chemical reactivity and they can be used instead of the halogens in preparative chemistry. Thus BrF_3 and ClF_3 convert metals or their oxides to the fluorides. In the liquid state, some interhalogens show electrical conductivity and this is attributed to self-ionization (p. 125). For example,

$$2ICl \rightleftharpoons I^+ + ICl_2^-$$

Use of these compounds as solvents has made possible the preparation of a whole new range of halogen compounds.

The stereochemistry of the polyatomic molecules has been interpreted in the light of the Sidgwick–Powell concept (p. 67).

Polyhalides

Many complex salts are known which contain polyhalide ions consisting of a central halogen joined to other halogen atoms. Iodine is the most common central atom: it may be combined with other iodines or with the atoms of other halogens.

The well-characterized polyiodides contain the ions I_3^-, I_5^-, I_7^- and I_9^-. The hydrated tri-iodide of sodium, $NaI_3.H_2O$, has been isolated. The higher polyiodides are formed only with larger cations, for example $KI_7.H_2O$, $(C_2H_5)_4NI_7$ and $RbI_9.3C_6H_6$. These compounds are prepared by reaction between the iodide and the stoichiometric amount of iodine in the appropriate solvent.

The bonding within such complex ions is covalent with the central iodine using its d orbitals for bond formation:

$$I^- + I_2 = (I{\rightarrow}I{-}I)^-$$

The I_3^- ions are linear but asymmetric with two different I—I distances.

Mixed polyhalides, that is, those which contain two or more halogens, are prepared by reaction between the simple halide and the appropriate halogen or interhalogen in the absence of a solvent.

$$RbI + Br_2 = RbIBr_2$$
$$CsBr + 2ICl = CsICl_2 + IBr$$

ICl_2^- and IBr_2^- are linear with iodine as the central atom.

The tetrachloroiodates are among the most stable of this class. These are prepared by adding iodine to solutions of the simple chloride in HCl, followed by saturation with Cl_2. All the alkali metals form orange-red polyhalides of the type $MICl_4$ and a series of salts with dipositive cations (Mg^{2+}, Ca^{2+}, Co^{2+}, Ni^{2+} and Mn^{2+}) is also known. In aqueous solution, dissociation occurs to form the metal chloride and ICl_3, the latter then hydrolyses to iodate.

The $[ICl_4]^-$ ion is square planar. This shape is derived from an octahedral arrangement in the iodine atom of the six electron pairs: two of these are lone pairs at the apices of the octahedron and the remaining four, directed towards the corners of a square, are bonding pairs.

Positive Iodine and Bromine

Considerable experimental evidence has been adduced to support the existence of the iodinium ion (I^+). This includes

(i) conductivity studies which suggest that iodine dissociates according to the equation
$$2I_2 \rightleftharpoons I^+ + I_3^-$$

(ii) the migration of part of the iodine to the cathode when ICl or IBr in glacial acetic acid is electrolysed:
$$2ICl = I^+ + ICl_2^-$$

(iii) the isolation of various salts containing iodine co-ordinated by organic compounds; for example, $I(py)NO_3$ prepared by treating silver nitrate, iodine and pyridine (py) in a non-aqueous solvent:
$$AgNO_3 + py + I_2 = I(py)NO_3 + AgI$$

The bare iodinium ion would have only 6 valency electrons. Co-ordination

9+M.A.I.C.

by an organic molecule stabilizes I^+ by completion of the octet as in $(I \leftarrow py)^+$. Similarly, it has been suggested that the hydrolysis of iodine proceeds by way of the formation of a hydrated iodinium ion:

$$I_2 + H_2O \rightleftharpoons H_2OI^+ + I^-$$
$$H_2OI^+ \rightleftharpoons HIO + H^+$$

(*iv*) the characteristic blue colour of iodine in oleum solution is attributed to the presence of I^+.

Iodine reacts with 100 per cent nitric acid to form iodyl nitrate, $IONO_3$, which appears to contain tripositive iodine. Other compounds in which iodine shows this valency state are I_4O_9, I_2O_4 and $I(CH_3COO)_3$.

Positive compounds of bromine, containing this halogen in a $+1$ oxidation state include $Br(py)_2ClO_4$ and $Br(py)_2NO_3$. BrF_3 and N_2O_5 react together in a non-aqueous solvent to produce bromine trinitrate, $Br(NO_3)_3$, which appears to contain tripositive bromine.

Astatine

Our knowledge of the chemistry of this element is based on radiochemical studies of its co-precipitation behaviour with iodine and the heavy elements of adjacent periodic groups. The longest-lived isotope of astatine is ^{211}At, with a half-life of 8·3 h. This has such a high specific activity that chemical operations are not feasible even with milligram quantities because of the intense heating and radiation effects.

Astatine was first identified as a product of the bombardment of bismuth with α-particles: ^{209}Bi (α, 2n) ^{211}At. It is isolated from the irradiated bismuth by vacuum sublimation and so astatine, in its volatility, resembles iodine. It shows other similarities in appearing to form astatide (At^-), astate (AtO_3^-) and hypoastatite (AtO^-) ions. Astatine is co-precipitated with bismuth and antimony from HCl solutions by H_2S. This suggests an insoluble sulphide may be formed and hence is evidence for greater metallic character than found in iodine.

10

THE COMPARATIVE CHEMISTRY OF THE TRANSITION ELEMENTS

THE transition and inner transition elements consist of the four series

Sc (21) to Cu (29),
Y (39) to Ag (47),
La (57) to Au (79)
and Ac (89) to Lw (103).

In each of these series the electronic configuration in the occupied shell of highest principal quantum number remains constant whilst an inner quantum shell is progressively filled up as the atomic number increases. This is shown in *Table 2.4* (p. 36).

In the elements from Sc to Cu, Y to Ag, and Hf (72) to Au, a penultimate *d* sub-shell is filled up and many of the properties associated with transition metals are due to the presence of at least one *d* electron. The Group III A elements Sc, Y and La, by definition transitional in the atomic state, are present in many of their compounds as tripositive ions which have an inert-gas configuration. They do not show many of the properties typical of the transition elements as a class and it is therefore appropriate to consider their chemistry separately.

The elements immediately following La constitute the inner transition series. These are the lanthanides, Ce (58) to Lu (71), in which the $4f$ sub-shell is being filled. The lanthanides have a strong tendency to form tripositive ions and in doing so are like the other Group III A elements, Sc, Y and La. These three elements and the lanthanides are collectively known as the rare earths.

Chemical and physical evidence supports the existence of a second series of inner transition elements following Ac (89). These are called the actinides, in which the $5f$ sub-shell is incomplete, and they include the artificially prepared transuranic elements from Np (93) onward. The actinides, by analogy with the lanthanides, conclude with Lw (103).

PROPERTIES OF THE TRANSITION ELEMENTS

These are Ti (22) to Cu, Zr (40) to Ag, and Hf to Au. They are all metals, generally of high densities, low atomic volumes and high melting and boiling points (*Table 10.1*). The structures of the elements have been described earlier (p. 87). The physical properties of the metals and their ability to form alloys with one another have led to their technological application on the largest possible scale. Iron is the outstanding example of this. Its ores are plentiful, the metal itself can be readily extracted therefrom and its properties may be modified extensively by alloying with other metals or by combination with carbon.

The metals vary widely in their chemical reactivity. The earlier members of a series undergo highly exothermic reactions to form stable compounds, whilst the later members are generally far less reactive. The older designation of platinum, gold, *etc.*, as noble metals is based upon their reluctance to form

Table 10.1. The properties of the d *transition metals*
(See *Table 10.8* for Group I B)

	IV A	V A	VI A	VII A	VIII		
	Ti	V	Cr	Mn	Fe	Co	Ni
Atomic number	22	23	24	25	26	27	28
M.p. (°C)	1725	1715	1830	1247	1528	1490	1452
B.p. (°C)	3260	~3500	~2300	2030	2735	3100	2840
Atomic radius (Å)	1·32	1·22	1·17	1·17	1·16	1·16	1·15
Ionic ⎱ M^{2+} (Å)	0·90	0·88	0·84	0·80	0·76	0·74	0·72
radius ⎰ M^{3+} (Å)	0·76	0·74	0·69	0·66	0·64	0·63	0·62
	Zr	Nb	Mo	Tc	Ru	Rh	Pd
Atomic number	40	41	42	43	44	45	46
M.p. (°C)	2100	1950	2600		~2400	~1966	1555
B.p. (°C)	~3600	~5100	~4800		~4200	~3900	3170
Atomic radius (Å)	1·45	1·34	1·29		1·24	1·25	1·28
	Hf	Ta	W	Re	Os	Ir	Pt
Atomic number	72	73	74	75	76	77	78
M.p. (°C)	2300	3010	3400	3150	~2700	2454	1774
B.p. (°C)	~5200	~6000	~5700		~4600	~4500	~3800
Atomic radius (Å)	1·44	1·34	1·30	1·28	1·26	1·26	1·29

Table 10.2. Heats of formation of the principal oxides for the reaction:
Metal + Oxygen = Metallic oxide + Y kcal

Oxide	Y (kcal/ mole)	Oxide	Y (kcal/ mole)	Oxide	Y (kcal/ mole)
TiO_2	225·5	V_2O_5	373	CrO_3	138·4
ZrO_2	258·2	Nb_2O_5	463·2	MoO_3	180·3
HfO_2	271·5	Ta_2O_5	499·9	WO_3	200·8
MnO	92·0	Fe_2O_3	196·5	CoO	57·2
		RuO_2	52·5	RhO	21·7
Re_2O_7	297·5	OsO_4	93·4	IrO_2	40·1
NiO	58·4	CuO	37·1		
		Cu_2O	39·84		
PdO	20·4	Ag_2O	7·31		
		Au_2O_3	−19·3		

compounds with oxygen. The change in reactivity is well illustrated by the heats of formation of the principal oxides (*Table 10.2*).

The properties of transition metals can be conveniently summarized into five sections, each of which is dealt with in turn below.

1. Variable Valency

This arises because of the presence of a partially filled *d* sub-shell and is illustrated by *Tables 10.3, 10.4* and *10.5*, which list the binary compounds with oxygen, fluorine and chlorine respectively.

Table 10.3. The oxides of the transition metals

IV A	V A	VI A	VII A	VIII			I B
							Cu_2O (b, w.a.)
TiO (b)	VO (b)	CrO (b)	MnO (b)	FeO (b, w.a.)	CoO (b, w.a.)	NiO (b)	CuO (am.)
Ti_2O_3 (b)	V_2O_3 (b)	Cr_2O_3 (am.)	Mn_2O_3 (b)	Fe_2O_3 (am.)	(Co_2O_3)	(Ni_2O_3)	
TiO_2 (am.)	VO_2 (am.)	CrO_2 (a)	Mn_3O_4 MnO_2 (am.)	Fe_3O_4	Co_3O_4 (CoO_2)	(NiO_2)	
	V_2O_5 (am.)	CrO_3 (a)					
			Mn_2O_7 (a)				
							Ag_2O (b, w.a.)
	NbO	(Mo_2O_3)			RhO Rh_2O_3 (RhO_2)	PdO (b) Pd_2O_3 (PdO_2)	AgO
ZrO_2 (am.)	NbO_2 (a)	MoO_2		RuO_2			
	Nb_2O_5 (a)	Mo_2O_5 (am.)					
		MoO_3 (a)	Tc_2O_7 (a)				
				RuO_4			
			(Re_2O_3)		Ir_2O_3	Pt_2O_3	Au_2O Au_2O_3 (a, w.b.)
HfO_2 (am.)	TaO_2 (a)	WO_2	ReO_2 (am.)	OsO_2	IrO_2 (b)	PtO_2 (am.)	
	Ta_2O_5 (a)						
		WO_3 (a)	ReO_3 Re_2O_7 (a)	OsO_3		PtO_3	
				OsO_4 (a)			

b = basic;   w.b. = weak basic;   a = acidic;   w.a. = weak acidic   am. = amphoteric
Brackets around a formula indicate the compound has not been prepared in a pure state.

Table 10.4. The fluorides of the transition metals

IV A	V A	VI A	VII A	VIII			I B
TiF_3 TiF_4	VF_3 VF_4 VF_5	CrF_2 CrF_3 CrF_4 CrF_5	MnF_2 MnF_3	FeF_2 FeF_3	CoF_2 CoF_3	NiF_2	CuF CuF_2
							Ag_2F, AgF AgF_2
ZrF_4	NbF_3 NbF_5	MoF_3 MoF_4 MoF_5 MoF_6	TcF_6	RuF_3 RuF_5	RhF_3 RhF_4	PdF_2 PdF_3	
HfF_4	TaF_5	WF_6	ReF_4 ReF_5 ReF_6 ReF_7	OsF_4 OsF_5 OsF_6	IrF_3 IrF_4 IrF_6	PtF_4 PtF_5 PtF_6	AuF_3

Oxides and their Derivatives—The transition metals Ti to Cu all show an oxidation state of +2 in their monoxides, MO. These compounds are ionic and have basic properties. The first three, TiO, VO and CrO, are strong

Table 10.5. The chlorides of the transition metals

IV A	V A	VI A	VII A	VIII			I B
							$CuCl$
$TiCl_2$	VCl_2	$CrCl_2$	$MnCl_2$	$FeCl_2$	$CoCl_2$	$NiCl_2$	$CuCl_2$
$TiCl_3$	VCl_3	$CrCl_3$	$MnCl_3$	$FeCl_3$			
$TiCl_4$	VCl_4	$CrCl_4$					
							$AgCl$
$ZrCl_2$		$MoCl_2$			$RhCl_2$	$PdCl_2$	
$ZrCl_3$	$NbCl_3$	$MoCl_3$		$RuCl_3$	$RhCl_3$		
$ZrCl_4$	$NbCl_4$	$MoCl_4$	$TcCl_4$	$RuCl_4$			
	$NbCl_5$	$MoCl_5$					
			$TcCl_6$		$IrCl$		$AuCl$
	$TaCl_2$	WCl_2		$OsCl_2$	$IrCl_2$	$PtCl_2$	
$HfCl_3$	$TaCl_3$	WCl_3	$ReCl_3$	$OsCl_3$	$IrCl_3$	$PtCl_3$	$AuCl_3$
$HfCl_4$	$TaCl_4$	WCl_4		$OsCl_4$	$IrCl_4$	$PtCl_4$	
	$TaCl_5$	WCl_5	$ReCl_5$				
		WCl_6	$ReCl_6$				

reducing agents and their salts are easily oxidized. From MnO onward, however, the $+2$ state is much less readily oxidized and the salts derived from the oxides are stable in aqueous solution.

The formation of the dipositive ion M^{2+} involves the loss of a pair of s electrons and higher valency states must therefore involve one or more d electrons. For example, titanium has the valency electrons $3d^2 4s^2$. By the loss of the $4s$ electrons, Ti^{2+} is formed; further removal of a d electron produces Ti^{3+}. Both these states of titanium are characterized by strong reducing properties. The most stable oxidation state is Ti^{IV}, present in weakly acidic aqueous solutions as the titanyl ion, TiO^{2+}. The simple cation Ti^{4+} occurs in the ionic dioxide rutile and has the electronic configuration of argon $(1s^2 2s^2 2p^6 3s^2 3p^6)$. The instability of Ti^{II} and Ti^{III} can thus be related to the tendency to lose 2 and 1 electrons respectively in attaining this inert gas configuration.

Cations isoelectronic with Ti^{4+} but of higher charge (namely V^{5+}, Cr^{6+} and Mn^{7+}) are unknown. The extremely high polarizing power which such ions would possess means that in practice the monatomic ions do not exist but that covalencies are formed. For example, strongly-acid solutions of vanadium (V) contain the cations VO^{3+} and VO_2^+; in weakly-acid or alkaline solutions, vanadate, VO_4^{3-}, and its condensed forms are present.

Another feature of the first transition series is that the highest stable oxidation state is three for the metals beyond Mn. Thus Fe^{III} is the highest state stable in aqueous solution. Mn^{2+} is also noteworthy for its stability. This ion contains five $3d$ electrons and thus represents the half-way stage in the filling up of the $3d$ sub-shell. According to Hund's rule of maximum multiplicity, the five d electrons are arranged with parallel spins in each of the available orbitals. At the end of the titanium series the $3d^{10}$ cations Cu^+ and Zn^{2+} illustrate the stability of a completed shell of 18 electrons*.

It appears that so far as the first series of transition metals is concerned there are three especially stable electronic arrangements; those in which the $3d$ sub-shell is completely empty, half-filled or completely filled.

---

* The elements of Group II B, zinc, cadmium and mercury, are not by definition transition metals. It is, however, appropriate to consider their chemistry immediately after that of Group I B because the dipositive ions Zn^{2+}, Cd^{2+} and Hg^{2+} have a complete d^{10} sub-shell like the unipositive ions of I B, Cu^+, Ag^+ and Au^+.

250

Variability in valency is shown by the formation of several oxides by most of the transition metals. High oxidation states are associated with acidic properties of the oxide and when the metal is showing its highest possible (group) valency, there is often some similarity with the representative elements of the same periodic group. Thus Mn_2O_7, manganese heptoxide, and its related acid, $HMnO_4$, permanganic acid, are comparable with Cl_2O_7, chlorine heptoxide, and $HClO_4$, perchloric acid.

An examination of the oxides formed by the metals of the second and third transition series (*Table 10.3*) shows the preference for higher oxidation states. A maximum oxidation state of eight is reached in Group VIII by Ru and Os in contrast to the much lower oxidation states shown by the Fe–Co–Ni triad. Another significant difference between the first series and the other two is that the metals of the first form simple cations much more readily than the elements of the second and third series, which show a much stronger tendency to complex formation even in aqueous solutions of their simple salts.

Fluorides—These are listed in *Table 10.4* and in the oxidation states of the transition metals show similar trends to those observed for the oxides. Thus the low oxidation states predominate in the second half of the first series. Higher oxidation states are shown by the heavier metals and a maximum of 7 is reached at Re in the third series. (The so-called 'octafluoride' of osmium has recently been shown to be the hexafluoride, OsF_6.) The lower fluorides, such as the difluorides MnF_2, FeF_2, CoF_2 and NiF_2, are ionic solids. The highest fluorides of the heavier metals in Groups VI, VII and VIII are either reactive low-melting solids or volatile liquids. Some fluorides, such as MnF_3, CoF_3 and AgF_2 are used as fluorinating agents in place of fluorine itself.

Chlorides—The binary chlorides show lower oxidation states of the metal than the fluorides. This is at least partly due to the greater size of the chlorine compared with the fluorine atom. The non-existence of VCl_5, although VF_5 exists, may be related to the unfavourable size ratio of the metal and the halogen atoms which prevents the formation of five stable bonds to one metal atom.

The bonding is chiefly ionic in the lower chlorides although the increased polarizability of chloride ion often results in a different structural type from that of the corresponding fluoride. For example, $FeCl_2$, $CoCl_2$ and $NiCl_2$ have layer lattices (p. 100). The higher chlorides have mainly covalent properties as indicated by their volatility and lack of electrical conductivity in the liquid state.

The tendency for the heavier transition elements to form complex salts is well illustrated by the 'dichlorides' of Mo and Pd. Molybdenum (II) chloride exists as Mo_3Cl_6 molecules in ethereal and alcoholic solution. In the solid state, the structural units are the cation $Mo_6Cl_8^{4+}$ and chloride ions and the formula is best written as Mo_6Cl_{12}. The ion $Mo_6Cl_8^{4+}$ has eight chlorines at the corners of a cube and six molybdenums near the face centres. Anhydrous palladium (II) chloride has a square planar arrangement of chlorines around the metal and is formulated as a polymer:

251

Bromides and iodides, about which much less is known than the chlorides and fluorides, are not considered here.

2. Paramagnetism

This property is shown when one or more unpaired electrons is present in the atom or ion (p. 279) and so is a feature of the chemistry of transition metals.

In an ion of the first transition series, the experimentally determined paramagnetic moment is in close agreement with the value calculated for the spin interaction alone with the applied magnetic field. The observed and predicted values for the ions of this series are given in *Table 10.6*. The orbital

Table 10.6. Comparison of the calculated and observed paramagnetic moments of the simple ions of the first transition series

Ions	Unpaired electrons	Magnetic moment (Bohr magnetons)	
		Calculated from $\sqrt{4S(S+1)}$	Observed
K^+, Ca^{2+}, Sc^{3+}, Ti^{4+}	0	0	0
Ti^{3+}	1	1·73	1·7–1·8
Ti^{2+}, V^{3+}	2	2·83	2·8–3·1
V^{2+}, Cr^{3+}	3	3·87	3·85–3·9
Cr^{2+}, Mn^{3+}	4	4·90	4·8–4·9
Mn^{2+}, Fe^{3+}	5	5·92	5·85–5·95
Fe^{2+}, Co^{3+}	4	4·90	5·0–5·6
Co^{2+}	3	3·87	4·3–5·3
Ni^{2+}	2	2·83	2·9–3·4
Cu^{2+}	1	1·73	1·9–2·1
Cu^+, Zn^{2+}	0	0	0

contribution to the magnetic moment appears to be almost completely quenched and the reason for this is that the $3d$ electrons are unshielded from the influence of the immediate environment of the metal ions (either the neighbouring ions in a solid lattice or the solvent molecules in solution). The close correspondence between the experimental and calculated 'spin-only' moments for this series forms the basis of Pauling's 'magnetic criterion of bond type' (p. 153).

In the case of the second and third transition series—the lanthanides and the actinides—the orbital contributions to the paramagnetic moment must be important because only when these are combined with the spin components can reasonable agreement be obtained between experimental and calculated values. This is accounted for by the suggestion that the $4d$ and $5d$ electrons and the $4f$ and $5f$ electrons are screened by filled outer electronic shells from strong interaction with the environment. Hence an important orbital contribution to the magnetic moment.

3. Formation of Coloured Ions

The violet colour of the hydrated Ti^{3+} ion is due to the transition of its single d electron between two energy levels (p. 157). The other transition metal ions containing one or more d electrons are also coloured because the absorption of energy in the visible region of the spectrum can again take place to bring about electronic transitions. The colours of the hydrated ions of the first period of transition metals are summarized in *Table 10.7*.

The colour of an ion is modified extensively by complex formation or by a change in its oxidation state. We have already described how the approach of a ligand alters the energies of the *d* electrons of the metal ion and hence the magnitude of the energies of the electronic transitions possible therein. A

Table 10.7. The colours of the hydrated ions of the first transition series

Number of d electrons	Number of unpaired electrons	Oxidation state and colour of hydrated ion
0	0	Ti^{IV}, colourless
1	1	Ti^{III}, violet; V^{IV}, blue (as VO^{2+})
2	2	V^{III}, green
3	3	V^{II}, violet; Cr^{III}, violet
4	4	Cr^{II}, blue; Mn^{III}, violet
5	5	Mn^{II}, pink; Fe^{III}, yellow
6	4	Fe^{II}, green
7	3	Co^{II}, pink
8	2	Ni^{II}, green
9	1	Cu^{II}, blue
10	0	Cu^{I}, colourless

wide range of colours is shown by the compounds of a single transition metal and its very name is sometimes an expression of this property. For instance, iridium (Latin *iris*, rainbow-coloured), chromium (Gr. *chrōma*, colour) and rhodium (Gr. *rhodon*, rose-red)

4. Complex Formation

The complexes of the transition metals are discussed elsewhere (Chapter 6) and examples are also to be found in the succeeding pages.

5. Interstitial Compounds

These have already been described earlier (p. 102) and nothing more will be added here.

GROUP IVA

Titanium

The most stable oxidation state is +4. The lower states of +3 and +2 are also known.

Titanium (II)

The oxide TiO is a non-stoichiometric compound obtained by heating a mixture of TiO_2 and Ti. It is oxidized to Ti^{III} salts by acids with the evolution of hydrogen. $TiCl_2$, made by the reduction of $TiCl_4$ with sodium amalgam, is a black powder which is oxidized by water. $TiBr_2$ and TiI_2 are also known.

9*   253

Titanium (III)

The oxide Ti_2O_3 is made by heating TiO_2 with carbon. Its basic nature is shown by reaction with H_2SO_4 to form the sulphate.

Ti^{III} salts are most conveniently prepared by the reduction of Ti^{IV} solutions with zinc and acid or electrolytically. Two hexahydrates of $TiCl_3$, one violet and the other green, are known. These resemble the isomers of $CrCl_3 . 6H_2O$ (p. 257). Hydrated $Ti_2(SO_4)_3$ is isomorphous with the corresponding Fe^{III} salt and forms alums such as $RbTi(SO_4)_2 . 12H_2O$ and $CsTi(SO_4)_2 . 12H_2O$. The Ti^{3+} ion thus resembles other metal ions of the same charge and similar size (Cr^{3+}, Fe^{3+} and Al^{3+}). The chloride and sulphate are both used in volumetric analysis as powerful reducing agents. The oxidation potential of Ti^{4+}/Ti^{3+} is $+0.04$ V. Ti^{III} salts are readily oxidized even by atmospheric oxygen or water. The hydrated Ti^{3+} ion is coloured violet and the formation of this colour on the reduction of Ti^{IV} serves as a useful qualitative test for the element.

Titanium (IV)

Titanium dioxide, TiO_2, occurs in nature largely as rutile (p. 174) and more rarely as anatase and brookite. The first two are tetragonal crystals; brookite is rhombic. It is insoluble in water and dilute acids but slowly dissolves in concentrated H_2SO_4 or fused alkali hydrogen sulphates. Titanium (IV) sulphate is formed under these conditions. This salt is easily hydrolysed by boiling with water with the production of β-titanic acid, H_4TiO_4. The addition of ammonium hydroxide to an acid solution of a Ti^{IV} salt precipitates another form of this, α-titanic acid. These α- and β-forms are analogous to the two forms of stannic acid (p. 214), the α-acid being much more reactive than the β-acid. Thus α-titanic acid dissolves in caustic alkali solution to form alkali titanates corresponding with the formulae $M_2^ITiO_3$ and $M_2^ITi_2O_5$. Titanates may alternatively be prepared by the fusion of TiO_2 with alkali carbonates. Certain titanates occur in nature, for instance $CaTiO_3$ as perovskite and $FeTiO_3$ as ilmenite.

In neutral or acid solution Ti^{IV} salts are coloured deep orange by hydrogen peroxide. From concentrated solutions, peroxytitanic acid, H_4TiO_5, is precipitated as a gel of variable water content. This is a derivative of titanic acid in which one —OH group has been replaced by —O—OH:

$$\begin{array}{ccc} HO & & OH \\ & \diagdown \; \diagup & \\ & Ti & \\ & \diagup \; \diagdown & \\ HO & & O\text{—}OH \end{array}$$

Hydrolysis of Ti^{IV} compounds takes place readily in solution. Partial hydrolysis gives compounds containing the titanyl ion, TiO^{2+}. The four tetrahalides are known and are characteristically covalent. $TiCl_4$, prepared by the chlorination of TiO_2 in the presence of carbon, is an important intermediate in the large-scale production of titanium metal. It is a colourless liquid, b.p. 136°C, which is rapidly hydrolysed by water:

$$TiCl_4 + 2H_2O = TiO_2 + 4HCl$$

Derivatives of the tetrahalides are the complex hexahalotitanate (IV) ions,

254

$[TiF_6]^{2-}$ and $[TiCl_6]^{2-}$.   In its tetrahalides, therefore, titanium again shows marked resemblances to the representative elements of Group IV.

Zirconium and Hafnium

These two elements are difficult to separate chemically because of their very close similarity in atomic and ionic radii.   Indeed hafnium was not discovered until 1922 when it was identified spectroscopically in zirconium minerals. Ion-exchange and solvent extraction methods (p. 189) have proved to be most successful in effecting separation.

Zirconium and hafnium are tetravalent in almost all their compounds. Some lower-valent compounds have been prepared, such as $ZrCl_3$ and $ZrCl_2$, but these are only stable in the solid state and no reaction in aqueous solution comparable with the reduction of Ti^{4+} to Ti^{3+} takes place with either Zr or Hf.

The dioxides ZrO_2 and HfO_2 are amphoteric, with acidic properties less pronounced than those of TiO_2.   The chemistry of both the elements in aqueous solution is dominated by the marked tendency to form complex ions, e.g. $[ZrF_6]^{2-}$, $[ZrF_8]^{4-}$, $[ZrO(SO_4)_2]^{2-}$, $[Zr(C_2O_4)_4]^{4-}$, etc.

GROUP V A

Vanadium

The known oxidation states are $+2$ to $+5$ inclusive, of which the $+5$ is the most stable.

Vanadium (II) and (III)

The oxides VO and V_2O_3 are formed in the reduction of V_2O_5 by hydrogen. Compounds of intermediate composition such as $VO_{1.35}$ have also been made. VO and V_2O_3 react with acids to form vanadium (II) and (III) salts respectively.   The oxidation potential for V^{3+}/V^{2+} is -0.255 V and that for VO^{2+}/V^{3+} is $+0.36$ V and so both V^{II} and V^{III} have marked reducing properties.   Thus V^{II} liberates hydrogen from dilute acids:

$$V^{2+} + H_3O^+ = V^{3+} + \tfrac{1}{2}H_2 + H_2O$$

Vanadium (II) salts, conveniently prepared by the reduction of vanadium (V) in acid solution using zinc amalgam, are often isomorphous with the corresponding iron (II) salts.   For instance, $VSO_4 . 7H_2O$ is isomorphous with $FeSO_4 . 7H_2O$, as is $K_4V(CN)_6 . 3H_2O$ with $K_4Fe(CN)_6 . 3H_2O$.

The most stable vanadium (III) compounds are the sulphatovanadates (III), such as $NH_4V(SO_4)_2 . 6H_2O$, prepared by the electrolytic reduction of a solution of V_2O_5 in H_2SO_4.   Sulphates of the alum type are also formed but these are oxidized slowly in solution by atmospheric oxygen.   The hexacyano-vanadate (III) salts are comparable in constitution with the hexacyano-complexes of Cr^{III}, Fe^{III} and Co^{III} but are less stable.

Vanadium (IV)

The oxide VO_2 is made by the mild reduction of V_2O_5 using oxalic acid. Its amphoteric nature is illustrated by solubility in acids to form the blue

255

vanadyl (containing VO^{2+} ions) salts and reaction with caustic alkalis to form vanadates (IV), such as $M_2^I(V_4O_9) . 7H_2O$. Vanadyl chloride, $VOCl_2$, can be prepared by the hydrolysis of VCl_4:

$$VCl_4 + H_2O = VOCl_2 + 2HCl$$

The tetrachloride, VCl_4, is a dark-red liquid, b.p. 154°C, which can be prepared by chlorination of the metal. The properties of VCl_4 are consistent with covalent bonding within the molecule. It reacts with HF to produce VF_4.

Vanadium (V)

Divanadium pentoxide, V_2O_5, can be prepared by heating ammonium metavanadate, NH_4VO_3. It is also the main product when finely divided vanadium is ignited in air. It is an acidic oxide which, whilst only slightly soluble in water, dissolves readily in alkali to form vanadates (V). The simple orthovanadate ion, VO_4^{3-}, exists only in strongly alkaline solution. The addition of H^+ produces condensed oxy-anions:

$$2VO_4^{3-} + 2H^+ \rightleftharpoons [V_2O_7]^{4-} + H_2O \text{ at pH } 10\text{--}12$$

$$[V_2O_7]^{4-} + VO_4^{3-} + 4H^+ \rightleftharpoons [V_3O_9]^{3-} + H_2O \text{ at pH } \sim 9$$

$$[V_3O_9]^{3-} + [V_2O_7]^{4-} + 4H^+ \rightleftharpoons [V_5O_{14}]^{3-} + 2H_2O \text{ at pH } 7$$

Further decrease in pH causes the eventual formation of a red colloidal dispersion of hydrated V_2O_5. Finally, when the pH is less than 1, the vanadium forms an oxy-cation:

$$V_2O_5 + 2H^+ \rightleftharpoons 2VO_2^+ + H_2O$$

The smaller vanadate ions are colourless; $[V_5O_{14}]^{3-}$ is orange-yellow and condensation beyond this is accompanied by an intensification of colour. The VO_2^+ ion is pale yellow.

The vanadates (V) resemble the phosphates in their marked tendency to condense (although the method of formation of condensed oxy-anions is different, p. 224) and like the arsenates have weak oxidizing properties.

In alkaline or weakly acid solution, vanadium (V) reacts with H_2O_2 to form the yellow diperoxovanadate ion, $[VO_2(O_2)_2]^{3-}$.

VF_5 is the only oxygen-free halide of vanadium (V). It is made by the disproportionation of VF_4 (into VF_5 and VF_3). The halides VOF_3, $VOCl_3$ and $VOBr_3$ are more readily obtained. For instance, dry HCl gas reacts with heated V_2O_5 in the presence of P_2O_5 to form $VOCl_3$:

$$V_2O_5 + 6HCl = 2VOCl_3 + 3H_2O$$

Niobium and Tantalum

Like zirconium and hafnium, these two metals are difficult to separate from one another. Isolation is best achieved using modern selective techniques (p. 189).

The +5 state is the most stable and the lower-valent states are obtained with increasing difficulty on passing from vanadium to tantalum. Blue Nb^{III} solutions are obtained by the reduction of Nb^V solutions with zinc and HCl. Ta^V, however, is unaffected in these conditions.

The pentoxides, like V_2O_5, are acidic. Pentahalides such as NbF_5, TaF_5,

$NbCl_5$, $TaCl_5$ and $NbBr_5$ are known. These are chiefly covalent and are easily hydrolysed to give hydrated pentoxides. A variety of halo-complexes are also known, including $[NbOF_5]^{2-}$, $[NbOF_6]^{3-}$, $[NbF_7]^{2-}$, $[TaF_7]^{2-}$ and $[TaF_8]^{3-}$.

GROUP VI A

Chromium

The important oxidation states, discussed below, are +2, +3 and +6. Other states shown are +1 (in the complex $[Cr(dipy)_3]ClO_4$ where dipy = dipyridyl), +4 (in CrF_4, $CrCl_4$ and CrO_2) and +5 (in CrF_5).

Chromium (II)

The oxide CrO is prepared by dissolving the mercury out of chromium amalgam with dilute nitric acid. It is readily oxidized to Cr_2O_3.

Cr^{II} salts can be made by the reduction of Cr^{III} with zinc in acid solution in the presence of CO_2 or some other inert atmosphere to prevent oxidation. The salts are very strong reducing agents in aqueous solution as indicated by the oxidation potential of -0.41 V for the Cr^{3+}/Cr^{2+} couple. The Cr^{II} state is stabilized by complex formation as in chromous hydrazine sulphate, $CrSO_4 . (N_2H_4)_2H_2SO_4$, which, unlike simple Cr^{II} salts, is quite stable in air. Cr^{II} salts resemble those of Fe^{II} because of the similarities in ionic size of the metal, but they are more strongly reducing.

Chromium (III)

The oxide Cr_2O_3 is obtained by the thermal decomposition of ammonium dichromate. The hydrated form is precipitated by the addition of hydroxyl ions to solutions of Cr^{III} salts. The hydrate, chromic hydroxide, is soluble in acids to form chromium (III) salts and in caustic alkalis to form chromites (the chromium is present here in the form of anions like $[Cr(OH)_6]^{3-}$).

The simple chromium (III) salts are like those of Al^{III} and Fe^{III} in their properties; for example, Cr^{III} forms double sulphates like the alums.

The distinctive property of the Cr^{3+} ion is its very strong ability to form complexes. In solutions of chromium (III) chloride, for instance, aquo-complexes are present. Crystallization produces a deep-green hexahydrate, from which only two molecules of water can be removed easily and from which, in solution, only one third of the chlorines present can be immediately precipitated by silver nitrate. Because of this the compound has been formulated as $[CrCl_2 . (H_2O)_4]Cl . 2H_2O$. Two other hexahydrates have been obtained: one, pale green in colour, is $[CrCl . (H_2O)_5] . Cl_2 . H_2O$; the other, a violet complex, is $[Cr(H_2O)_6]Cl_3$.

Many complexes are known which contain ammonia. The co-ordination number of the metal is again 6 as in the salts $Cr(NH_3)_6X_3$, where X is a uni-negative anion such as halide. Replacement of 1, 2 or more ammonias by water molecules leads to a series of aquo-derivatives: complex anions result when the ammonia is partly or wholly replaced by negative ions, leading eventually to $[CrX_6]^{3-}$. In its range and stability of complexes Cr^{III} shows a striking resemblance to Co^{III}.

Chromium (VI)

The polymeric oxide CrO_3 is prepared by acidifying saturated dichromate solution with concentrated sulphuric acid. It is a deep-red crystalline solid which reacts with water to form chromic, H_2CrO_4, and dichromic, $H_2Cr_2O_7$, acids. The acids themselves are known only in solution but the salts can be isolated in the solid state. The alkali metal chromates and dichromates are soluble in water. The salt, potassium dichromate, $K_2Cr_2O_7$, finds particular application as a primary standard in volumetric analysis. It is an oxidizing agent, being itself reduced to Cr^{III}:

$$Cr_2O_7^{2-} + 6e^- + 14H^+ \rightleftharpoons 2Cr^{3+} + 7H_2O \quad E° = +1.33 \text{ V}$$

The chromate ion is tetrahedral: the dichromate ion is composed of two CrO_4 tetrahedra joined together by sharing one oxygen:

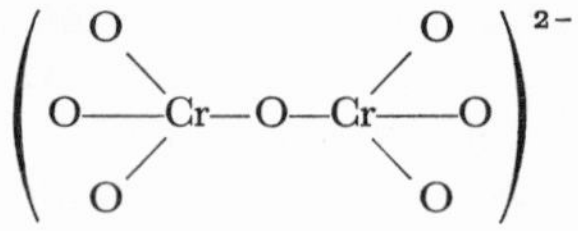

Further condensation occurs in acid solution to tri- and tetrachromate, $[Cr_3O_{10}]^{2-}$ and $[Cr_4O_{13}]^{2-}$ respectively.

The action of H_2O_2 on chromate (VI) solutions gives a variety of peroxo-chromates. Two series are known: the blue compounds, containing $[Cr_2O_{12}]^{2-}$; and the red peroxochromates which contain $[CrO_8]^{3-}$.

Molybdenum and Tungsten

These two elements show marked resemblances to each other because of the lanthanide contraction. The most stable oxidation state is $+6$, although the lower states $+2$ to $+5$ inclusive are also known.

The trioxides, MO_3, are acidic. In aqueous solution they give rise to oxy-acids which show a great tendency to form polyacids of high molecular weight. Some of these are formed from one acid only and are then known as isopolyacids. Examples of their salts are $(NH_4)_6(Mo_7O_{24}).4H_2O$, ammonium paramolybdate, and $K_6(H_2W_{12}O_{40}).18H_2O$, potassium metatungstate. The heteropolyacids are another group which contain a second acid besides either molybdic or tungstic acid. Derivatives of these are important in quantitative analysis, for example, ammonium phosphomolybdate, $(NH_4)_3PMo_{12}O_{40}$, which is used for the gravimetric analysis of phosphorus.

Both metals form many complexes and this property is made use of to stabilize the lower-valent states, for instance, Mo^{IV} and W^{IV} are appreciably stabilized in their octacyano-complexes, $[Mo(CN)_8]^{4-}$ and $[W(CN)_8]^{4-}$ respectively.

GROUP VII A

Manganese

The important oxidation states are $+2$, $+4$ and $+7$. Others known are $+1$, $+3$, $+5$ and $+6$. The Mn^{2+} ion is very stable compared with the divalent ions of Ti, V and Cr and so the electronic arrangement $3d^5$ is regarded as particularly stable.

Manganese (II)

The oxide MnO, obtained when the higher oxides of Mn are reduced by hydrogen or CO, is basic and reacts, for instance, with HCl to form manganese (II) chloride, $MnCl_2$. This and other salts of Mn^{II} are stable in the anhydrous state and also in acid solution. In alkaline solution, $Mn(OH)_2$ is formed and this is slowly oxidized by air to $MnO_2 \cdot xH_2O$.

Manganese (III)

The oxide Mn_2O_3 can be made by heating Mn^{II} salts in air or oxygen. Heating to above 900°C converts it to Mn_3O_4, formulated as a mixed oxide, $2Mn^{II}O \cdot Mn^{IV}O_2$. Mn_2O_3 has basic properties and dissolves, for example, in sulphuric acid to form manganese (III) sulphate, $Mn_2(SO_4)_3$. This and other Mn^{III} salts have a low stability and are reduced to Mn^{II} in acid solution. In neutral solution, hydrolysis takes place to $Mn(OH)_3$ which is then oxidized to hydrated MnO_2. $Mn_2(SO_4)_3$ forms double sulphates and alums, such as $CsMn(SO_4)_2 \cdot 12H_2O$. Other known salts of Mn^{III} include MnF_3.

Manganese (IV)

Manganese dioxide, MnO_2, occurs in nature as pyrolusite. It has extremely low solubility in water and to this property can be attributed its apparent stability. It is amphoteric, reacting both with acids to give manganese (IV) salts, and with alkalis to form manganates (IV), containing MnO_3^{2-}. For example, in cold concentrated HCl, MnO_2 dissolves to form the complex ion $[MnCl_6]^{2-}$. The simple chloride $MnCl_4$ has not been isolated in the pure state. Manganese (IV) compounds are not stable in solution, being oxidized to manganate (VI) in alkaline solution and showing a strong tendency to undergo reduction to Mn^{II} in acid solution.

Manganese (V) and (VI)

Some manganates (V), containing the blue ion MnO_4^{3-}, have been prepared. For example, the reduction of K_2MnO_4 at $-5°C$ in 12 M NaOH by an equivalent of sulphite yields crystalline $Na_3MnO_4 \cdot 10H_2O$. Magnetic susceptibility measurements have been used to show the presence of Mn^V in this compound; it is isomorphous with Na_3VO_4.

Manganates (VI) containing the green ion MnO_4^{2-} are made by the oxidation of MnO_2 in the presence of fused alkali. The alkali metal manganates are stable only in the solid state in the absence of CO_2 or in strongly alkaline media and undergo disproportionation in water or dilute acids:

$$3Mn^{VI}O_4^{2-} + 2H_2O \rightleftharpoons 2Mn^{VII}O_4^- + Mn^{IV}O_2 + 4OH^-$$

Manganese (VII)

The oxide Mn_2O_7 is obtained by the action of concentrated H_2SO_4 on $KMnO_4$. It reacts with water to form a solution of permanganic acid, $HMnO_4$. This acid, although it cannot be isolated in the anhydrous state, appears to be very strong and it acts as a powerful oxidizing agent. The most important salt of the acid is the potassium one which can be prepared by the electrolytic oxidation of manganate (VI):

$$MnO_4^{2-} - e^- = MnO_4^-$$

Potassium permanganate is a deep-purple, almost black, solid which dissolves in water to give a characteristic red-violet solution. It is extensively used in volumetric analysis as an oxidizing agent. In acid solution the following reaction occurs:

$$MnO_4^- + 8H^+ + 5e^- = Mn^{2+} + 4H_2O \quad E^\circ = +1.51 \text{ V}$$

Its reaction with a reducing agent is initially slow but is accelerated by the increasing concentration of Mn^{2+} during the reaction or by the deliberate prior addition of Mn^{2+}. The reaction between Mn^{2+} and MnO_4^- produces low concentration of Mn^{3+} and MnO^{2+} which both rapidly oxidize the reducing agent:

$$Mn^{2+} + MnO_4^- = MnO^{2+} + MnO_3^-$$

followed by

$$Mn^{2+} + MnO_3^- + 4H^+ = MnO^{2+} + Mn^{3+} + 2H_2O$$

In alkaline or neutral solution, MnO_4^- is reduced according to

$$MnO_4^- + 4H^+ + 3e^- = MnO_2 + 2H_2O: \quad E^\circ = +1.695 \text{ V}$$

No condensed oxy-anions of Mn comparable with those of Cr or V appear to exist.

The oxides of Mn illustrate very clearly the decrease in basic property and increase in acid character as the oxidation state of the metal increases.

Technetium and Rhenium

Traces of technetium occur naturally. It was first prepared, however, in 1947 by the following nuclear reaction:

$$^{98}_{42}Mo \, (n, \gamma) \, ^{99}_{42}Mo \xrightarrow{-\beta} {}^{99}_{43}Tc \xrightarrow[2.12 \times 10^5 \text{ yr}]{-\beta} {}^{99}_{44}Ru$$

It is mainly obtained from the fission products of uranium and in its chemistry resembles rhenium rather than manganese.

Rhenium, an extremely rare element, was first identified in 1925. The +4 and +7 oxidation states are important. The enhanced stability of the higher valency states of rhenium compared with those of manganese is shown by the properties of one of its most stable compounds, potassium perrhenate, $KReO_4$. This is quite stable; it does not have the marked oxidizing ability of $KMnO_4$ and is not decomposed by alkali.

GROUP VIII

Iron

The most stable oxidation states are +2 and +3. The unstable states of +4, +5 and +6 are also known. The sudden fall in maximum stable oxidation state from +7 to +3 in passing from Mn to Fe is attributable to the extra stability of the half-filled $3d$ sub-shell, since Fe^{3+}, like Mn^{2+}, has the electronic configuration $3d^5$.

Iron (II)

The oxide FeO is formed on heating iron (II) oxalate in the absence of air. The crystalline compound invariably contains less iron than that required by the (ideal) formula FeO (p. 101). Although FeO does have basic properties, iron (II) salts are best prepared by dissolution of the metal in the appropriate acid.

In acid solution, Fe^{II} salts are fairly stable in the presence of air and require the presence of a strong oxidizing agent to convert them to Fe^{III} (see below). Iron (II) hydroxide, $Fe(OH)_2$, is precipitated by the addition of alkali to a Fe^{II} salt solution and is very easily oxidized to Fe^{III}. $Fe(OH)_2$ is amphoteric and dissolves in concentrated NaOH to form a ferrate (II)—$Na_4Fe(OH)_6$.

Iron (II) sulphate is technically the most important salt of iron. The heptahydrate, $FeSO_4.7H_2O$, is isomorphous with the heptahydrates of the other transition metal sulphates. It forms double sulphates such as Mohr's salt, $(NH_4)_2SO_4.FeSO_4.6H_2O$.

When complexed with cyanide ion, Fe^{II} is much more stable than the simple hydrated Fe^{2+} ion. Thus $E°$ for Fe^{3+}/Fe^{2+} is $+0.771$ V whilst $E°$ for $[Fe(CN)_6]^{3-}/[Fe(CN)_6]^{4-}$ is $+0.36$ V. These figures should be compared with the corresponding ones for simple and complexed Co^{II} and Co^{III} (p. 117).

Iron (III)

The hydrated oxide Fe_2O_3 is precipitated by adding alkali to an iron (III) solution. It is amphoteric and forms iron (III) salts with acids and ferrates (III), like $NaFeO_2$, with alkali.

Fe_3O_4 is a double oxide, formulated as $Fe^{II}O.Fe^{III}_2O_3$, which occurs extensively in nature as the ore magnetite.

Fe^{III} salts are hydrolysed to a large extent in aqueous solution but the hydrolysis can be repressed by the addition of acid:

$$FeCl_3 + 3H_2O \rightleftharpoons 3HCl + Fe(OH)_3$$

In the vapour state, $FeCl_3$ dimerizes in a similar manner to $AlCl_3$:

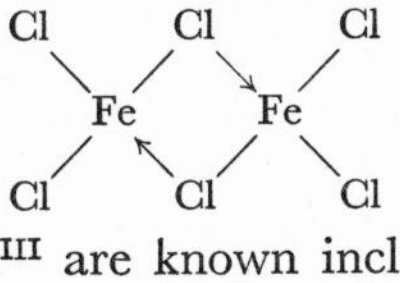

Numerous complexes of Fe^{III} are known including the hexacyanoferrates (III), containing $[Fe(CN)_6]^{3-}$, and the thiocyanate complexes, $[Fe(CNS)]^{2+}$, $[Fe(CNS)_2]^+$, *etc.*

Iron (IV)

This state is exemplified by the unstable ferrates (IV) and the complex $[FeCl_2.2C_6H_4(As(CH_3)_2)_2](FeCl_4)_2$, in which the cation is

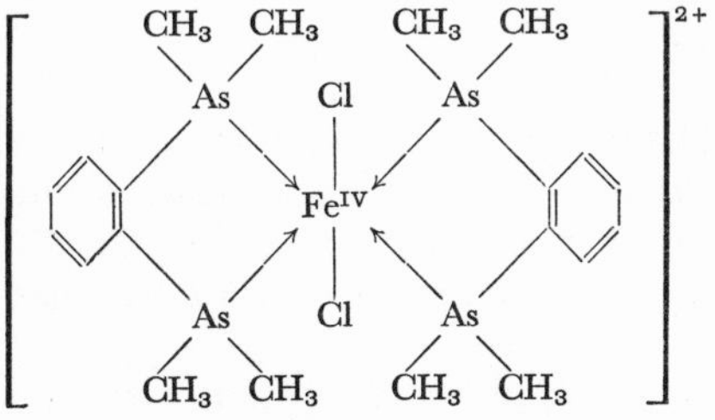

Iron (VI)

This state is exemplified by the very unstable ferrates (VI), containing the anion FeO_4^{2-}, obtained when Fe^{III} is oxidized by NaOCl in strongly alkaline solution:

$$2 Fe(OH)_3 + 3 ClO^- + 4 OH^- = 2 FeO_4^{2-} + 3 Cl^- + 5 H_2O$$

Reduction by water takes place with the loss of oxygen and the precipitation of $Fe(OH)_3$. The formation of ferrates (VI) is the last example in the first transition series of the active use of most of the *d* electrons in compound formation.

Cobalt

The chief oxidation state of Co in its simple salts is $+2$; in its complexes, it is $+3$. The unstable $+4$ state is also known (in the oxides CoO_2 and Co_3O_4, formulated as $2 Co^{II}O \cdot Co^{IV}O_2$, and the double oxides Sr_2CoO_4 and Ba_2CoO_4). The tetracyano complex of Co^0, $[Co(CN)_4]^{4-}$, is mentioned elsewhere (p. 128).

Cobalt (II)

The oxide CoO is prepared by heating $Co(OH)_2$ or $CoCO_3$ in the absence of air. In the presence of oxygen, freshly precipitated $Co(OH)_2$ is oxidized to hydrated Co_2O_3. In the presence of strong oxidizing agents, further oxidation to hydrated CoO_2 occurs.

Simple Co^{II} salts are stable in solution; E° for Co^{3+}/Co^{2+} is $+1\cdot82$ V. A dilute solution of a cobalt (II) salt is pink in colour due to the hexahydrated ion $[Co(H_2O)_6]^{2+}$. On the addition of HCl or metallic chlorides, the colour changes through violet to blue as the chloride ion concentration increases. This is associated with the formation of halide complexes $[CoCl]^+$, $CoCl_2$, $[CoCl_3]^-$ and $[CoCl_4]^{2-}$. Double salts containing $[CoCl_4]^{2-}$, such as $Cs_2 CoCl_4 \cdot CsCl$, are also blue.

Cobalt (II) salts give a precipitate with cyanide ions which has the composition, $Co(CN)_2 \cdot 2H_2O$. Treatment of this with KCN solution gives a solution from which crystals of the complex potassium pentacyanocobaltate (II), $K_3Co^{II}(CN)_5$, separate out. This is only stable in a hydrogen atmosphere and is very readily converted to $K_3Co^{III}(CN)_6$. This behaviour is typical of Co^{II} complexes for these in general are easily oxidized to the stable Co^{III} complexes. The oxidation potential, E°, for $[Co^{III}(CN)_6]^{3-}/[Co^{II}(CN)_5]^{3-}$ is $-0\cdot83$ V and should be compared with that for the simple ions (see above). The key to the high stability of Co^{III} complexes is to be found in their electronic configuration (p. 154).

Cobalt (III)

CoF_3, prepared by the action of fluorine on $CoCl_2$, decomposes to CoF_2 and F_2 on heating and is a valuable fluorinating agent. $Co_2(SO_4)_3 \cdot 18H_2O$, formed when a cold concentrated solution of $CoSO_4$ containing H_2SO_4 is oxidized electrolytically, is similarly unstable and has strong oxidizing properties.

In contrast, a great multiplicity of Co^{III} complexes is known. For example,

NH_3 and CN^- are very firmly complexed by Co^{III} and the resulting compounds have proved of special interest in the development of theoretical ideas on co-ordination (p. 134). Not only are many mononuclear complexes known like $[Co(NH_3)_6]^{3+}$ and $[Co(CN)_6]^{3-}$, but there exists also a wide range of poly-nuclear complexes in which two or more metal atoms are present in the complex. The latter are exemplified by dodecamminehexoltetracobalt (III) salts:

$$\left[Co\left(\begin{array}{c} HO \\[0.2em] \diagdown \\[-0.3em] \diagup \\[0.2em] HO \end{array} Co(NH_3)_4 \right)_3 \right] X_6$$

Nickel

The oxidation state of $+2$ is by far the most common, but the higher states of $+3$ and $+4$ are also known. Lower states of $+1$ and 0 are found in the complexes $K_2[Ni(CN)_3]$ and $K_4[Ni(CN)_4]$ respectively.

Nickel (II)

The oxide NiO is formed when Ni^{II} salts such as $NiCO_3$ and $Ni(NO_3)_2$ are heated. It dissolves in acids forming Ni^{II} salts. This represents the stable state of nickel in aqueous solution.

Nickel (II) readily forms complex ions with ammonia such as $[Ni(H_2O)_2(NH_3)_4]^{2+}$ and $[Ni(NH_3)_6]^{2+}$. For this reason, many nickel salts are insoluble in water but dissolve in ammoniacal solutions. The maximum covalency of 6 is not often reached in Ni^{II} complexes and the lower value of 4 is more common, as in the square planar $[Ni(CN)_4]^{2-}$, the complex with dimethylglyoxime (p. 144), etc.

Nickel (III)

The anhydrous oxide has not been isolated but hydrated Ni_2O_3 has been precipitated by oxidizing Ni^{II} in alkaline solution with bromine. This hydrate loses water on heating to form $Ni_2O_3.H_2O$, which then decomposes to NiO with the evolution of oxygen and water vapour. On heating NiO with BaO in an oxygen atmosphere, the compound $Ba_2Ni_2O_5$ is obtained. The formation of this is evidence for the amphoteric character of Ni^{III}.

Stable complexes of Ni^{III} have been prepared: these include bis(triethyl-phosphine) tribromonickel (III), which is of special interest as an example of a 5 co-ordinate square-pyramidal complex:

$$\begin{array}{ccc} & Br & \\ Br & | & P(C_2H_5)_3 \\ & \diagdown \; \downarrow \; \diagup & \\ & Ni & \\ & \diagup \quad \diagdown & \\ (C_2H_5)_3P & & Br \end{array}$$

Also known is the complex ion $[NiCl_2.2C_6H_4(As(CH_3)_2)_2]^+$ which contains octahedrally co-ordinated Ni^{III}.

263

Nickel (IV)

The action of chlorine on Ni^{II} in alkaline medium gives precipitates containing up to 1·9 atoms of oxygen per atom of nickel. The nickel is therefore substantially in the $+4$ state. Such substances are very strongly oxidizing and will convert, for example, Mn^{2+} to MnO_4^- in acid solution. Barium nickelate (IV) has been made by the reaction at 700°C between oxygen and an equimolar mixture of $Ba(OH)_2$ and NiO.

Other examples of Ni^{IV} are K_2NiF_6, made by the fluorination of a 2:1 molar mixture of KCl and $NiCl_2$, and the complex ion $[NiCl_2 . 2C_6H_4(As(CH_3)_2)_2]^{2+}$, made by the oxidation of the monovalent ion of this composition using HNO_3 and $HClO_4$.

The Platinum Metals

These are ruthenium (Ru), rhodium (Rh), palladium (Pd), osmium (Os), iridium (Ir) and platinum (Pt). They almost invariably occur with one another and are often found native. They are rare because of their siderophile nature.

Important valency states are as follows (those of iron, cobalt and nickel are also included for comparison):

Fe (II), (III)	Co (II), (III)	Ni (II)
Ru (IV), (VIII)	Rh (III)	Pd (II)
Os (VI), (VIII)	Ir (IV)	Pt (II), (IV)

A number of other states is also known.

The affinity for oxygen decreases from left to right as we approach I B, the sub-group containing the noble metals silver and gold. All six elements have a relatively much higher affinity for sulphur. As well as the simple sulphides, many complexes are formed containing sulphur as the ligand atom. Numerous other complexes are known and even the apparently simple compounds like $PdCl_2$ have a complex structure (p. 251).

GROUP I B

Commonly referred to as the coinage metals, copper (Cu), silver (Ag) and gold (Au) have the electron configuration $(n-1)d^{10}ns^1$. Apart from the fact that they exhibit monovalency and have electrical conductivity, there is little resemblance to the alkali metals. As one would expect, there is a strong resemblance between Ni, Pd and Pt and the corresponding elements in this sub-group; the nickel sub-group elements have only one electron less than the coinage metals in each case and because energy differences involved are small, the differences in chemical behaviour are only slight.

The high ionization potentials cause considerable covalent character in the compounds of this group. Each member shows more than one oxidation state (*Table 10.8*). With gold, the main oxidation state of three is largely a complexed one and the ion Au^{3+} is not formed. A study of the ionization potentials (*Table 10.8*) indicates that the monovalent ions are the most stable *in vacuo*, but in assessing the relative stability of the different oxidation states in

Table 10.8. *The properties of the coinage metals*

		Cu	Ag	Au
Atomic number		29	47	79
Electron configuration		$3d^{10}4s^1$	$4d^{10}5s^1$	$5d^{10}6s^1$
Melting point (°C)		1083	960	1063
Boiling point (°C)		2580	2180	2700
Ionization potential	1st	178·1	174·7	212·6
(kcal/g atom)	2nd	467·9	495·3	472·7
Atomic radius (Å)		1·17	1·34	1·34
Ionic radius (Å)	M^+	0·96	1·26	1·37†
	M^{2+}	0·72*	—	—
	M^{3+}	—	—	0·87*
Oxidation states		I, II, (III)	I, II, (III)	I, III

* Estimated values.　　　　† See p. 75.

solution the effect of hydration must be considered and it is found that whereas silver is less resistant to reduction with increasing charge on the cation, copper and gold show the reverse behaviour in their common oxidation states. In the case of copper, the respective ionization potentials of $Cu \rightarrow Cu^+$ and $Cu \rightarrow Cu^{2+}$ are 178·1 and 468·1 kcal/g atom; hence cuprous copper, Cu^I, is more stable by an amount of 290 kcal/g atom. The hydration energies of the two oxidation states are, however, 115·3 and 537·3 kcal respectively; thus in solution cupric copper, Cu^{II}, is the more stable by an overall energy difference of 132 kcal. Cuprous compounds are only stable in the presence of water if they are insoluble or complex, otherwise disproportionation occurs according to

$$2\,Cu^+ = Cu^{2+} + Cu$$

(see also p. 116).

With silver the unipositive oxidation state is stable with respect to disproportionation of this nature. The dipositive and tripositive states, although stable in the solid, have oxidation potentials that exceed that required for the oxidation of water. Consequently, in aqueous solution these states are unstable.

With gold, the problem is complicated by hydrolysis but the oxidation states Au^I and Au^{III} bear a similar relationship to one another as do the $+1$ and $+2$ states for copper, that is to say Au^I is unstable with respect to disproportionation into Au^{III} and metallic gold.

Compounds

Oxides

Monoxides of the general formula M_2O have all been characterized. Their preparation may be effected by precipitation by caustic alkali. It becomes increasingly difficult as the group is descended to obtain them free from water; cuprous oxide may be precipitated from aqueous solution without water of crystallization whereas gold (I) oxide is precipitated as a hydrate and attempts to dehydrate this lead to decomposition with loss of oxygen. Compared with the alkali metal oxides they are less soluble, more covalent and generally feebly basic. The basicity does not vary regularly in the group and Ag_2O is the most basic. The thermal stability of the monoxides towards decomposition into the metal and oxygen decreases from Cu_2O to Au_2O. Structurally Cu_2O and Ag_2O are isomorphous; unlike the monoxides of Group I A which have the antifluorite structure, these are more covalent and have 4:2 co-ordination.

In the divalent state, cupric oxide, CuO, is well characterized, silver (II) oxide is less well characterized and Au^{II} oxide is unknown.

Cupric oxide, which can be obtained either by direct oxidation of the metal or by heating the hydroxide, nitrate or carbonate, is weakly basic. Decomposition to Cu_2O occurs at 900°C.

A black solid of composition AgO may be prepared by the oxidation of silver nitrate with persulphate ion in alkaline media and although this solid dissolves in sulphuric acid with the evolution of oxygen, tests for peroxide are negative. Recent results have shown that the solid is diamagnetic and not paramagnetic as originally reported. Two different types of silver atom are present in the crystal; one is two co-ordinate, the other four co-ordinate. The composition is probably $Ag^I Ag^{III} O_2$.

The corresponding oxide of gold is unknown. Addition of alkali to solutions of Au^{III} results in the formation of the amphoteric hydroxide $Au(OH)_3$. This compound exhibits greater acidic character than $Cu(OH)_2$ and readily dissolves in hot alkali to form aurates (AuO_2^-). Thermal decomposition of this hydroxide yields Au_2O_3.

Halides

The copper (I) halides, CuX, exhibit greater covalent character than those of silver (I). This is shown by their crystal structures; for the former zinc blende is found, whereas for the latter, except AgI, the structure is that of sodium chloride.

Copper (I) chloride and bromide are prepared by the reduction of Cu^{2+} by reagents such as metallic copper, sulphur dioxide or stannous chloride in the presence of the appropriate halogen hydracid. The iodide may be prepared by reducing Cu^{2+} with iodide ion alone.

The halides of Au^I with the exception of AuF are known. Disproportionation occurs in water to Au^{III} and metallic gold for the chloride and bromide. The iodide, however, resembles CuI in being stable under these conditions.

For divalent copper there is again a certain degree of covalent bond character. The tendency of copper to form co-ordinate square planar complexes is shown in the structure of the anhydrous chloride and bromide which have the chain structures

The dihydrate $CuCl_2 . 2H_2O$ also contains square planar co-ordinated copper. This configuration arises from extreme distortion of an octahedral grouping around the metal (p. 161). Thermally unstable, the chloride and bromide decompose at high temperatures into the halogen and the cuprous halide.

Silver (II) halides are unknown except for AgF_2 which may be prepared by fluorination of silver or silver salts. Like other compounds of Ag (II) it is strongly oxidizing as is indicated by the redox potential of $+1.98$ V for the Ag^{2+}/Ag^+ couple.

All four halides of Au^{III} are known, the stability decreasing from AuF_3 to AuI_3. Even in the solid state the iodide is unstable at ordinary temperatures and decomposes to iodine and gold (I) iodide. The fluoride, unlike the chloride and bromide, which are prepared by direct combination of the metal and X_2, is best prepared by reaction between gold and BrF_3, forming the intermediate $AuBrF_6$ which is thermally decomposed at 150°C to AuF_3. The iodide may be prepared by the reaction between $KAuCl_4$ and concentrated potassium iodide solution. In the solid, as well as in the vapour phase, dimeric molecules of the chloride and bromide are formed, illustrating the great tendency of gold in this oxidation state to form 4 co-ordinate complex compounds:

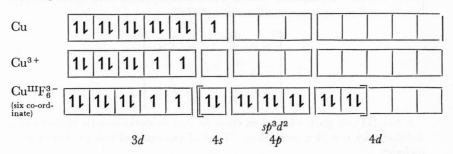

An anomalous sub-fluoride Ag_2F is formed by cathodic reduction of silver (I) fluoride; this has a layer lattice and is intermediate between a salt and a metal in behaviour.

Complexes

In addition to the simple halides, a number of complex halides are formed. Thus copper forms species of the type $[Cu^IX_2]^-$, $[Cu^{II}X_4]^{2-}$. Halo-complexes such as $[CuX_4]^{2-}$ and $[CuX_3(H_2O)]^-$ are numerous in the dipositive oxidation state and the change from solid to solution is accompanied by colour variations. In the solid state, $[CuCl_4]^{2-}$ is brown but in solution, colours varying from yellow-green to blue are obtained according to the degree of hydration.

In $K_3Cu^{III}F_6$, the observed paramagnetism corresponds to the presence of two unpaired electrons indicating an outer orbital complex.

Cu	$\boxed{1\downarrow\,1\downarrow\,1\downarrow\,1\downarrow\,1\downarrow\;\;1}$			

| Cu^{3+} | $\boxed{1\downarrow\,1\downarrow\,1\downarrow\,1\;\;1}$ | | | |

| Cu^{III}F$_6^{3-}$ (six co-ordinate) | $\boxed{1\downarrow\,1\downarrow\,1\downarrow\,1\;\;1}$ | $\boxed{1\downarrow}$ | $\boxed{1\downarrow\,1\downarrow\,1\downarrow}$ | $\boxed{1\downarrow\,1\downarrow}$ |

$$sp^3d^2$$

3d	4s	4p	4d

Silver also forms complexes of the same type, *e.g.* $[Ag^ICl_2]^-$ and $[Ag^{III}F_4]^-$.

Four co-ordinate gold complexes such as $[AuCl_4]^-$ and $[AuBr_4]^-$ are well known; this co-ordination is retained when hydrolysis occurs to complexes such as $[AuOCl_3]^{2-}$. In compounds such as $CsAuCl_3$ the empirical formula suggests the presence of Au^{II} but it has been shown that these are correctly formulated as $[Au^ICl_2.Au^{III}Cl_4]^{2-}$.

A wide variety of other anionic and cationic complexes are found. The principal co-ordination numbers exhibited are two and four.

In the +1 oxidation state, complexes of the type $[M(CN)_2]^-$ and $[M(NH_3)_2]^+$ are formed and linear co-ordination is found for this co-ordination number two. Stable complexes are formed between phosphine and arsine derivatives and the metal halides MX. These are of the type $R_3P{\rightarrow}AuX$ (monomeric) and $(C_2H_5)_3As{\rightarrow}CuI$ (tetrameric). In the latter compound, as in many others, a tetrahedral configuration around copper is assumed as shown in *Figure 10.1*.

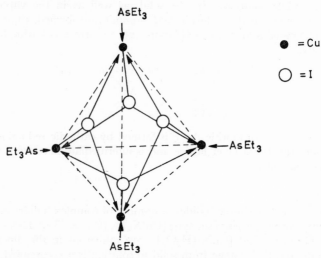

Figure 10.1. Structure of the complex between triethylarsine and Cu^I iodide

In the dipositive oxidation state, 4 co-ordinate paramagnetic copper complexes are commonly formed and these are square planar (p. 161). In addition to the halo-complexes, cyanide $[Cu(CN)_4]^{2-}$ and ammine $[Cu(NH_3)_2]^{2+}$ complexes are also formed. Stable chelate compounds with donor oxygen, sulphur and nitrogen are characteristic of Cu^{II},

e.g.

$$\left[\begin{array}{c} \overset{H_2}{H_2C-N} \qquad \overset{H_2}{N-CH_2} \\ | \qquad\quad Cu \qquad\quad | \\ \underset{H_2}{H_2C-N} \qquad \underset{H_2}{N-CH_2} \end{array} \right]^{2+}$$

Silver (II), in particular when co-ordinated to pyridine-type molecules, is stabilized by complex formation. Typical examples of this oxidation state include:

$$[Ag(py)_4]S_2O_8; \quad [Ag(\alpha\text{-pic})_2]S_2O_8 \text{ and } [Ag(dipy)_2](ClO_4^-)_2$$

where py = pyridine; α-pic = α-picoline and dipy = dipyridyl.

The tripositive oxidation state is exemplified by gold which forms 4 co-ordinate complexes that have a square planar arrangement of the co-ordinated groups. A number of arsine and phosphine type complexes are known such as $(CH_3)_3P{\rightarrow}AuX_3$. Some simple and alkyl substituted cyano-complexes are formed; the simple cyano-complexes show the same instability as AuI_3 but alkyl substituted complexes like $(C_3H_7)_2AuCN$ are stable and in fact are tetrameric:

$$
\begin{array}{ccc}
& C_3H_7 & & C_3H_7 \\
& | & & | \\
C_3H_7-\!\!\!& Au & \!\!\!-C\!\equiv\!N\!\rightarrow\!\!\!& Au \!\!\!-C_3H_7 \\
& \uparrow & & | \\
& N & & C \\
& ||| & & ||| \\
& C & & N \\
& | & & \downarrow \\
C_3H_7-\!\!\!& Au & \!\!\!\leftarrow\!N\!\equiv\!C-\!\!\!& Au \!\!\!-C_3H_7 \\
& | & & | \\
& C_3H_7 & & C_3H_7 \\
\end{array}
$$

GROUP II B

This sub-group comprises the three metals zinc (Zn), cadmium (Cd) and mercury (Hg). The atoms have the electron configuration $(n-1)d^{10}ns^2$ and the removal of one or two electrons might be expected to give rise to the formation of mono-positive and dipositive oxidation states respectively. The existence of the $+1$ oxidation state in the case of mercury has been well established but there is no reliable evidence for this state with either zinc or cadmium.

Compared with the elements of the A sub-group, compounds of zinc, cadmium and mercury in the dipositive state are considerably more covalent in character. The stability of the inner d^{10} core is such that oxidation states higher than two are not formed. Complexes are, however, very common; these are tetrahedral where 4 co-ordinate and octahedral where 6 co-ordinate.

Table 10.9 summarizes the general physical properties of the group.

Table 10.9. The properties of the Group II B metals

		Zn	Cd	Hg
Atomic number		30	48	80
Electron configuration		$3d^{10}4s^2$	$4d^{10}5s^2$	$5d^{10}6s^2$
Melting point (°C)		419·4	320·9	$-38·87$
Boiling point (°C)		906	765	356·6
Ionization potential	1st	216·6	207·3	240·5
(kcal/g atom)	2nd	414·2	389·7	432·4
Atomic radius (Å)		1·25	1·41	1·44
Ionic radius (Å)	M^{2+}	0·74	0·97	1·10

Mercury shows a few peculiarities:

(*i*) it is a liquid at normal temperatures,
(*ii*) it is capable of forming amalgams,
(*iii*) it has an ionization potential comparable with that of radon, showing the increased inert character of the outermost s electrons.

Compounds

Mercury (I) Compounds

Compounds of this oxidation state are numerous and most oxidizing agents are capable of converting mercury to either Hg^I (the mercurous) or

Hg^{II} (the mercuric) state. The oxidation potentials for these two couples are

$$Hg^{I} \rightarrow Hg \qquad E^{\circ} = +0.789 \text{ V}$$
$$\text{(at } 25°C)$$
$$Hg^{II} \rightarrow Hg \qquad E^{\circ} = +0.854 \text{ V}$$

The corresponding oxidation potential for the couple Hg^{II}/Hg^{I} is $+0.92$ V. In the presence of excess mercury the product of oxidation is Hg^{I} since the equilibrium constant of the reaction

$$Hg + Hg^{II} \rightleftharpoons 2Hg^{I}$$

is approximately 160. In the absence of excess mercury, or in reactions where the mercury (II) compound is less soluble than the mercury (I) compound, the formation of Hg^{II} is favoured.

The oxide, hydroxide and cyanide of Hg^{I} have not been isolated, being unstable with respect to disproportionation to Hg and the corresponding Hg^{II} compound.

Most Hg^{I} compounds are only sparingly soluble in water, the main exceptions to this being the nitrate, chlorate and perchlorate.

The constitution of the mercurous ion is of considerable interest. In contrast to the cuprous ion, evidence is conclusive in formulating the mercurous ion as a diatomic species:

$$(Hg—Hg)^{2+}$$

There are several pieces of experimental evidence to support this contention:

(i) X-ray crystal analysis of mercurous chloride indicates the presence of distinct Cl—Hg—Hg—Cl units.

(ii) Electrochemical data from the concentration cell

Hg	Hg^{I} nitrate 0.1 M (c_2) in dil. HNO_3	Hg^{I} nitrate 0.01 M (c_1) in dil. HNO_3	Hg

The potential of the cell at 25°C is 0.028 V. The theoretical equation relating potential (E) to the concentrations (c_1 and c_2) is

$$E = \frac{RT}{nF} \log_e \frac{c_2}{c_1}$$

where n is the electron change. Using this expression and substituting for the constant R gives $n=2$. Hence in the cell the reaction is $2Hg = (Hg)_2^{2+} + 2e^-$.

(iii) Conductivity measurements on solutions of mercurous nitrate indicate the presence of a bi–univalent salt and not a uni–univalent salt.

(iv) Determinations of the concentration of Hg^{I} and Hg^{II} in solutions obtained by shaking excess mercury with mercuric nitrate until equilibrium is attained. The two possible reactions are

$$Hg + Hg^{2+} \rightleftharpoons 2Hg^+$$

and

$$Hg + Hg^{2+} \rightleftharpoons Hg_2^{2+}$$

270

Evaluation of the equilibrium constants for each reaction using the experimental data gives consistent values for the second reaction only.

Compounds of the Dipositive Oxidation States

Oxides

Both zinc and cadmium on exposure to air yield surface coatings of the oxide, in contrast to mercury. Mercury forms an oxide only on heating in air. The thermal stability of the oxides is noteworthy; on heating, zinc and cadmium oxides sublime without decomposition but mercury oxide decomposes to mercury and oxygen.

The basic character varies in the same manner as the monoxides of sub-group I B; thus cadmium oxide is most basic. Compared with the corresponding oxides of sub-group II A elements, they are more resistant to attack by dilute acids. Zinc oxide shows amphoteric character and dissolves in alkali with the formation of the zincate ion $[ZnO_2]^{2-}$.

Halides

The halides show less ionic character than those of sub-group II A. The increase in covalent character as the group is descended is illustrated by the small conductivity of zinc chloride in the fused state, compared with mercuric chloride which is non-conducting. This increase in covalent character is also shown by the properties of the halides in aqueous solution; zinc and cadmium halides are soluble to form ions but mercuric chloride, for example, although soluble in water, is not ionized and is present as undissociated $HgCl_2$.

Cadmium halides show a great tendency to autocomplex as indicated by conductivity measurements on the concentrated aqueous solutions. Ions such as $[CdX_3]^-$ and $[CdX_4]^{2-}$ are formed. Zinc shows less tendency to complex in this way and shows a great inclination to form hydrated ions in aqueous solution. Mercury forms 4 co-ordinate complexes of the type $[HgX_4]^{2-}$ in the presence of excess of the anion.

Complexes

Zinc (II) and cadmium (II) form a wide variety of tetrahedral complexes particularly where nitrogen is present to act as donor atom. Thus strong complexes are formed with ammonia, amines such as o-phenanthroline and also molecules where both nitrogen and oxygen are present to act as donor atoms, e.g. 8-hydroxyquinoline and ethylenediaminetetracetic acid.

Mercury (II) also forms stable ammine complexes. The general products of interaction between mercury (II) and ammonia gas under anhydrous conditions are ammonobasic compounds. Mercuric chloride reacts with aqueous ammonia to form 'infusible white precipitate' or mercury (II) amidochloride, $HgNH_2Cl$:

$$HgCl_2 + 2NH_3 = HgNH_2Cl + NH_4Cl$$

If the reaction is carried out in the presence of excess ammonium chloride the product is diammine mercury (II) chloride $Hg(NH_3)_2Cl_2$.

Mercuric oxide reacts with ammonia to form Millon's base:

$$2HgO + NH_3 + H_2O = (HOHg)_2NH_2OH$$

271

the anhydride of which is the parent compound of Nessler's reagent, $OHgNH_2I$, used for the detection of small amounts of ammonia.

GROUP III A

The elements of this sub-group are called the rare earths and comprise scandium (Sc), yttrium (Y), lanthanum (La) and the elements from cerium (Ce) to lutetium (Lu). The latter group, cerium, *etc.*, constitute an inner transition series corresponding to the filling up of the $4f$ quantum level and are termed the *lanthanide elements* (*Table 10.11*).

Table 10.10. The properties of scandium, yttrium and lanthanum

		Sc	Y	La
Atomic number		21	39	57
Electron configuration		$4s^2 3d^1$	$5s^2 4d^1$	$6s^2 5d^1$
Melting point (°C)		1420	1500	920
Boiling point (°C)		2480	3230	3370
Ionization potential	1st	151·3	147·1	129·4
(kcal/g atom)	2nd	295·2	282·0	263·6
	3rd	570·7	470·4	470·4
Atomic radius (Å)		1·44	1·62	1·69
Ionic radius (Å)	M^{3+}	0·81	0·93	1·15

Table 10.11. Physical properties of the lanthanide elements

Element	Atomic number	Symbol	Electron configuration	Ionic radius (Å) (M^{3+})
Cerium	58	Ce	$4f^2 6s^2$	1·11
Praseodymium	59	Pr	$4f^3 6s^2$	1·09
Neodymium	60	Nd	$4f^4 6s^2$	1·08
Promethium	61	Pm	$4f^5 6s^2$	1·06
Samarium	62	Sm	$4f^6 6s^2$	1·04
Europium	63	Eu	$4f^7 6s^2$	1·03
Gadolinium	64	Gd	$4f^7 5d^1 6s^2$	1·02
Terbium	65	Tb	$4f^9 6s^2$	1·00
Dysprosium	66	Dy	$4f^{10} 6s^2$	0·99
Holmium	67	Ho	$4f^{11} 6s^2$	0·97
Erbium	68	Er	$4f^{12} 6s^2$	0·96
Thulium	69	Tm	$4f^{13} 6s^2$	0·95
Ytterbium	70	Yb	$4f^{14} 6s^2$	0·94
Lutetium	71	Lu	$4f^{14} 5d^1 6s^2$	0·93

In their chemical behaviour, scandium and yttrium show strong resemblances to the lanthanides. The elements are electropositive metals and the characteristic oxidation state found for all of them is $+3$; certain lanthanides also show either $+2$ or $+4$. These additional states are usually associated with the elements where electron loss occurs to form ions which have a particularly stable electron configuration. Three arrangements of especial stability should be noted. These are $4f^0$ (in La^{3+}, Ce^{4+}), $4f^7$ (in Eu^{2+}, Gd^{3+}, Tb^{4+}) and $4f^{14}$ (in Yb^{2+}, Lu^{3+}).

In the lanthanide elements, the addition of the electrons to the $4f$ shell has little effect upon the size of the ions which show a gradual decrease with

increase in atomic number. This lanthanide contraction (p. 93) is responsible for the great chemical similarity within the group and has an important
influence on succeeding groups. Because of the close similarity in both
chemical and physical properties, the separation of the lanthanides had proved
a difficult task for many years. In recent years the development of ion-
exchange and solvent extraction methods has resulted in the efficient separation
of the lanthanides (p. 192).

Some physical properties of the first three elements of the rare earth group
are given in *Table 10.10*.

Oxidation States

In the tripositive oxidation state, which in many cases is the only state found,
there is a close similarity in chemical properties between the rare earths.
The oxides in this state are strong bases, the strength being related to ionic
size. Thus scandium oxide is the least basic and the basic power falls from
La_2O_3 to Lu_2O_3.

Oxidation states other than $+3$ are found; cerium, praseodymium and
terbium form the $+4$ oxidation state; samarium, europium and ytterbium form
the $+2$ oxidation state.

In the $+4$ state, the rare earths tend to resemble the metals of Group IV A.
In the $+2$ state, their chemical properties are like those of the alkaline earth
metals.

Magnetic Susceptibility and Colour

The magnetic susceptibilities of the trivalent ions do not obey the spin-only
formula (see p. 280) because of the contribution made to the magnetic moment
by the orbital moments of the $4f$ electrons. *Figure 10.2* shows the magnetic
moments of the ions M^{3+} from lanthanum to lutetium.

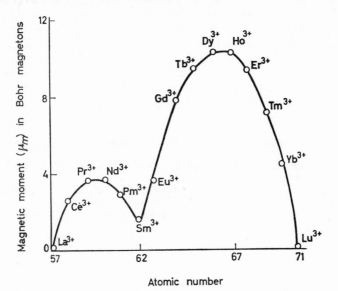

Figure 10.2. Magnetic moments of the lanthanide ions (M^{3+})

Solutions of many of the trivalent ions are distinctly coloured and correlation between the number of f electrons present and colour has been found. The ions with n more electrons than La^{3+} are observed to have similar colours to those with an extra $(14-n)$ electrons; thus, praseodymium and thulium are both green in their $+3$ state and neodymium and erbium are red-coloured in the $+3$ state.

The Actinide Series

These are actinium (Ac), thorium (Th), protoactinium (Pa), uranium (U) and the elements beyond uranium up to atomic number 103. The preparation of the transuranic elements has been dealt with earlier (p. 21). There is little doubt that in this series of elements the $5f$ level is being filled. In contrast to the lanthanides, several oxidation states are found for each of the earlier members of this series and chemically some of the elements show a strong resemblance to certain families of transition elements. Thus thorium shows a stable oxidation state of $+4$ and in many ways behaves as a sub-group IV A metal, and is more electropositive than hafnium. Similarly, uranium, as it forms many compounds in which its oxidation state is $+6$, shows a strong resemblance to sub-group VI A.

The $+3$ oxidation state becomes increasingly important as the atomic number increases. For example, Np^{III} and Pu^{III} are immediately oxidized in aqueous solution when access of air is permitted. However, Cm^{III} is very stable and is indeed the only oxidation state observed for this element in aqueous solution. It is this fact, together with the strong paramagnetism of Cm^{3+} (comparable with Gd^{3+}), which suggests that the $5f$ shell is half filled at curium (96) and hence that a series of inner transition elements begins at actinium (89)

The separation of uranium from plutonium and fission products by solvent extraction (p. 188) and the use of ion-exchange resins for the production of uranium concentrates (p. 193) are important large-scale separation processes which have been developed because of the demand, both for military and for peaceful purposes, for fissionable materials. This requirement has also stimulated intensive research with the result that, for a number of the heavier metals, hitherto of little interest because few uses could be made of them, the chemical properties are now known in great detail.

SUGGESTED REFERENCES FOR FURTHER READING

BARNETT, E. de B., and WILSON, C. L. *Inorganic Chemistry*, 2nd edn, Longmans Green, London, 1957.

MOELLER, T. *The Chemistry of the Lanthanides*, Reinhold, New York, 1963.

SANDERSON, R. T. *Chemical Periodicity*, Reinhold, New York, 1960.

SNEED, M. C., and BRASTED, R. C. *Comprehensive Inorganic Chemistry*, vols.I–VIII, Van Nostrand, New York, 1953–61.

APPENDIX I

PHYSICAL MEASUREMENTS IN INORGANIC CHEMISTRY

DIFFRACTION METHODS

X-ray Diffraction

THE x-ray analysis of crystals gives information on *interatomic distances* and on *the size of the unit cell*, that is the number of atoms which form a repeating unit in the crystal.

A crystal lattice acts as a three-dimensional diffraction grating towards x-rays. The crystal is composed of series of parallel planes of atoms and the incident x-rays are reflected by these planes. The x-rays reflected by one plane penetrate the crystal to a different extent compared with those reflected by an adjacent plane. Thus there is a certain path difference between reflections from the two planes. When the path difference equals an integral number of wavelengths, the x-rays reinforce one another. This is the condition represented by the Bragg relationship:

$$n\lambda = 2d \sin \theta$$

where n is an integer, λ is the wavelength of the x-rays, θ is the angle of incidence and d is the perpendicular distance between the planes:

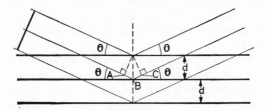

When a crystal is rotated in an x-ray beam, reflection or diffraction occurs whenever the Bragg condition is obeyed. The diffracted beam may be recorded on a photographic plate as a series of spots, each spot corresponding with a particular set of planes in the crystal. The mathematical analysis of the diffraction pattern gives the distribution of electron density in the crystal for the diffraction is caused primarily by the extra-nuclear electrons. Thus a picture of the structure can be built up consisting of sections of projections of the crystal lattice which show contours of equal electron density. The positions of the atoms are usually assumed to coincide with regions of maximum electron density.

Electron Diffraction

A beam of electrons, by virtue of its wave properties, gives rise to diffraction patterns when passed through a very thin section of a crystal or a gas at low

275

pressure.   As the beam consists of charged particles, it interacts with regions of high electrostatic potential and the contour maps obtained by analysis of the experimental results give the variation of this potential through the crystal or in the gas molecule.   This is determined by the distribution of the positively charged nuclei and the electrons around them.

Electron diffraction measurements give information on *bond lengths* and *interbond angles*.

Neutron Diffraction

Neutrons also show wave properties and hence can be diffracted by crystals. Neutron scattering by diamagnetic substances takes place largely by the interaction between the neutrons and the atomic nuclei in the crystal.   In contrast to x-ray and electron diffraction methods, which cannot detect the positions of hydrogen atoms with much certainty, neutrons are diffracted to a similar extent by hydrogen and many other much heavier atoms.   The method can be used in conjunction with x-ray analysis to give a complete picture of a crystal structure.   For example, the atoms other than hydrogen in a hydrogen-bonded structure can be located by x-rays and the hydrogen atoms themselves by neutron diffraction.

SPECTROSCOPY

Atomic Spectra

The experimental study of emission spectra led to the introduction of the four quantum numbers n, l, m_l and m_s in order to explain all the lines observed, for example, in the spectrum of an alkali metal vapour.   These quantum numbers are fundamental to the modern concept of *atomic structure* and to the *periodic classification of the elements* according to the distribution of electrons in orbitals of increasing energy.

The *ionization potentials* of an atom can also be determined from its emission spectrum.   The ionization potential is the amount of energy necessary to remove one electron completely from the gaseous atom.   Experimentally, it is observed that at a definite wave number $\bar{v}_i$, the line spectrum of an atom is replaced by a continuous region of radiation.   This region is the continuum and the lowest wave number for which the continuum is observed gives a direct measurement of the energy required to remove the electron.

The analysis of emission spectra has played a most important role in the *discovery of the chemical elements* in the nineteenth and twentieth centuries. When an element or one of its compounds is subjected to powerful excitation, either by a d.c. arc or by sparking, the very high temperatures attained cause the material to emit radiations of definite wave numbers.   These appear as spectral lines and are relatively few for the alkali metals: for transition and rare-earth metals however, the spectra are highly complex.   An emission spectrum may be recorded photographically and then examined at leisure to identify the element or elements present from the spectral lines observed. The analysis is made in a quantitative manner by comparison of the densities of the spectral lines obtained for an unknown sample with the densities produced from a series of standards of known composition.   Alternatively, a known amount of another element is added to the unknown sample as an internal standard so that comparison within the one spectrum is possible.

Molecular Spectra

Molecules also undergo electronic changes by the absorption or emission of electromagnetic radiation. The electronic spectrum of a molecule is more complex than that of an atom because, in addition to electronic energy changes, the vibrational and rotational energies usually change as well.

From studies of their spectra in the various energy regions (the ultra-violet, the visible, the infra-red, the microwave and the radio-frequency), compounds can be identified. For some simple molecules, infra-red and microwave studies give information on the *geometry of the molecule*. Another example is the determination of *dissociation energies* for diatomic molecules (p. 46).

THERMOCHEMISTRY

The heat of a reaction, defined as the energy absorbed or evolved as the reaction proceeds, is a quantity of great importance in inorganic chemistry. The heat of formation, defined as the heat evolved or absorbed when one mole of a compound is formed from its component elements at constant pressure (1 atmosphere) and at 25°C, is particularly useful. The heat change is always related to the elements and their compounds in their standard states, that is, the most stable physical state at 25°C. The magnitude of the heat of reaction is affected by the physical form of the participants. For instance, the heat evolved when one mole of gaseous SO_3 is formed from its elements is different from that given out when the same quantity of solid SO_3 is formed by an amount which equals the heat sublimation of SO_3.

The heat of formation is positive for an exothermic compound and negative for an endothermic compound. It must be remembered that $\Delta H°$, the heat content change for a reaction, is numerically the same as the heat of reaction but has the opposite sign. Thus $\Delta H°$ is positive for heat absorbed (an increase in $H°$, the heat content, means that the heat content of the products is greater than that of the reactants) and negative for heat evolved.

Heats of reaction can be measured experimentally by calorimetry, but only rarely can the heats of formation of inorganic compounds be determined directly in this way. More commonly, the heat changes for related chemical reactions are measured and these values used in calculation of the required heats of formation. The validity of the calculation depends on the thermochemical law, Hess's Law, which states that the heat liberated or absorbed in a chemical reaction is independent of the number and nature of the steps by which a reaction is brought about.

The heat content change, $\Delta H°$, can be determined in several ways. For example, in a reversible reaction it can be calculated from the equilibrium constants, K, determined over a range of temperature. This involves use of the van't Hoff Isochore:

$$\frac{\mathrm{d}}{\mathrm{d}T}(\log_e K) = \frac{\Delta H°_T}{RT}$$

where $\Delta H°_T$ refers to the heat of formation measured at the absolute temperature, $T°K$.

The heat content change, $\Delta H°$, can be used in conjunction with $\Delta S°$, the entropy change at 25°C, in order to calculate $\Delta G°$, *the standard free energy* change in the reaction. $\Delta G°$ is related to the other two quantities by the equation

$$\Delta G° = \Delta H° - T\Delta S°$$

The importance of the free energy concept is that $\Delta G°$ is always negative for a reaction which is thermodynamically possible and that the magnitude of $\Delta G°$ determines the affinity of the reactants for one another (p. 182). The rate of reaction, if indeed it proceeds at all at a measurable rate, is, of course, determined by kinetic factors.

Thermochemical data is necessary for the calculation of *experimental lattice energies* of ionic compounds by the Born–Haber cycle (p. 45). Not only is the heat of formation of the compound required but also the heat of vaporization of one or more of the reactants.

From heats of formation data, one can also arrive at values for *bond energies*, which serve to measure the strengths with which atoms are joined together. For diatomic molecules, the heat of formation of the molecule from its atoms is the same as the bond dissociation energy, which is the energy required to break the bond. These two quantities are not usually the same in the case of polyatomic molecules.

Bond dissociation energies can be found by a variety of experimental methods, some of which are :

(*i*) *Calorimetric method*—In some cases it is possible to measure the exothermic recombination of atoms or radicals.

(*ii*) *Electron-impact method*—Electrons of known energy are allowed to interact with molecules to produce ionization and dissociation. Under certain conditions, the lowest electron energy required to do this is equal to the sum of the dissociation energy and the ionization potential of the fragment. This is an experimental method for obtaining dissociation energies in polyatomic molecules.

(*iii*) *Spectroscopic method*—The ultra-violet spectrum of certain diatomic molecules affords a very accurate method for determining dissociation energies. For example, the ultra-violet spectrum of iodine is composed of bands gradually becoming closer together with increasing energy until the absorption is continuous. The convergence limit of the band spectrum to continuous absorption gives an accurate measure of the energy required to dissociate the excited iodine molecule.

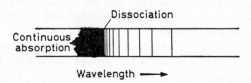

An illustration of the different values obtained for the average bond energy calculated from heat of formation data and the bond dissociation energy, measured, is given by the figures for a polyatomic molecule such as ammonia.

Thus the following heats of reaction can be used to calculate the average bond energy for N—H in ammonia:

$$\tfrac{1}{2}N_2 + \tfrac{3}{2}H_2 = NH_3 \text{ (g)} + 11\cdot04 \text{ kcal}$$
$$N = \tfrac{1}{2}N_2 \qquad +112\cdot9$$
$$3H = \tfrac{3}{2}H_2 \qquad +156\cdot27$$

By addition,

$$N + 3H = NH_3 \text{ (g)} + 280\cdot21$$

and the average N—H bond energy is therefore $93\cdot4$ kcal. The bond dissociation energy, *i.e.* that required to effect the reaction $NH_3 = {}^{\times}NH_2 + {}^{\times}H$, is 102 kcal. In this text, the values given for the bond energies in polyatomic molecules are always the average values calculated from thermochemical data*.

MAGNETISM

Two types of chemical compound can be distinguished according to their behaviour when placed in a magnetic field. *Diamagnetic* substances are less permeable to magnetic lines of force than is a vacuum and tend to move from the strong to the weak part of the magnetic field: *paramagnetic* substances show the opposite behaviour, that is they move from the weak to the strong part of the field.

Magnetism arises because of the interaction between the external magnetic field and the orbital electrons of the atoms. A special case of paramagnetism, known as ferromagnetism, occurs in a few metals, notably iron. This is the acquisition of a permanent magnetic moment by the metal because of the parallel orientation of magnetic particles in the crystalline lattice.

Diamagnetism is found for all chemical substances. It is caused by the interaction of an external field with the magnetic field produced by the movement of electrons in filled atomic orbitals. This results in an induced field which is directionally opposed to the applied field. Diamagnetism is independent of temperature but increases with atomic or molecular size and the diamagnetism of covalent compounds is approximately additive. Generally, however, its effect is much smaller than that of paramagnetism.

Paramagnetism arises whenever an atom, ion or molecule possesses one or more unpaired electrons. The presence of these causes the element to behave like a small permanent magnet. An applied magnetic field tends to align all these magnets in parallel. This tendency is opposed by thermal effects which favour a random arrangement of the magnets. Paramagnetism is found in the compounds of the transition metals, due to the presence of unpaired d electrons, in the lanthanides and actinides, due to the presence of unpaired f electrons, and in a few molecules such as O_2, NO, NO_2 and ClO_2, which contain an odd number of valency electrons.

Experimentally, a quantity known as the paramagnetic molar susceptibility χ_M is measured. This can be done using Gouy's method which essentially involves the study of the effect of an inhomogeneous magnetic field on a specimen suspended from one arm of a sensitive balance.

* The values are taken from COTTRELL, T. L. *The Strength of Chemical Bonds*, 2nd edn, Butterworths, London, 1958.

The molar susceptibility is given by

$$\chi_M = \frac{N\mu_M^2}{3RT}$$

where N is the Avogadro Number, μ_M is the magnetic moment and T is the absolute temperature

or

$$\mu_M = \sqrt{\frac{3RT\chi_M}{N}}$$

Magnetic moments are expressed in Bohr magnetons (B.M.). This is the magnetic moment of an electron spinning on its own axis and has the magnitude 5564 gauss cm/mole.

$$1 \text{ B.M.} = \frac{he}{4\pi mc}$$

where e = electronic charge, m = electronic mass, c = velocity of light and h = Planck's constant.

Both the spin and orbital motion of an electron contribute to the paramagnetic moment of an atom or ion. The spins of individual electrons are regarded as coupled together to give a resultant spin momentum (S), where n, the number of unpaired electrons, equals $2S$. Coupling of the orbital angular momenta of the electrons similarly gives a resultant orbital angular momentum (L). It has been shown theoretically that S and L combine together in such a way that the resultant magnetic moment, μ_M, is given by

$$\mu_M = \sqrt{4S(S+1)+L(L+1)}$$

For an ion of the first transition series the unpaired $3d$ electrons are unshielded from the effect of the immediate environment of the ion in the solid lattice or in solution and their orbital momenta are not affected significantly by an external magnetic field. Under such circumstances, the expression for μ_M reduces to $\sqrt{4S(S+1)}$ or $\sqrt{n(n+2)}$. The experimental evidence on which this conclusion is based is the close correlation observed between experimental values of μ_M and the theoretical values calculated for spin interaction only (*Table 10.6*).

For the metals of the second and third transition series (the lanthanides and the actinides) orbital contributions to the moment must be important, for only when these are taken into account as well as the spin component can reasonable agreement between predicted and experimental values be obtained. The observed paramagnetic moment is accordingly not simply related to the number of unpaired electrons present (*Figure 10.2*).

A study of paramagnetism in inorganic compounds provides much valuable information on the *number of unpaired electrons present in an ion or molecule* and is hence of great value in many cases in deciding upon the electronic configuration.

DIPOLE MOMENTS

Whenever a covalent bond is formed between two atoms of different electronegativities, a separation of electric charges occurs and a dipole is established.

If the two atoms are at a distance r apart and the charges on them are $+\delta$ and $-\delta$ respectively, then the dipole moment, μ, is δr. This is a vector quantity and the overall moment of a molecule containing several dipoles is the resultant of the component vectors.

The dipole moment of a covalent compound may be calculated from the effect which it has on the capacitance of a condenser. The ratio of the capacitance of the condenser when the compound is placed between the plates to the capacitance in a vacuum is the dielectric constant, ϵ. This is related to the molecular polarization, P, of a substance of molecular weight, M, and density ρ by the equation

$$P = \frac{\epsilon-1}{\epsilon+2} \cdot \frac{M}{\rho}$$

When a polar substance is placed in a uniform electric field, this tends to orient the permanent dipoles. There is the opposing thermal effect increasing with temperature, which tends to give random orientation of the molecules. The field also induces a dipole in the molecule which lasts only as long as the field is present.

Debye showed that P is of the form

$$P = A + \frac{B}{T}$$

where A is the contribution due to the induced dipole and B $(=4\pi N\mu^2/k)$ is that due to the permanent dipole.

When ϵ is determined at a series of temperatures, P can be calculated and plotted against $1/T$. If B, the slope, is zero, $\mu=0$. If the plot has a measureable slope, the dipole moment can be found from B.

Dipole moments are valuable in determining the *shapes of molecules and complexes*. One example only must suffice as an illustration. In the *cis*- and *trans*-isomers of the dichlorodiammines of platinum (II), (p. 136), the *cis*-isomer has a permanent dipole moment whilst the *trans*-isomer has none. These observations confirm the square-planar distribution of the four ligands about the metal atom (in the *trans*-form, the moments of the two Pt—Cl bonds are exactly opposite and so are those of the two Pt—N bonds). In many other instances, dipole moment measurements have been important in the solution of stereochemical problems.

SUGGESTED REFERENCES FOR FURTHER READING

Maron, S. H., and Prutton, C. F. *Principles of Physical Chemistry*, 3rd edn, Macmillan, New York, 1958.

Nyholm, R. S. 'Magnetism and inorganic chemistry', *Quart. Rev. chem. Soc., Lond.*, 7 (1953) 377.

Walker, S., and Straw, H. *Spectroscopy*, Vol. 1, Chapman & Hall, London, 1961.

Wheatley, P. J. *The Determination of Molecular Structure*, Clarendon Press, Oxford, 1959.

APPENDIX II

COMPOUNDS OF THE NOBLE GASES

THE preparation of the first true compound of xenon was achieved in 1962 by Bartlett, who, having utilized the strong oxidizing properties of PtF_6 to prepare dioxygenyl hexafluoroplatinate (V), $O_2^+PtF_6^-$, suggested that an analogous reaction might be expected to occur with xenon because of the similarity of the first ionization potential of molecular oxygen and of atomic xenon (approximately 275 kcal). The preparation of xenon hexafluoroplatinate (V) and some other xenon metal fluorides was soon achieved by the reaction at room temperature between xenon and the appropriate metal (VI) fluoride.

$$Xe + MF_6 = Xe^+MF_6^- \qquad (M = Pt, Pu, Ru, Rh)$$

Three xenon fluorides have been synthesized: XeF_6, by heating xenon with excess fluorine under pressure at 300°C; XeF_4, by heating xenon with fluorine at 400°C; and XeF_2 by irradiating a mixture of xenon and fluorine with light from a high pressure mercury arc. At room temperature these compounds are white crystalline solids, XeF_6 being the most volatile. Reduction by hydrogen occurs according to

$$XeF_n + n/2\ H_2 = Xe + nHF$$

a reaction that has proved useful in the analysis of these fluorides. Hydrolysis of the fluorides leads to a further series of xenon compounds. Thus, $XeOF_4$ is a colourless liquid formed by the incomplete hydrolysis of XeF_6 and XeO_3 is the end product of slow hydrolysis of XeF_6. Salts of xenic acid, $Xe(OH)_6$, result from alkaline hydrolysis of the hexafluoride.

The structures of xenon compounds, which may be predicted by simple electron pair repulsion, are

(cf. ICl_2^-) (cf. ICl_4^-) (cf. IF_6^-) (cf. IO_3^-)

The linear and square planar arrangements of XeF_2 and XeF_4 respectively have been confirmed experimentally. The experimental data on XeF_6 is consistent with a symmetrical, non-octahedral structure, presumably arising from sp^3d^3 orbitals. The XeO_3 structure is supported by crystallographic and infra-red data. Infra-red and Raman data support a square-pyramidal structure for $XeOF_4$ with oxygen replacing a lone-pair in the XeF_4 arrangement.

Fluorides of two other noble gases have also been reported. The preparation of KrF_4, which is much less stable than XeF_4, can be realized by the

282

passage of an electric discharge through mixtures of krypton and fluorine at liquid nitrogen temperatures, whereas the photolysis of a solid mixture of krypton and fluorine in an argon matrix at 20°K yields KrF_2. The existence of a radon fluoride has been established. Compounds of helium, neon and argon have yet to be prepared.

INDEX

Acceleration of charged particles, 16
Acetic acid, glacial, as a solvent, 123
Acetylacetone,
    beryllium (II) complex, 205
    chromium (III) complex, 161
    metal complexes, 143, 148, 187, 209
Acetylene molecule, bonding in, 64
Acids,
    Bronsted–Lowry concept, 118
    Cady and Elsey definition, 125
    Lewis concept, 125
    strength, 120
    table of, 119
Actinide contraction, 93
Actinides,
    oxidation states, 274
    preparation, 21–2
    separation, 192, 247
Actinium (^{235}U) decay series, 12
Activity of metal ions, 109
Alkali metals,
    comparative chemistry, 200–3
    complexes, 148
    cyclopentadienyls, 167
    extraction, 179
    occurrence, 170
    properties, 200
Alkaline earth metals,
    comparative chemistry, 203–5
    complexes, 148
    cyclopentadienyls, 167
    extraction, 179
    occurrence, 170
    properties, 203
Allotropy, 82
Alpha emission, 8
Aluminium,
    abundance in earth's crust, 171
    as reducing agent, 179, 183
    chloride,
        hydrolysis of, 209
        structure of, 206–9
    compounds, 131, 174, 178
    extraction, 170, 174
    structure of, 88
Alumino-silicates, 105, 171, 190
Americium,
    preparation, 21
    separation, 193
Ammonia,
    as base, 122, 133, 218
    preparation, 218
    reactions in liquid, 126
    self-ionization, 124

Ammonia (*contd*)
    shape of molecule, 65, 220
    solution of metals in, 127
Ammonium salts,
    oxidation of, 219
    thermal decomposition of, 218
Antimony,
    allotropes, 83–5
    compounds, 217–26
    extraction, 177
    occurrence, 170, 177
    properties, 217
Arsenic,
    acid, 122
    allotropes, 83–5
    compounds, 217–26
    extraction, 177
    occurrence, 170, 177
    properties, 217
Artificial disintegration of atomic nuclei,
    15–17
Astatine, 246
Atmophil elements, 170
Atomic radii, 74–6
Atomic spectra, 23, 24, 276
    and Bohr theory, 25–8
    Balmer series, 24
    hydrogen, 23–5

Balmer series, 24, 27
Barium,
    compounds, 203–5
    extraction, 173
    occurrence, 173
    properties, 203
    structure, 88
Bases,
    Bronsted–Lowry concept, 118
    Cady and Elsey definition, 125
    Lewis concept, 125
    strength, 120
Basicity of ligands, 150
Berkelium,
    preparation, 22
    separation, 193
Beryllium,
    acetylacetonate, 205
    basic acetate, 205, 229
    basic nitrate, 130
    compounds, 203–5
    extraction, 173, 181, 185
    occurrence, 170, 173
    properties, 203

Beryllium (*contd*)
 structure, 88
Beta emission, 8
Binding energy, 7
Bismuth,
 compounds, 217–26
 extraction, 177
 occurrence, 170, 177
 properties, 217
 structure, 83–5
Bohr magneton, 280
Bohr theory of atomic spectra, 25–8
Bond energy, 212, 239, 240, 241, 278
Bond length, 276
Borax bead test, 131
Boric acid, 122, 208
Born coefficient, 91
Born–Haber cycle, 45, 111, 239, 278
Boron,
 compounds, 206–9
 extraction, 174
 hydrides, 206–8
 nitride, 218
 occurrence, 174
 structure, 88
 trifluoride, 130, 207, 208
Brackett series, 24, 27
Bragg equation, 275
Bromine,
 compounds, 241–6
 extraction, 177, 241
 occurrence, 177
 preparation, 241
 properties, 239
 reaction with water, 241
 solvent extraction, 188
 structure, 81
 trifluoride, as a solvent, 126

Cadmium,
 chloride structure, 100
 compounds, 269–72
 extraction, 176
 iodide structure, 100
 occurrence, 170, 176
 properties, 269
 structure, 88
Caesium,
 chloride structure, 95, 97
 compounds, 200–2
 extraction, 173
 occurrence, 173
 oxide structure, 100
 properties, 200
 structure, 88
Calcium,
 abundance, 171
 complex with EDTA, 149–50
 compounds, 203–5

Calcium (*contd*)
 extraction, 173
 fluoride structure, 98, 100, 103
 occurrence, 173
 oxide formation, $\Delta G°$, 182
 preparation, 131
 properties, 203
 structure, 88
Carbides, 210
Carbon,
 allotropes, 85
 as reducing agent, 179, 183
 bond energies of compounds, 212
 compounds, 210–16
 dioxide,
  bonding in, 64
  preparation, 213
  properties, 213
  resonance formulations, 54, 64
 extraction, 174
 monoxide,
  bonding in, 60
  formation of carbonyls, 161–4
  preparation, 212, 214
  properties, 212, 214
  reduction by, 184
 occurrence, 174
 properties, 210
 suboxide, 212, 214
Carbonyls, 151, 155, 161–4
 hydrides, 164
Catenation, 211, 215, 228
Cathode rays, 1–3
Cementite, 103
Cerium,
 compounds, 272–4
 extraction, 174
 occurrence, 214
Chain reactions, 20
Chalcophil elements, 170
Chelating agents,
 bidentate, 142–5
 in solvent extraction, 186–7
Chelation, 133, 141, 150
Chemical cells, 109–17
Chlorine,
 abundance in earth's crust, 171
 extraction, 177
 occurrence, 177
 oxides, 242, 251
 oxy-acids, 123, 243
 preparation, 241
 properties, 239
 reaction with water, 241
 solvent extraction, 188
Chlorophyll, 148, 172
Chromium,
 compounds, 249, 250, 257–8
 dibenzene complex, 168
 extraction, 175, 179

Chromium (*contd*)
  hexacarbonyl, 162
  occurrence, 170, 175
  properties, 248
  structure, 87
Clathrate compounds, 199
Close-packing, 76–7
Cobalt,
  ammines, 134–5
  carbonyls, 162, 164
  complexes, 128, 154, 167
  compounds, 249, 250, 262–3
  extraction, 175, 178
  occurrence, 170, 175
  properties, 248
  structures, 87, 88
Complexes,
  and electroneutrality principle, 152
  definitions, 133
  factors influencing stability, 147–51
  stability constants, 138, 141, 146, 148,
    150, 151
  stereochemistry, 134–8
  theories of binding, 152–61
Complexones, 145
Conjugate acid and base, 119
Co-ordination,
  compounds—see Complexes
  number,
    in complexes, 133
    in crystals, 93
Copper,
  complexes, 141, 142, 150, 155, 156,
    160, 267
  compounds, 249, 250, 264–8
  extraction, 176, 178–9
  nitrate, preparation, 129
  occurrence, 170, 176
  properties, 265
  structure, 87
Covalent bond,
  and partial ionic character, 52–3
  in crystals, 77, 80, 88, 89
  nature of, 39, 40, 54–65
Cristobalite, 104
Crystal field theory, 157–61
Crystal radius, 90–2
Crystals,
  classification, 74
  parameters, 73
Cubic close-packing, 77, 88
Curium,
  preparation, 21–2
  properties, 274
  separation, 193
Cyanates, 212
Cyanides,
  complex, 151–9, 255, 258, 261, 262,
    263, 268–9
  in metal extraction, 163–4, 176, 178

Cyanides (*contd*)
  complex,
    oxidation potentials, 117
    preparation, 127–8
    structure, 97
Cyclopentadienyl complexes, 165–8

Dative bond, 39, 40, 41
Debye equation, 281
Degenerate orbital levels, 33
Demineralization of water, 191
Deuterium, 197
Deuteron, 16
Diagonal relationship, 92, 203
Diamagnetism, 279
Diamond,
  structure, 85, 97
  synthesis, 86
Diborane, structure, 207
Dielectric constant, 124, 281
β-Diketone complexes, 143
Dimethylglyoxime complexes, 143, 187
  263
Dinitrogen pentoxide, 221
Dinitrogen tetroxide, 129–30, 221
Dinitrogen trioxide, 221
Diphosphine, 219
Dipole moments, 53, 121, 280
Dipyridyl, 144
Dissociation energy, 46, 277
Dithizone, 143, 187
Dysprosium, 272

Effective atomic number, 151, 163
Effective nuclear charge, 90
Electrochemical series, 110
Electrode potentials, 109–17
  and equilibrium constants, 115–16
  factors affecting, 111–15
  sign of, 109
  stabilization and disproportionation of
    valency states, 116–17
  standard, 109
  table of, 114
Electron, 1
  charge on, 3
  configurations, 34–8
  diffraction, 275
  electric deflection of, 1
  energy levels, 32–4
  magnetic deflection of, 2
  mass, 3
  orbitals, 30–2
  ratio of charge to mass (*e/m*), 3
  spin, 28
  wave and particle nature of, 29
Electron affinity, 42, 44, 45, 46, 112, 149,
  228
Electron deficient molecules, 69, 207

Electron impact method, 278
Electronegativity, 52, 53
  and partial ionic character, 52, 53
  of Group IV B elements, 213
Electroneutrality principle, 152
Electrovalency, 39, 40, 41–54
Energy level diagram, 27, 33
  of the hydrogen atom, 27
Equilibrium constants and redox re-
    actions, 115
Erbium, 272
Eriochrome Black T, 147
Ethylenediaminetracetic acid
    (EDTA), 145, 148, 193
  acid dissociation constants, 146
  stability constants of metal com-
    plexes, 146, 148, 150
Ethylene molecule, bonding in, 62–3
Europium, 272
  extraction, 174
  ores, 174
Exclusion principle, 34
Extraction and distribution of the
  elements, 170ff.

Face-centred cubic close packing, 76
  octahedral holes in, 103
Fajans' rules, 48, 89, 96, 98
Feldspar, 105
Fermium, 22, 192
Ferrates,
  (IV), 261
  (VI), 262
Ferrocene, 165–7
Fission products, 19
Fluorides of transition metals, 249
Fluorine,
  dissociation of molecular, 239, 240
  extraction, 177, 241
  intercalation compounds, 86
  molecule, 59
  occurrence, 177
  oxygen compounds, 242
  properties, 238–41
  reaction with water, 241
Fluorite structure, 98, 100, 103
Fluorosulphonic acid, 128
Francium, 202–3

Gadolinium, 272–4
Gallium,
  compounds, 209–10
  extraction, 176, 181
  occurrence, 170, 176
  properties, 210
  structure, 88
Gamma radiation, 8

Geometrical isomerism, 135–8
Germanes, 211
Germanium,
  as a semiconductor, 80
  compounds, 211–16
  extraction, 176, 181
  occurrence, 170, 176
  oxidation states, 211
  properties, 210
  solvent extraction as GeCl$_4$, 188
  structure, 87
Gold,
  complexes, 267–9
  extraction, 176
  halides, 266–7
  occurrence, 170, 176
  oxidation states, 264–5
  oxides, 265–6
  properties, 265
  structure, 87
Gouy method, 279
Graphite structure, 86, 87

Haber process, 218
Hafnium,
  extraction, 174, 181, 255
  occurrence, 170, 174
  separation from zirconium, 143, 189,
    193
  structure, 87
Half-life, radioactive, 9
Halogens,
  occurrence, 170
  reactions, 241
Heat content change ($\Delta H°$), 277
Heat of formation, 277
  of transition metal oxides, 248
Heat of reaction, 277
Heavy ion bombardment, 22
Heinsenberg's uncertainty principle, 29
Helium,
  chemistry, 198–9
  properties, 199
  structure, 81
Heptasulphur imide, 238
Hess' law, 277
Hexacyanoferrate,
  (II), 152, 153, 159, 163, 164, 261
  (III), 152, 153, 261
Hexagonal close-packing, 77, 88
Hexammine cobalt (III) complex,
  and effective atomic number concept,
    152
  preparation of chloride, 133
Holmium, 272–4
Hund's rule, 34, 159, 250
Hybridization, 60–5
  and valence-bond approach to com-
    plexes, 152

Hydrazine, 219, 240
Hydrides, types, 196–7
  acidic and basic properties, 121
  of aluminium, 208
  of boron, 206–8
  of Group IV B, 212
    stability to hydrolysis, 212
  of Group V B, 217
    stereochemistry of, 220
  of Group VI B, 230
    heats of formation of, 230
    stereochemistry, 230
  of Group VII B, 241–2
  pK values, 121
Hydrogen, 195–8
  atomic,
    excited states, 27, 31
    ground state, 26, 30
  bonding, 69, 70, 71, 230, 240
  chloride,
    as Lewis acid, 125
    dissociation constant, 242
  compounds, 196
  extraction, 173
  fluoride,
    as ionizing solvent, 128
    dissociation constant, 242
  isotopes, 195, 197, 198
  ortho- and para-, 195
  non-stoichiometry of compounds with
    transition metals, 102
  structure, 81
  peroxide, 231–2, 240
  persulphide, 231
  properties, 195
Hydrolysis, 119, 120, 211, 226
Hydrometallurgy, 178
Hydroxides, 122
Hydroxylamine, 219
8-Hydroxyquinoline,
  metal complexes, 142, 187
  stability constants of, 151

Ice, structure, 69–70
Ilmenite, 171, 174
Indium,
  compounds, 209
  extraction, 176
  occurrence, 170, 176
  properties, 210
  structure, 88
Inert gases,
  chemistry, 198–200, 282
  occurrence, 170
  properties, 199
  structure, 81
Inert-pair effect, 41, 211, 217, 230
Inner complexes, 141–4, 187
Interbond angles, 276

Intercalation compounds, 86
Interhalogens, 89, 244
Intermetallic compounds, preparation in
    liquid ammonia, 127
Interstitial compounds, 102
  hydrides, 103, 197
  nitrides, 218
Iodine,
  compounds, 241–6
  evidence for the iodinium ion, 245
  extraction, 177
  occurrence, 177
  properties, 239
  reaction with water, 241
  solvent extraction, 188
  structure, of elementary, 81
Ion-association and solvent extraction,
    187
Ion exchange,
  chromatography, 191
  liquid ion-exchangers, 188
  order of cationic affinities for resins,
    191
  separation procedures using, 190–4
  synthetic organic resins, 190
  zeolites, 190
Ionic bond in inorganic compounds,
    88–90
Ionic potential, 172
Ionic product, 121
Ionic structures, 93ff
Ionization potential, 42, 43, 45, 149, 276
Iridium,
  compounds, 162, 249, 250
  extraction, 176
  occurrence, 170, 176
  structure, 87
Iron,
  abundance in earth's crust, 171
  carbonyls, 138, 162, 181
  complexes, 152–3, 158–9
  compounds, 249, 250, 260–2
  cyclopentadienyl complex, 163
  extraction, 175, 179, 180
  interstitial compounds with carbon,
    103
  occurrence, 170, 175
  (II) oxide, non-stoichiometry, 101,
    261
  properties, 248
  structures, 87
  (II) sulphide, non-stoichiometry, 101
Iron (III) chloride, extraction by ether,
    187
Irving-Williams order, 149
Isobaric change, 11
Isotopes, 4–7
  abundance, 5
  detection of, 4–5
  masses, 6

Isotopic masses, relationship between chemical and physical, 6

K-capture, 11, 22
Kaolin, 106
Kroll process, 179
Krypton,
  properties, 199
  structure, 81

Lanthanide contraction, 93
Lanthanides,
  complexes, 148, 192
  compounds, 273–4
  definition of, 247
  extraction, 174
  hydrides, 197
  ores, 174
  properties, 272
  separation, 192
Lanthanum, structure, 87
Lattice energy, 46–9, 278
Layer lattice, 89, 100
LCAO approximation, 57
Lead,
  compounds, 211–6
  desilverization, 190
  extraction, 176
  occurrence, 170, 176
  properties, 210
  structure, 87
Lewis acids and bases, 125
Ligand-field theory, 161
Ligands, 133, 139
  properties affecting stability constants, 149
Lithium,
  complexes, 148
  compounds, 200–2
  extraction, 173
  halide structures, 96–7
  occurrence, 171, 173
  properties, 200
  structure, 88
Lithophil elements, 170
Lutetium,
  extraction, 174
  occurrence, 174
  properties, 272–3
  separation, 191–3
Lyman series, 24, 27

Madelung constant, 47, 91
Magnesium,
  abundance in earth's crust, 171
  as liquid extractant, 190
  complexes, 148, 149

Magnesium (contd)
  compounds, 203–5
  extraction, 131, 173, 178
  ores, 171, 173
  properties, 203
  structure, 88
Magnetic criterion of bond type, 153, 252
Magnetic susceptibility, 279
Manganese,
  complexes, 149, 162, 164
  compounds, 258–60
  disproportionation of oxidation states, 116
  extraction, 175
  occurrence, 170–5
  properties, 248
  solvent extraction, 187
  structure, 87, 88
Mass defect, 6
Mass number, 5
Mass spectrograph, 4
Mass spectrometer, 4
Mercury,
  complexes, 150, 271
  compounds, 269–72
  extraction, 176
  occurrence, 170, 176
  properties, 269
  solvent extraction, 188
  structure, 88
Metal indicators, 146
Metallic bond, 77
Metals,
  complexes, 133–68
  extraction, 178–80
  inner transition, 247
  occurrence, 170–2
  purification, 180–1
  solutions in ammonia, 127
  stability of complexes, 147–9
  structures, 87–8
  transition, 247
Metaphosphate bead test, 132
Mica, 106
Mohorovicic discontinuity, 171
Molecular orbital theory, 57–60, 161
Molecular polarization, 281
Molecular spectra, 277
Molybdenum,
  complexes, 162, 251, 258
  compounds, 249, 250, 258
  extraction, 175
  occurrence, 170, 175
  properties, 248
  refining, 181
  structure, 87
Mond process, 161, 180
Mulliken nomenclature for molecular orbitals, 60

Neodymium, 148, 272–4
Neon, 81, 199
Neptunium, 21, 274
  decay series, 14
Nernst equation, 110, 113–6
Nernst partition law, 186
Nessler's reagent, 272
Neutron, 6, 16
  capture, 21, 22
  diffraction, 276
  irradiation, 18
Nickel,
  complexes, 121, 155, 167, 263–4
  compounds, 249, 250, 263–4
  extraction, 176
  occurrence, 170, 176
  properties, 248
  structure, 87
  tetracarbonyl, 155, 161, 180
Niobium,
  compounds, 256–7
  extraction, 175, 185
  occurrence, 170, 175
  properties, 248
  separation from tantalum, 189, 193
  structure, 87
Nitric acid, 123, 222
Nitric oxide, 60, 67, 221
Nitrides, 217
Nitrogen,
  bonding in molecular, 59
  halides, 225
  occurrence, 170
  oxides, 220
  oxy-acids, 222
  properties, 217
  structure, 81
Nitromethane structure, 55
Nitroprusside, 164
Nitrosonium salts, 129
Nitrosyls, 163
Nitrous acid, 122, 222
Nitrous oxide, 221
Noble gases, compounds, 282
Non-aqueous solvents, 123–32
Non-stoichiometric compounds, 101
Nuclear fission, 19–20
Nuclear fuel, 20, 188
Nuclear fusion, 20–1
Nuclear reactions, 15–18

Octahedral holes, 102
Olefin complexes, 164
Olivine, 171
One-electron bonds, 67
Orbitals,
  atomic, 30–2
  hybridization, 60–5
  molecular, 57–60

Osmium,
  compounds, 162, 188, 249, 250, 251
  extraction, 176
  occurrence, 170–6
  properties, 248
  structure, 87
  valency states, 264
Oxidation potential, 109–17
Oxidation state, 39
Oxides, 131, 228, 231, 249, 251
Oxonium ion, 118, 130, 229
Oxy-acids, 222, 233, 243
  Pauling's rules for strength of, 122
Oxygen,
  bonding in molecular, 59
  compounds, 228–38
  occurrence, 170
  properties, 228
  structure, 81
Ozone, 68

Palladium,
  complexes, 127, 165, 251
  compounds, 249, 250, 251, 264
  extraction, 176
  occurrence, 170, 176
  properties, 248
  structure, 87
Paramagnetism, 59, 60, 152, 252, 279–80
Parkes process, 190
Partition law, 186
Paschen series, 24, 27
Pauli exclusion principle, 34
Pegmatites, 172
Perchloric acid, 123, 243, 251
Periodic acids, 243–4
Periodic classification, 34
Peroxo-acids, 231, 232, 235, 254, 256, 258
Phosphine, 219–20
Phosphonitrilic halides, 227
Phosphorus,
  abundance in earth's crust, 171
  allotropes, 83
  extraction, 177
  halides, 120, 225–7
  occurrence, 170, 177
  oxides, 220, 223
  oxy-acids, 123, 222–4
  properties, 217
Pi-bonds, 58–60, 63–5
Pile, 20
Platinum,
  complexes, 136–8, 142, 154, 164, 281
  compounds, 249, 264
  extraction, 176
  occurrence, 170, 176
  properties, 248
  structure, 87

Platinum metals, 176, 264
Plutonium,
    oxidation states, 274
    preparation, 11, 21
    separation from uranium, 188
    solvent extraction, 188
Polonium, 8, 238
Polyacids, 258
Polyhalides, 244
Polynuclear complex, 263
Positive rays, 3–5
Positron emission, 11, 17, 18
Potassium,
    abundance in earth's crust, 171
    compounds, 168, 200–2
    dichromate, 258
    extraction, 173
    occurrence, 173
    permanganate, 260
    properties, 200
    structure, 88
Praseodymium, 272–4
Promethium, 272–4
Protoactinium, 274
Proton, 4
    solvated, 118, 196
Protonated double bond, 207
Protonic acids, 118, 123
Pyrometallurgy, 178–85
Pyroxenes, 105

Quanta, 23
Quantum numbers, 26–32
Quartz, 104, 213

Radial density, 30
Radioactive decay, 8
    series, 9–14
Radioactive isotopes, 9–14
    as tracers, 20
    uses, 20, 141
Radioactivity,
    artificial, 17–19
    natural, 7–14
Radium, 8, 203
Radius ratio, 94
Radon, 198
Rare earths,
    compounds, 272–4
    definition, 247
    extraction, 174
    occurrence, 170, 174
    properties, 272
    separation, 191
Redox reactions, 108
Reduction, 108
Refining of metals, 180
Residual bond, 77, 81. 88, 100

Resonance, 54
Reversible reactions, 115
Rhenium,
    compounds, 162, 249, 250, 260
    extraction, 175
    occurrence, 170, 175
    properties, 248
    solvent extraction, 187
    structure, 87
Rhodium,
    complexes, 162, 165
    compounds, 249, 250, 264
    extraction, 176
    occurrence, 170, 176
    properties, 248
    structure, 87
Rubidium,
    compounds, 200–2
    extraction, 173
    occurrence, 171, 173
    properties, 200
    structure, 88
Ruthenium,
    complexes, 162
    compounds, 249, 254, 264
    extraction, 176
    occurrence, 170, 176
    properties, 248
    solvent extraction, 188
    structure, 87
Rutile, 98, 100, 174
Rydberg constant, 24, 27

Samarium,
    chemistry, 272–4
    extraction, 174
    occurrence, 174
Scandium,
    extraction, 174
    ores, 174
    properties, 272
Scattering of α-particles, 11, 15
Schroedinger wave equation, 30
    solutions to, 30–3
Scintillation counting, 8
Screening constant, 90
Screening effect, 42
Selenides, 229, 231
Selenium,
    allotropes, 83
    compounds, 230, 232–3, 236–7
    extraction, 177
    occurrence, 170, 177
    properties, 228
Semi-conductors, 79, 80
    purification by zone-refining, 181
Shapes of molecules and ions (for non-transitional elements), 65
Siderophil elements, 170

Sigma bonds, 57
Silanes, 211–12
  preparation, 126, 211
Silica, 89
  gel, 214
  properties, 213
  structures, 104
Silicates,
  occurrence, 171
  structures, 103–6
Silicon,
  abundance in earth's crust, 171
  as reducing agent, 179, 183
  as semi-conductor, 80
  bond energies of bonds involving, 212
  bond with oxygen, character of, 105
  carbide, 88
  compounds, 211–16
  extraction, 174, 181
  occurrence, 170, 174
  properties, 210
  structure, 87
  tetrachloride,
    hydrolysis, 211
    solvolysis in liquid ammonia,
Silicones, 216
Silver,
  amine-complexes, 150
  as a liquid extractant, 190
  chloro-complexes, 140
  compounds, 265–9
  extraction, 170
    by hydrometallurgy, 178
  halides, structure, 240
  occurrence, 170, 176
  properties, 265
  structure, 87
  tetrafluoroborate preparation, 128
  thiosulphate complexes, 140
Slag, formation in pyrometallurgical processes, 131, 180
Sodium,
  abundance in earth's crust, 171
  chloride, non-stoichiometry, 102
    structure, 74, 89, 95, 97
  compounds, 200–2
  extraction, 173
  ores, 173
  preparation, 131
  properties, 200
  salts in solution, 120
  structure, 88
Solubility and lattice energy, 51
Solvent extraction, 140, 186–90
Solvents, non-aqueous, 123–32
Spectroscopy, 276–7, 278
Spinel, 171
Stability constants,
  definition, 139

Stability constants (contd)
  experimental determination, 139–41
  factors influencing magnitude of, 147
  for metal–EDTA complexes, 146
Stabilization,
  of Co (III) by complex formation, 154
  of valency states, 116
Standard,
  electrode potential, 109–17
  free energy, 108
  hydrogen electrode, 109
Stannic acids, 214
Stationary state, 25
Stellar energy, 21
Stereochemistry,
  of co-ordination compounds, 134–8
  of molecules and ions of the non-transition metals, 65–8
Strontium,
  compounds, 203–5
  extraction, 173
  ores, 173
  properties, 203
  structure, 88
Sulphides, 228, 231
Sulphur,
  allotropes, 82, 83
  compounds with nitrogen, 237
  dioxide,
    as non-aqueous solvent, 130
    solvent extraction of, 188
    structure, 68, 232
  extraction, 177
  halides, 228, 230, 236, 240
  hydrides, 230–2
  occurrence, 170, 177
  oxides, 232–3
  oxy-acids, 123, 233–5
  oxy-ions, structure, 234
  properties, 228
  reaction with alkali metals in liquid ammonia, 127
  trioxide, 68, 233
Sulphuryl chloride, 236
Superoxides, 201

Talc, 106
Tantalum,
  compounds, 256–7
  extraction, 175
  occurrence, 170, 175
  preparation, 131
  separation from niobium, 189, 193
  structure, 87
Technetium,
  extraction, 175
  preparation, 260
  structure, 87
Tellurides, 229, 231

Tellurium,
  allotropes, 83
  extraction, 177
  halides, 230, 236
  hydride, 230
  occurrence, 170, 177
  oxides, 232–3
  properties, 228
Terbium,
  chemistry, 272–4
  (IV) oxide, non-stoichiometry of, 102
Tetrahedral holes, 102
Tetrasulphur tetranitride, 237
Thallium
  compounds, 209–10
  extraction, 176
  occurrence, 170, 176
  structure, 88
Thermochemistry, 277
Thionic acids, 234
Thionyl,
  bromide, 130
  halides, 235–6
Thiosulphate, 234–5
  oxidation by halogens, 113
Thorium,
  decay series (4n), 10
  extraction, 174
  ores, 174
Three-electron bonds, 67
Thulium, 272–4
Tin,
  allotropy, 87
  compounds, 168, 210–16
  extraction, 176
  occurrence, 170, 176
  properties, 210
Titanates, 254
Titanic acids, 254
Titanium,
  abundance in earth's crust, 171
  compounds, 249, 250, 253–5
  extraction, 174, 179, 181, 185
  (III) ion, colour of hydrated, 157,252
  occurrence, 170, 174
  (II) oxide, non-stoichiometry of, 101
  preparation, 131
  properties, 248
  structure, 87
Transition metals,
  carbonyls, 151
  coloured ions of the first period, 253
  comparative chemistry, 247–74
  complexes with unsaturated hydro-
    carbons, 165
  cyclopentadienyls, 165–7
  oxides, heats of formation, 248
  paramagnetism of ions, 252
  properties, 248
  stabilities of complexes, 149

Transition metals (contd)
  structures, 87, 88
  trends in ionic radii, 93
  variable valency, 149, 248–52
Transuranic elements,
  chemistry, 274
  preparation, 21–2
Tridymite, 104
Tritium, 198
Tungsten,
  bronzes, non-stoichiometry of, 87
  carbide, 179
  compounds, 162, 249, 250, 258
  extraction, 175, 179
  occurrence, 170, 175
  structure, 87

Uncertainty principle, 29
Unit cell, 74, 275
Univalent radius, 90
  relation to crystal radius, 91
Unsaturated hydrocarbons, formation of
    metal complexes, 164–8
Uranium,
  compounds, 274
  concentrates, 193
  decay series for ^{238}U $(4n+2)$, 12
  extraction, 174, 178, 185
  occurrence, 172
  ores, 174
  solvent extraction of uranyl ion, 187–9
Uranyl ion, formation of tris(carbonato)
    complex, 142

Valence-bond theory, 56, 60–5, 152
Valency,
  and oxidation state, 39
  primary, 134
  secondary, 134
Vanadium,
  compounds, 249, 250, 255–6
  complexes, 162, 167, 255
  extraction, 175
  occurrence, 170, 175
  structure, 87
Van Arkel's method, 179, 181
Van der Waals bond, 81
Van't Hoff isochore, 277
Variable valency, 248–52

Water,
  demineralization, 191
  ionic product, 121
  maximum density, 70
  solvent properties, 118
  stereochemistry of molecule, 65, 230
Wave mechanics, 29

Weathering of igneous rocks, 172
Wurtzite structure, 97, 98

Xenon, compounds, 198–200
X-ray diffraction, 275

Ytterbium, 272–4
Yttrium,
  compounds, 272
  extraction, 174
  ores, 174
  structure, 87

Zeise's salt, 164
Zeolites, 105
  ion-exchange properties, 190
Zinc,
  blende, structure, 97–8, 103
  chloro-complexes, 140
  compounds, 271–2

Zinc (*contd*)
  electrolytic preparation, 179
  extraction, 176
  occurrence, 170, 176
  oxide, non-stoichiometry, 102
  properties, 269
  structure, 88
Zirconium,
  compounds, 255
  extraction, 174, 181, 185
  occurrence, 170, 174
  separation from hafnium, 143, 189,
    193
  structure, 87
Zone refining, 181
Zone theory of metals, 78–80

α-emission, 8
α-particles, scattering of, 11, 15
γ-radiation, 8
π-bonds, 58–60, 63–5
σ-bonds, 57

MADE AND PRINTED IN GREAT BRITAIN BY WILLIAM CLOWES AND SONS, LIMITED,
LONDON AND BECCLES

The Periodic Table
(Based on the 'Aufbau' principle)

H 1	He 2																
Li 3	Be 4																
		B 5	C 6	N 7	O 8	F 9	Ne 10										
Na 11	Mg 12																
		Al 13	Si 14	P 15	S 16	Cl 17	Ar 18										
K 19	Ca 20							Sc 21	Ti 22	V 23	Cr 24	Mn 25	Fe 26	Co 27	Ni 28	Cu 29	Zn 30
		Ga 31	Ge 32	As 33	Se 34	Br 35	Kr 36										
Rb 37	Sr 38							Y 39	Zr 40	Nb 41	Mo 42	Tc 43	Ru 44	Rh 45	Pd 46	Ag 47	Cd 48
		In 49	Sn 50	Sb 51	Te 52	I 53	Xe 54										
Cs 55	Ba 56							La 57	Hf 72	Ta 73	W 74	Re 75	Os 76	Ir 77	Pt 78	Au 79	Hg 80
		Tl 81	Pb 82	Bi 83	Po 84	At 85	Rn 86										
Fr 87	Ra 88							Ac 89	104								

←—— Representative Elements ——→←—— Transition Elements ——→